Competition Math

for Middle School

J. Batterson

ArtofProblemSolving.com

Please contact the author, Jason Batterson, at
batterson@artofproblemsolving.com to suggest
additions, corrections, or clarifications.

Published by AoPS Inc.
10865 Rancho Bernardo Rd, Suite 100
San Diego, CA 92127

ISBN: 978-1-934124-20-8

Printed in the United States of America

*Cover: The 2009 state championship team from Ligon Middle School at
the MATHCOUNTS chapter round: Peter Luo, Jason Liang, Tejas
Sundaresan, and Calvin Deng (who went on to place 4th in the national
MATHCOUNTS written contest.)*

For
The Beast List

Contents

Table of Contents

Introduction

About six years ago I got my first real taste of the math that is contained in this book. A student asked me how many different rectangles could be formed by tracing the lines of a standard chessboard. My first instinct was to start plowing through the possibilities. After a few fruitless minutes looking for an organized approach to the problem, the student mercifully showed me the trick (which is presented on page 87 of this text). I was instantly hooked.*

In the next few years I joined Mr. Rohan Lewis in coaching the math team at Ligon Middle School. In addition to being an extraordinarily gifted math student, Rohan had been exposed to competition level problem solving in middle and high school. He is primarily responsible for my early introduction and education in the world of hard math at the middle school level.

As a student I was rarely challenged. The competition that my school took part in was a city wide Math Bowl which we nearly won during my 6th grade year, and then ran away with for the next two years. I can recall a specific question that drew cheers from the crowd when I answered it very quickly, "How many feet are there in 2 miles?".

This was the extent of the difficulty in the competitions I was exposed to, almost strictly computation and basic algebra. This book is for students who are like I was, interested in challenging math that is not typically taught in the standard classroom.

Perhaps even more so, this book is for teachers. It is teachers who have the greatest opportunity to expose gifted math students to the kinds of problems that are found in the major national competitions. MATHCOUNTS, the AMC series, and various other exams expose students to a level of problem solving rarely found in today's classrooms.

For a teacher interested in coaching for these competitions, the biggest hurdle to overcome is usually ego. It is not easy being outsmarted by 12 and 13-year-olds at every practice for most

*There are $(_9C_2)^2 = 1,296$.

adults. As you begin, keep in mind that even coaches with years of experience have a very difficult time keeping up with their best kids.

In 2008 I was fortunate enough to attend a coaching clinic sponsored by the North Carolina Council for Teachers of Mathematics. I quickly discovered that there is a real need for a book like this. Not every teacher or coach has the opportunity to be guided into the world of competition mathematics the way I was, surrounded by experienced and talented individuals. There are many problems in this text that I would never have been able to figure out without a willingness to ask, "How did you do that so fast?". This book is filled with the answers I received.

As teachers, we owe it to our best students to provide the kinds of interesting and challenging problems which will help them continue to see that there is magic in mathematics. This book was written to provide just enough guidance to allow a teacher, parent, coach, tutor, or other adult familiar with standard algebra the opportunity to bring hard math problems to the students who can solve them.

Using This Book

This is my first book, and as such, there were numerous things that I got wrong. This 2019 revision includes minor updates and corrections, mostly in the solutions section..

The book was designed to be read from front to back, with each chapter relying on some of the material from previous chapters. A strong foundation in pre-algebra is necessary before approaching most of the math in this text. Although it was written for middle-school level competition, it was written with the very best students in these competitions in mind, and many of the units are appropriate for gifted high-schoolers. If you are already familiar with much of the material, it is less important to begin at the beginning and end at the end.

You should not get discouraged if you can only solve a few of the problems in this book on your first try. The problems are supposed to be difficult, and there are problems and sections that may require several careful readings and attempts, even over the course of several months or even years. You may find it useful to come back to a section you didn't understand at first after seeing similar problems in practices or competitions.

I always recommend that you read the solutions, even when you get a problem correct (but please, attempt every problem first). A lot of the teaching in this text occurs within the solutions. In reading through a solution, you may find a different method than the one you used to solve a problem that will be useful on a future problem (although I am sure there will be times when a more elegant solution can be achieved than the one presented).

There are plenty of problems in this book to get you started, but practice is essential and there are many wonderful sources for anyone looking to find additional problems and materials.

Old copies of MATHCOUNTS and AMC contests are available for sale through their web sites: *www.unl.edu/amc* and *www.mathcounts.org*. Thousands of wonderful problems can be purchased for countless hours of enjoyment. If you don't enjoy these problems, quick... tear this page out before your parents see it! I made a serious effort to include most of the major topics found on these major national math competitions so that you can reference a topic that is giving you difficulty in these problem sets.

After you have ordered lots of supplementary problem sets from AMC and MATHCOUNTS, there is no greater resource for gifted middle-school math students than my new employer, *artofproblemsolving.com* (AoPS). AoPS proved an invaluable resource for me long before I began working there. I own all of their books and they are well worth the money I spent on them. More importantly, the site provides a community for gifted math students looking for others who, like themselves, enjoy a good hard math problem.

What is With the Numbering?

I grew up on Martin Gardner puzzle books and other texts which provided answers in the back. The answers were always in the same order as the problems. What this meant was that if I wanted to see an answer, I usually ran the risk of seeing the next answer, or perhaps even the next several answers.

I made an effort to prevent this possibility by numbering the problems backwards within the text. For example, the following problems occur in order on page 29:

1.140
1.240
1.340
...

The **1** at the start of the problem simply means that it is in Chapter 1. After that, if you reverse the last three digits you can see that these problems are actually numbered in order... just backwards: **041**, **042**, and **043**. This allows you to find a problem in the chapter relatively quickly (once you get used to the system). For example, I know that problem **1.720** will be near the beginning of chapter 1 (because it is problem 27 when read backwards), while **1.721** will be much later in the chapter. (It is problem 127... I know, this seems confusing right now, hopefully you will get used to it).

The answer key and solutions are listed in order with the numbers as shown, for example:

1.140
1.141
1.150
...

I know this could very well be a major complaint about the book, so I have provided blank answer keys available for printing on my web site for students who would like to keep their answers organized and check their answers quickly.

I considered reorganizing and using the standard method, but I believe that the benefits outweigh the drawbacks of this numbering system. If it is a little hard to find the solution a student is looking for, perhaps they will go back to the problem for long enough to figure it out on their own.

Where do the Problems Come From?

I wrote the problems in this book with inspiration from a variety of sources. Most were inspired by the two major national middle grades math competitions: the AMC competition series and MATHCOUNTS. Others were inspired by problems I have seen in state and local subject area competitions. Some are completely original, while others that I think are completely original may inevitably turn up in old contests, perhaps even in contests I have never seen before.

With about 800 problems and examples in the text, it is likely that many are very similar or even identical to previously published competition problems. In most cases this will be because the problems are obvious: the height of a stack of circles, the sum of a number's factors, the number of paths on a grid, or the probability of a dice roll. In some cases, the problem is less obvious but elegant in a way that lends itself to being written by several people without collaboration.

Some problems are just classics that can be seen everywhere. In these cases I have usually attempted to modify the problem (when I first read problem **1.240** it involved watermelons, and have seen it since in various other forms). In some cases, a classic is a classic in part because it cannot be significantly altered. I included some of these in the text (problem **1.441** for example). I apologize in advance to anyone who has written a similar or identical problem to one found in this text. Included below are links to the competitions and resources that I have read in the past and whose problems inspired many of the ones included in this text. I have found these to be great sources of problems for practice and review and encourage anyone reading this book to frequent the following sites:

MATHCOUNTS: www.mathcounts.org
AMC: amc.maa.org
Math League: www.themathleague.com
MOEMS: www.moems.org
Purple Comet Math Meet: www.purplecomet.org
Art of Problem Solving: www.artofproblemsolving.com
The North Carolina State High School Math Contest:
      courses.ncssm.edu/goebel/STATECON/state.htm
      Wake Tech Regional Competition:
      mathandphysics.waketech.edu/contest.php
The Alabama State High School Math Contest (great for Geometry):
      mcis.jsu.edu/mathcontest

Algebra
Chapter I

The ability to write, manipulate, and solve equations is perhaps the most critical skill for middle-school math competitions. Assigning and manipulating variables in equations and expressions is useful and often necessary for solving problems in each of the other chapters in this text.

I begin this chapter (and this book) with some assumptions. Readers should have a strong foundation in pre-algebra. This includes but is not limited to an understanding of the correct order of mathematical operations, common mathematical symbols and their use, the commutative, associative, and distributive properties, and a basic understanding of the coordinate plane. You must also be able to solve multi-step linear equations for a given variable. Perhaps most importantly, young students should work hard to develop strong number sense and computational skills with integers, fractions, decimals, and percents.

If you do not have all of the skills above, you are probably not ready to begin with this book. If you are a very strong math student who simply hasn't been taught or exposed to these skills, it is possible that an adult or older sibling will be able to fill-in the gaps for you as you progress through this text.

1.1: Variables and Equations

"What are all of these letters doing in my math problems?"

This is the reaction of many students when they are first exposed to Algebra. A variable is a lower-cased letter assigned to represent an unknown quantity. Perhaps the most fundamental skill necessary for competing in mathematical competitions in the middle grades is the ability to write and solve equations.

Example: Angela is three years older than twice her brother Thomas' age. If Angela is 17, how old is Thomas?

Reasoning: Many bright young math students with fast computational skills will quickly be able to find Thomas's age (7), but when the problems become more difficult, simple computational skills are not enough. Practice writing equations even when guess-and-check or computational methods are sufficient:

Angela is three years older than twice Thomas's age.
$$a \quad = \quad 3 \quad\quad + \quad\quad 2 \quad t$$

Translating words into algebra is a skill that comes with practice. We substitute Angela's age into the equation above and solve for t to get $t = 7$. If you don't know how to do this, find a teacher or other adult to help you solve this equation, and then solve lots more like it. Here are a few basic equations to practice with. Solve each for x:

1.100	$3x - 7 = 8$	**1.200**	$2 - 3x = 7$
1.300	$2x - 7 = 8 - x$	**1.400**	$3(x - 4) = 8 - 2x$
1.500	$\dfrac{x-7}{2} = 4$	**1.600**	$\dfrac{2}{3}x - 5 = \dfrac{6-x}{3}$

Writing Equations:

There are a variety of common categories of problems that are typically solved by writing an equation and then solving for a variable.

Consecutive Integer Problems.

Example: The sum of five consecutive integers is 80. What is the smallest of these integers?

Reasoning: It is often recommended that students label the integers x, $x + 1$, $x + 2$, $x + 3$, and $x + 4$. The equation is then:

$$x + (x+1) + (x+2) + (x+3) + (x+4) = 80$$

Combining like terms we get $5x + 10 = 80$ or $x = 14$.

Do you see why it may be easier to label the middle number x in this case? It is important to remember that you are solving for the middle number this time:

$$(x-2) + (x-1) + x + (x+1) + (x+2) = 80$$

Combining like terms we get $5x = 80$ or $x = 16$, so the smallest number is $x - 2 = 14$.

Often, problems will involve consecutive even or odd integers, in which case each number is two bigger than the one before it: x, $x + 2$, $x + 4$, $x + 6$, etc.

Perimeter Problems.

Example: The height of a rectangle is three centimeters more than twice its length. If the perimeter of the rectangle is 60cm, what is its area?

Reasoning: Label the side lengths x and $2x + 3$. Solving for x in the perimeter equation $2x + 2(2x + 3) = 60$ gives us $x = 9$. Substituting to find the height gives us 21 cm. The area is therefore $9(21) = 189$cm^2.

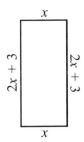

Distance equals rate (speed) times time: *d=rt*.
Perhaps the most common equation used in middle school
level math competitions is the formula relating
distance, rate, and time. Begin by solving the
equation for rate and time:

$$\frac{d}{r}=\frac{rt}{r} \text{ so } t=\frac{d}{r} \text{ and } \frac{d}{t}=\frac{rt}{t} \text{ so } r=\frac{d}{t}$$

Most students just use $d = rt$ and solve where necessary
instead of trying to remember all three.

Example: Marlon jogs two miles to the park in 25 minutes,
turns around, and takes another 55 minutes to walk
the same path back to his house. What is his
average speed for the round-trip?
Reasoning: The round-trip is four miles and takes 80
minutes or 4/3 hours:

$$4 = \frac{4}{3}r \text{ gives us } r = 3\text{mph}$$

Example: On a bike ride, Calvin starts at home and goes up
a long hill for 30 minutes at just 6mph. At the top, he
turns around and rides home along the same path at
a speed of 18mph. What is his average speed for
the round-trip?
Reasoning: The common mistake is to assume that Calvin
averages (6 + 18)/2 = 12mph. This is not correct.
Calvin spends much more time riding uphill than he
does riding downhill. In this problem, the hill is 3
miles long (he rides for 30 minutes up the hill at
6mph), so his round-trip distance is 6 miles. He
makes it down the hill three times faster than he
rides up the hill, so it takes one-third as long (10
minutes) for a total time of 40 minutes (2/3 hour).

$$6 = \frac{2}{3}r \text{ gives us } r = 9\text{mph}.$$

Finding a shortcut: Harmonic Mean.

Often you will be given two different rates and asked to find
their average. For example, in the previous bike
riding example, we did not need to know how far
Calvin rode his bicycle. Regardless of how far he
rode up and down the hill, his average speed for the
trip would be the same.

Consider the following:

Example: The water from a swimming pool evaporates at a
rate of 6 gallons per hour in the shade and 19 gallons
per hour in the sun. For several weeks in August,
the amount of water lost to evaporation in the shade
was equal to the amount lost in the sun. What was
the average rate of evaporation from the pool?

Reasoning: This is an uphill/downhill bicycle problem in
disguise. The same amount of water is lost in the
sun as is lost in the shade. First, let's find a number
of gallons evaporated that is easy to work with. The
LCM of 6 and 19 is $6 \cdot 19 = 114$. We will find the
time it takes for 114 gallons to evaporate in the shade
and the time that it takes to evaporate in the sun. In
the shade it takes $114/6 = 19$ hours to evaporate and
in the sun it takes $114/19 = 6$ hours. This gives us a
total of 25 hours to evaporate 228 gallons. The
average rate of evaporation is $228/25 = 9.12$ gallons
per hour.

Example: Calvin rides his bicycle again up a hill and then
back home. On the way up he averages a miles per
hour, and on the way home he averages b miles per
hour. What is his average speed for the entire trip in
terms of a and b?

Use ab as the length of the hill and a process similar
to the previous example before reading ahead.

Reasoning: If we use ab as the length of the hill, it will take Calvin $ab/a = b$ hours to ride up the hill and it will take $ab/b = a$ hours to ride back down the hill. The total distance traveled will be $2ab$ miles and the total time will be $a + b$ hours. This gives us his average speed for the entire trip, called the **harmonic mean** of a and b:

$$\text{Harmonic mean of } a \text{ and } b\text{:} \quad \frac{2ab}{a+b}$$

Remember that this formula will only work when the distance traveled (or water evaporated, as in the previous example) is equal for both rates.

This can be a very powerful tool in problem solving.

Example: What is Alicia's average speed on her walk to school if she walks halfway at 2mph and runs the rest of the way at 7mph?

Reasoning: The harmonic mean is: $\dfrac{2 \cdot 2 \cdot 7}{2 + 7} = \dfrac{28}{9} = 3.\bar{1}\,\text{mph.}$

Example: The battery in a portable music player is guaranteed to last 17 hours without charging if it is used with headphones and 3 hours if it is used with speakers. If you use headphones and speakers for equal amounts of time, how many minutes will a fully charged battery last?

Reasoning: You get 3 hours per battery with speakers and 17 hours per battery with headphones. The harmonic mean is $2(3)(17)/20 = 5.1$ hours or 306 minutes. We can check this to see that $5.1/2 = 2.55$ hours of listening on speakers will use $2.55/3 = 85\%$ of the battery's life. 2.55 hours with headphones will use $2.55/17 = 15\%$ of the life of the battery.

Moles Digging Holes: A variation of $d = rt$.

Example: It takes 7 minutes for 7 moles to dig 7 holes. How long will it take 8 moles to dig 8 holes?

Reasoning: Of course, the problem is stated to encourage the immediate response of 8 minutes. Begin by approaching this problem with some basic reasoning. Imagine one mole working on one hole at a time. Each mole takes 7 minutes to dig 1 hole. Now imagine all the moles working together on 1 hole. It takes 7 moles 1 minute to complete each hole. Either scenario leads us to reason that 1 mole can complete 1/7 of a hole in a minute.

With 8 moles working on 8 holes, it is easiest to assign 1 mole to each hole. Each mole takes 7 minutes to finish, so it takes 8 moles 7 minutes to dig 8 holes.

It is often useful to find a formula for use on problems that are more complicated. This is not necessary for all problems, but more complicated situations are often more easily approached with a formula.

Example: 5 moles can dig 4 holes in 3 minutes. How many minutes will it take for 9 moles to dig 6 holes?

Reasoning: The work w (holes dug) done by m moles in time t (in minutes) at a constant rate r (holes per minute) is similar to the $d = rt$ formula: $w = rt(m)$. We can plug-in the values we know and solve for r:

$4 = r \cdot 3 \cdot 5$ gives us $r = \dfrac{4}{15}$ (holes/min./mole).

Plug this value in for r along with $m = 9$ and $w = 6$ to solve for the time it takes 9 moles to dig 6 holes.

$6 = \dfrac{4}{15} \cdot t \cdot 9$ gives us $t = \dfrac{15}{36} \cdot 6 = \dfrac{15}{6} = 2.5$ minutes.

Moles Digging Holes: Using a formula: $w = rt(m)$.

Example: 5 hoses can fill 10 small tanks in 80 minutes or 6 large tanks in 90 minutes. What is the least amount of time it will take for 10 hoses to fill 8 small tanks and 8 large tanks?

Reasoning: We use the formula $w = rt(h)$ to figure out how long it takes for one hose (h) to fill one of each type of tank.
Small tanks: $10 = r \cdot 80 \cdot 5$ gives us $r = 1/40$. One small tank can be filled with one hose in 40 min.
Large tanks: $6 = r \cdot 90 \cdot 5$ gives us $r = 1/75$: One large tank can be filled with one hose in 75 minutes.

The tanks will take $8 \cdot 40 + 8 \cdot 75 = 920$ minutes to fill. If all 10 hoses are used efficiently, it will take 92 minutes to fill all 16 tanks.

Practice: Moles Digging Holes.

1.900 If 3 men can paint 4 rooms in 9 hours, how many hours and minutes will it take for one man to paint one room, assuming he can work at the same rate alone?

1.010 Nine beavers can build 1 dam in 5 hours. How long will it take for 15 beavers working together to build 2 dams?

1.110 A team of 4 students participating in a math competition can solve 9 problems correctly in 30 minutes. How many problems should a team of 5 students be able to solve correctly in 40 minutes?

1.210 Jeremy can solve a Rubik's cube in 4 minutes. Michael is very fast and can solve 5 cubes in 12 minutes. Working together, what is the fewest number of minutes it will take for them to solve 10 cubes?

Practice: Variables and Equations.

1.310 Molly's father James is three years less than three
times her age. How many years from now will
Molly's father be twice her age if James is 33 today?

1.410 The sum of four consecutive even integers is equal to
three times the smallest number. What is the sum of
the four integers?

1.510 The length of a rectangle is three times its width. If
the perimeter of the rectangle is 32cm, what is its
area?

1.610 When Anil drives to work on the highway he averages
45 miles per hour for the trip. When Anil uses the
back roads, he can only average 36 miles per hour.
The trip on the back roads is 3 miles shorter and
takes 5 more minutes than the highway route. How
many miles long is the highway route?

1.710 A hexagon and pentagon share the property that the
side lengths of each are consecutive integers, and the
perimeter of each is 45cm. What is the difference in
length between the short side of the pentagon and
the short side of the hexagon?

1.810 Kris runs half of the distance to school averaging
6mph. He jogs the rest of the way to school averaging 4mph, and the whole trip takes him 25 minutes.
How many minutes will it take him to run the same
way home if he averages 8mph the whole way?

1.910 Tobey can mow a lawn in 50 minutes. Working
together, Tobey and Nick take only 30 minutes to
mow the same lawn. How long would it take Nick
to mow the lawn alone?

1.2: Linear Equations

The length of this text is not sufficient to provide a complete or even a thorough discussion of linear equations. The following information is only intended to cover the basics of writing and graphing linear equations.

Sometimes an equation contains two unknowns. The simplest of these are called linear equations, and usually relate variables x and y in the form:

$$y = mx + b$$

In the equation above which is called the **slope-intercept form** of a linear equation, m is called the slope of the equation, and b is called the y-intercept.

The graph of a linear equation is a straight line. The first time you graph a linear equation, it is useful to first create a list of coordinate pairs (x, y) as shown to develop an understanding of the relationship between the graph and the equation.

$$y = \frac{1}{2}x + 4$$

(x, y)
$(-6, 1)$
$(-4, 2)$
$(-2, 3)$
$(0, 4)$
$(2, 5)$
$(4, 6)$
$(6, 7)$

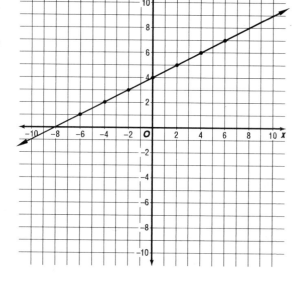

Slope:

The slope of the graph of a linear equation is its rise over its run. It is the ratio of the change in the value of y to the change in x. For example, in the graph of the equation on the previous page, y increases by 1 when x is increased by 2, giving a slope of 1/2. The slope of an equation written in slope-intercept form is the coefficient of x.

On the graph of an equation, the easiest way to determine the slope of a line is to find two points on the line. Working from left to right, count how far you must go up and over to get from one point to the next. If you go down and over, the slope is negative. Below are some examples of slopes graphed on the coordinate plane:

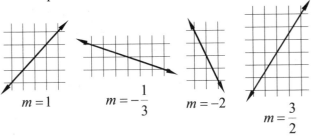

$$m = 1 \qquad m = -\frac{1}{3} \qquad m = -2 \qquad m = \frac{3}{2}$$

Of course, you can also determine the slope of a line without a graph. To find the rise, subtract the y-coordinates. To find the run, subtract the x-coordinates. Given a pair of coordinates (x_1, y_1) and (x_2, y_2):

$$\text{Slope} = m = \frac{rise}{run} = \frac{y_2 - y_1}{x_2 - x_1}$$

Example: Find the slope of the line passing through the following coordinates: $(7, -2)$ and $(-4, -1)$.

Solution: The slope is $m = \dfrac{-1 - (-2)}{-4 - 7} = \dfrac{1}{-11} = -\dfrac{1}{11}$.

Intercepts:

The intercepts of a graph are the points where the line of the equation crosses the *x* and *y*-axis. The *x*-intercept occurs where the line crosses the *x*-axis. It is the point where *y* equals zero. The *y*-intercept occurs where the line crosses the *y*-axis. It is the point where *x* equals zero. These are easiest to see on a graph.

The *x*-intercept is at (6,0).

The *y*-intercept is at (0, 5).

The intercepts are often given as a single coordinate. It is assumed that the intercepts occur where the opposite coordinate is zero.

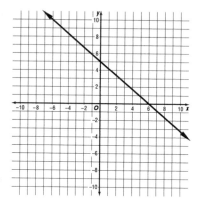

To find the intercepts of an equation without graphing, set the opposite coordinate to zero and solve the resulting equation.

Slope-Intercept Form:

As noted earlier, the most common form of a linear equation is called slope-intercept form. In the equation $y = mx + b$, *m* represents the slope of the graph of the line and *b* represents the *y*-intercept.

Slope-intercept form is easy to relate to real-world relationships, where *b* represents a starting value and *m* represents a rate of change. For example, the cost (*c*) of a phone call that costs $0.49 to connect and $0.09 per minute (*m*) could be represented by the equation $c = .09m + .49$.

Examples: Write an equation in slope-intercept form for each line graphed on the coordinate plane below.

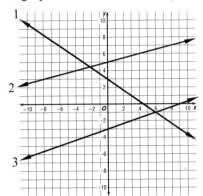

Solutions:

1. $y = -\dfrac{2}{3}x + 3$ 2. $y = \dfrac{1}{4}x + 5$ 3. $y = \dfrac{1}{3}x - 3$

Point-Slope Form:

Given two points on the graph of an equation or a point and the slope of an equation, the equation of a line graphed on the coordinate plane can be written in point-slope form. The equation of a line which passes through (x_1, y_1) and has slope m can be written:

$$y - y_1 = m(x - x_1)$$

Example: Write an equation in slope-intercept form for the line passing through $(10, 3)$ and $(-5, 9)$.

Reasoning: First we find the slope. Use the slope formula:

$$m = \frac{9 - 3}{-5 - 10} = \frac{6}{-15} = -\frac{2}{5}.$$

Use $(10, 3)$ to write an equation in point-slope form:

$y - 3 = -\dfrac{2}{5}(x - 10)$. Solving for y we get $y = -\dfrac{2}{5}x + 7$.

Alternatively, you can also use the same point and slope in the equation $y = mx + b$ to solve for b.

Standard Form:

The standard form of a linear equation is $Ax + By = C$. In correct standard form, $A > 0$, and there is no common divisor of A, B, and C. There are some nice properties of an equation written in standard form. For example, you can simply set x to zero and solve for y to get the y-intercept: (C/B), and vice-versa to get the x-intercept: (C/A).

The slope is easy to recognize as well. Prove to yourself that $-(A/B)$ will always give the slope of an equation written in standard form by solving the standard form equation for y (convert it into slope-intercept form).

Perhaps most importantly, standard form is how most linear equations are written on competition questions and answer choices.

Parallel and Perpendicular Lines:

Two lines with the same slope are parallel.

Two lines are perpendicular if the products of their slopes is equal to -1. In other words, perpendicular slopes are negative reciprocals of each other.

Horizontal and Vertical Lines:

The slope of a horizontal line is zero. The slope of a vertical line is undefined (because the denominator of the slope is zero and division by zero is undefined).

A horizontal line will be of the form $y = k$ (where k is some constant), for example, $y = 3$. The equation $y = 3$ is a horizontal line which passes through the y-axis at the point (0, 3).

A vertical line will be of the form $x = k$, for example, $x = 4$ is a vertical line passing through the x-axis at (4, 0).

Practice: Linear Equations.

1.020 What is the slope of the line that passes through $(-9,9)$ and the origin $(0,0)$?

1.120 Find the sum of the x and y intercepts of the equation $3x - 5y = 8$. Express your answer as a common fraction in simplest terms.

1.220 Write the standard form equation for the line which passes through $(1,-1)$ and $(-5,-5)$.

1.320 What is the slope of the line perpendicular to the graph of the equation $4x - 2y = 3$?

1.420 The graph of the equation $y = 2x + b$ passes through the point $(b,-3)$. Find b.

1.520 What is the area of the right triangle bounded by the graph of the equation $y = -\frac{2}{3}x + 12$ and both coordinate axis?

1.620 If the graphs of the lines $2x - 5y = 7$ and $10x + by = 7$ are perpendicular, what is the value of b?

1.720 Write the standard form of the equation which has the x and y-intercepts of the equation $y = \frac{4}{9}x - 8$ switched.

1.820 What length of the graph of $y = \frac{4}{3}x - 8$ is within the 4th quadrant? (See section **5.3**).

1.920 Integral coordinates x and y are selected such that $0 \le x \le y \le 5$. How many distinct values of m are possible if the graph of the equation $y = mx$ passes through the point (x, y)?

1.3: Systems of Equations

Often it is necessary to write two or more equations to represent the relationships between multiple variables. Solving for the variables in these equations is called solving a **system of equations**. There are two common techniques used when solving a system of equations: substitution and elimination.

Substitution: You have probably already used substitution many times. The simplest case of substitution involves problems like the following:

Example: Evaluate $2a - 3b + 7c$ for $a = 5$, $b = 4$, and $c = -3$.

Solution: In this case, we just substitute (5) for a, (4) for b, and (-3) for c to get $2(5) - 3(4) + 7(-3) = -23$.

A second simple case where substitution is used occurs where we are solving for one variable, given the value of another:

Example: What is the value of x in the equation $y = 2x - 4$ when $y = 7$?

Solution: Substituting, we get $7 = 2x - 4$, or $x = 11/2$.

The same process is used when two equations are given. Although this looks more complicated, the process is the same.

Example: What is the value of y in the equation $y = 2x - 4$ when $x = y - 5$?

Solution: Substituting $(y - 5)$ for x in the first equation, we get $y = 2(y - 5) - 4$. Solving for y we get $y = 14$. If we are interested in knowing the value of x as well, we can then substitute $y = 14$ into either equation to get $x = 9$.

Systems of Equations: Substitution.

Sometimes equations will not be as simple.

Example: Find $x + y$ if $x + 3y = 4$ and $x - 2y = -4$.

Reasoning: We can use substitution to solve this system of
   equations, but we first need to solve for one of the
   variables. In the first equation it is easy to solve for
   x: $x = -3y + 4$. We can substitute $(-3y + 4)$ for x in
   the second equation: $(-3y + 4) - 2y = -4$. Solving
   for y we get $-5y = -8$, or $y = 8/5$. We can substitute 8/5 for y in either equation (I used the first) to
   get $x + 3(8/5) = 4$, which gives us $x = -4/5$.
   Therefore, $x + y = (-4/5) + (8/5) = 4/5$.

Systems of Equations: Elimination.

The addition property of equality states:
   if $a = b$, then $a + c = b + c$.
   Similarly, if $a = b$, and $c = d$, then $a + c = b + d$.
   See if you can figure out how this helps us solve a
   system of equations like this one:

$$2x + 5y = -4$$
$$3x - 5y = 19$$

When we add the equations above, the $+5y$ and
the $-5y$ cancel each other out, leaving us with:

$$
\begin{array}{r}
2x + 5y = -4 \\
+\ 3x - 5y = 19 \\
\hline
5x \qquad = 15
\end{array}
$$

This gives us $x = 3$. Substituting into either of the two
   equations, we get $y = -2$. It deserves mentioning
   that **the solution of a system of equations is the
   point of intersection for the graphs of the two
   equations:** $(3, -2)$ is the point of intersection for the
   graphs of the equations above. Linear equations
   which are parallel have **no solution** unless they
   coincide, in which they have **infinite solutions**.

Systems of Equations: Elimination.

Equations usually need to be manipulated before being added so that one variable will be eliminated.

Example: What are the coordinates of the point of intersection for the graphs of the following equations?

$$2x + 3y = 21$$
$$3x - 4y = -45$$

Reasoning: We will manipulate the equations so that when added, the x variable will be eliminated:

$$3(2x + 3y = 21)$$
$$-2(3x - 4y = -45)$$

Multiplying gives us the following equations which are added to eliminate the x variable:

$$6x + 9y = 63$$
$$\underline{-6x + 8y = 90}$$
$$17y = 153$$
$$y = 9$$

Plugging 9 into either equation for y and solving for x gives us $x = -3$. The lines intersect at $(-3, 9)$.

Example: Three chocolate bars and five lollipops cost $3.70, while four chocolate bars and two lollipops cost $3.30. How much will it cost to buy one of each?

Reasoning: We will write and solve a system of equations:

$$4(3c + 5l = 3.70) = 12c + 20l = 14.80$$
$$-3(4c + 2l = 3.30) = \underline{-12c - 6l = -9.90}$$
$$14l = 4.90$$
$$l = 0.35$$

Plugging in $0.35 for the cost of a lollipop, we get $0.65 for the cost of a chocolate bar, or $1.00 for one of each. Always look for shortcuts. In the problem above, if we add the original equations we get $7c + 7l = 7$, or $c + l = 1$ (which is what we were asked to find).

Systems of Equations: Common Word Problems

***d=rt* Example:** Kelly and Jason are going out for a run. Kelly leaves two minutes before Jason. If Kelly runs seven miles an hour and Jason runs nine miles per hour, how long will it take for Jason to catch up to Kelly?

Reasoning: If we call the amount of time in minutes Jason runs *t*, we call the time Kelly runs $(t + 2)$. The distance Kelly has run *t* minutes after Jason begins is given by the equation:

$$d = 7\left(\frac{t+2}{60}\right), \text{ and for Jason: } d = 9\left(\frac{t}{60}\right).$$ When

Jason catches Kelly, the distance they have each run

will be equal, so we can solve $9\left(\dfrac{t}{60}\right) = 7\left(\dfrac{t+2}{60}\right)$ for

t to get 7 minutes. Note that the conversion from minutes to hours (/60) was not actually necessary here, but it is always good to be cautious when dealing with units.

Upstream/Downstream Example: Paddling upstream, Jake can travel at a rate of 3mph relative to the shore. Paddling downstream, Jake can travel 8mph relative to the shore. How fast can Jake paddle in still water?

Reasoning: We will use *p* to represent the speed at which Jake can paddle in still water, and *c* to represent the speed of the river current. Paddling downstream, Jake's speed is the sum of his paddling speed and the speed of the current $(p + c)$. Traveling upstream his speed is $(p - c)$. This gives us the equations:

$$p + c = 8$$
$$p - c = 3$$

Solving the system using elimination gives us $p = 5.5$mph.

Systems of Equations: Common Word Problems

Age Example: Today, Pamela is four times as old as her brother Thomas. In eight years, Pamela will only be twice as old as Thomas. How many years from now will Pamela be three times as old as Thomas?

Reasoning: We will label the current ages of Pamela and Thomas p and t. In eight years, their respective ages will be $p + 8$ and $t + 8$. This allows us to write the system of equations:

$$p = 4t$$
$$p + 8 = 2(t + 8)$$

Solving the system, we get their current ages: 4 and 16 years. We want to determine how many years it will take for Pamela to be three times Thomas's age (we could guess-and-check quickly, but let's do the math). Using x to represent the number of years it will take for Pamela to be 3 times Thomas' age:

$$p + x = 3(t + x)$$
$$\text{so } 16 + x = 3(4 + x)$$

Solving for x gives us 2 years (Thomas is 6, Pamela is 18).

Three Equations and Three Variables: Find (x, y, z) for:

$$2x + y + z = 9$$
$$x + 2y + z = 6$$
$$3x + 3y - z = 24$$

The goal is to create two equations with two variables. Adding the first and third equations eliminates the z variable. Adding the second and third equations also eliminates z. This leaves us with the two equations:

$$5x + 4y = 33$$
$$\text{and } 4x + 5y = 30$$

Solve this system for x and y, and plug the values in to get z. Complete this one your own. The solution is $(5, 2, -3)$.

Systems of Equations: Cheating the System.
Often, there is no need to write a system of equations if a
  little common sense will work:

Example: A cycling shop has bicycles and tricycles. If the
  shop currently has 42 cycles with a total of 90
  wheels in its inventory, how many tricycles does the
  shop have?

Reasoning: *Begin by assuming they have all bicycles.* If
  they had nothing but bicycles, there would be 84
  wheels. We need 6 more wheels. Add a wheel to
  each of six bicycles to get a total of 6 tricycles.

Example: Bradley scores 34 points in a basketball game by
  making 12 baskets. If each basket was worth either
  2 or 3 points, how many three-pointers did Bradley
  make?

Reasoning: Like the cycle problem, we *begin by assuming Bradley only made two-point shots.* Twelve
  baskets would give him 24 points. We need 10 more
  points, so he must have made 10 three-point shots.

Example: Melinda needed to mail a package. She used
  $0.02 stamps and $0.10 stamps to mail the package.
  If she used 15 stamps worth $.78, how many $0.10
  stamps did she use?

Reasoning: If she used fifteen $0.02 stamps they would be
  worth $0.30, so we need $0.48 more. Exchanging a
  $0.02 for a $0.10 adds $0.08, so we need 48/8 = 6
  $0.10 stamps.

Try It! In a parking lot there are motorcycles and cars.
  You count 104 wheels, and your friend counts 30
  vehicles. How many cars are there? The answer is
  at the bottom of the next page.

Practice: Systems of Equations.

1.030 The sum of two numbers is 20 and their difference is 5. What is the smaller of the two numbers?

1.130 Shannon has a pocket full of quarters and dimes. If she has 18 coins for a total of $2.40, how many quarters does she have?

1.230 In 2005, a man and his son were looking at a collection of paintings. The young boy looked at the dates on two paintings and noticed that the first year was exactly twice the second. His father noticed that the second painting was exactly three times the age of the first. How old was the first painting in 2005?

1.330 Working together: Al, Bob, and Carl can lift 240 pounds. Bob, Carl, and Dan can lift 250 pounds. Carl, Dan, and Al can lift 260 pounds, and Al, Bob and Dan can lift 270 pounds. How many pounds can all four men lift if they work together? (Find the trick!)

1.430 Kenny is playing on the mall escalator. He can run up the down escalator in 30 seconds, and it takes him 6 seconds to run up the up escalator. How many seconds would it take Kenny to run up the flight of stairs that is between the escalators?

1.530 Shane thinks of three integers. Added two at a time, their sums are 37, 41, and 44. What is the product of the three integers?

1.630 Four neighbors go to purchase letters to spell their house numbers at a local hardware store. Each letter is priced separately. The first neighbor (who lives in house number one) purchases the letters **ONE** for $2. The second neighbor buys **TWO** for $3, and the third pays $5 for the letters to spell **ELEVEN**. How much will the letters in the word **TWELVE** cost the fourth neighbor?

1.4: Ratios, Proportions, and Percents

A **ratio** is a relationship between two quantities, usually expressed as a fraction or by separating the two quantities by a colon. When ratios represent part-to-whole relationships they are usually represented as fractions, for example: three out of every five students are girls would be represented as 3/5. A ratio that compares two quantities usually uses a colon, for example, the ratio of girls to boys in the above example would be 3:2, meaning there are three girls for every two boys.

A **percent** is simply a part-to-whole ratio in which the whole is 100. For example, 45% means "45 out of 100".

The following statements all represent the same relationship:
> The ratio of girls to boys is 3:2.
> 3/5 of the students are girls.
> 60% of the students are girls.

A **proportion** is a comparison of two ratios that are equal, for example:

$$\frac{45}{100} = \frac{9}{20}$$

Two ratios are called proportional if they are equal. Often we are asked to find a missing value in a proportion, for example, solve for x in the following proportion:

$$\frac{5}{8} = \frac{x}{9}$$

There are many ways to solve for x, but the most common is to use *cross products*. In a proportion, cross-products are always equal. To demonstrate why this works, consider using a common denominator:

$\dfrac{5}{8} = \dfrac{x}{9}$ means $\dfrac{5 \cdot 9}{8 \cdot 9} = \dfrac{8x}{8 \cdot 9}$, therefore $5 \cdot 9 = 8x$.

Solving for x gives us $x = 45/8$ or 5.625.

Ratios:

If we say that the ratio of boys to girls in a classroom is 4 to
5, this means that for every 4 boys there are 5 girls,
or for every 9 students, 4 are boys (and for every 9
students, 5 are girls). It is often easiest to see a ratio
as a part-to-whole relationship.

Example: There are red, white, and blue marbles in a bag in
the ratio 2:3:4. If the bag contains 108 marbles, how
many of them are blue?

Reasoning: For every 9 marbles: 2 are red, 3 are white,
and 4 are blue. We can divide the 108 marbles into
12 groups of 9, each with 4 blue marbles for a total
of $12 \cdot 4 = 48$ blue marbles.

Even easier, four of every nine marbles are blue, so:

$$\frac{4}{9}(108) = 48 .$$

Example: The Reiter family uses three different-sized
scoops to serve mashed potatoes: blobs, globs, and
gobs. 2 blobs are equal to 1 glob, and 5 globs equal 3
gobs of mashed potatoes. A bowl holds 12 gobs of
potatoes. How many blobs are there in the bowl?

Reasoning: Problems like these often use confusing
sounding terms that are easy to mix-up. Solving
these quickly in your head can be very frustrating.
Most of the time you need to work backwards:
5 globs equal 3 gobs, so 12 gobs would equal 20
globs. Since each glob equals 2 blobs, 20 globs equal
40 blobs (so 12 gobs = 20 globs = 40 blobs).

This is easy to mess-up. If you have time, it is easier to set
up a ratio with all three terms, multiplying ratios
where necessary: blobs to globs to gobs = 10:5:3.
With 12 gobs, we get 40:20:12, or 40 blobs.

Solving Proportions:

Cross-Products: If $\dfrac{a}{b} = \dfrac{c}{d}$ then $\dfrac{ad}{bd} = \dfrac{bc}{bd}$ so $ad = bc$.

Note that if $\dfrac{a}{b} = \dfrac{c}{d}$, then $\dfrac{a}{c} = \dfrac{b}{d}$ and $\dfrac{d}{c} = \dfrac{b}{a}$, etc.

All of these share the same cross-products.

Example: A recipe calls for 5 cups of flour and 3 cups of sugar. You only have 4 cups of flour. How many cups of sugar should you use if all 4 cups of flour are used?

Reasoning: It is easy to set-up a proportion for this one:

$$\frac{5}{3} = \frac{4}{s} \text{ gives us } 5s = 12 \text{ or } s = 2\frac{2}{5}.$$

Scale Factor: Maps and models use a scale factor to indicate the ratio between the size of the map or model and the actual size of what is being represented. These are usually basic proportion problems.

Example: Tommy is constructing a model boat. The scale of the model is 1/4 inch = 1 foot. If the model of the boat is 14 inches long, how long is the real boat?

Reasoning: This one (and many problems like it) are easy to do in your head. If 1/4 inch equals one foot, then one inch equals 4 feet, and 14 inches equals $14 \cdot 4 = 56$ feet. Setting this up as a proportion looks like this:

$$\frac{1/4}{1} = \frac{14}{x}.$$

Using cross-products: $\dfrac{1}{4}x = 14$, so $x = 56$ feet.

Shadow lengths: The length of an object's shadow is directly proportional to its height. For example, if a 6ft object casts an 8ft shadow, then a 9ft object will cast a 12ft shadow (in the same location and at the same time of day).

Example: Carly, who is 5 inches taller than her brother Bailey casts a shadow that is a foot longer than his. If Carly is 50 inches tall, what is the length in inches of Bailey's shadow?

Reasoning: To solve this using a proportion, we will use C and B to represent the heights of Carly and Bailey, with c and b representing their shadows. Note that $B = C - 5$ and $b = c - 12$.

$$\frac{C}{c} = \frac{B}{b}, \text{ so } \frac{C}{c} = \frac{C-5}{c-12}. \text{ Substitute: } \frac{50}{c} = \frac{50-5}{c-12}.$$

Solving for c using cross-products, we get $50c - 600 = 45c$, so $c = 120$. If Carly's shadow is 120 inches long, Bailey's is 12 inches shorter, or 108 inches.

Doing this in your head is easy once you recognize that the *differences* between proportional values are also proportional (in the same ratio). Carly is 5 inches taller and has a shadow that is 12 inches longer, so the ratio of her height to her shadow length is 5:12. Since she is 50 inches tall, her shadow is 120 inches long (making Bailey's shadow 108 inches long).

This means:

$$\text{If } \frac{a}{b} = \frac{c}{d}, \text{ then } \frac{a}{b} = \frac{a+c}{b+d} = \frac{a-c}{b-d} = \frac{c}{d}.$$

Percents and Percent of Change:

A percent is a special ratio meaning "per hundred". A proportion can be used to convert any ratio into a percent. For example, to convert "3 out of 16" into a percent, the proportion below can be used:

$$\frac{3}{16} = \frac{x}{100}.$$

Cross products give us: $16x = 300$, so $x = 18\frac{3}{4}\%$.

Alternatively, divide and move the decimal point:

$$\frac{3}{16} = 0.1875 = 18.75\%.$$

To find a percent of a value, it is easiest to convert the percent to a decimal and multiply. For example, to find 15% of 80 we can just multiply $0.15(80) = 12$. It is also possible to solve many percent problems in your head with good number sense. Looking at the problem above, 15% is 3 out of 20, which is equal to 12 out of 80.

A **percent of change** is the ratio of the change to the original amount (expressed as a percent).

Example: Find the percent of decrease on the cost of a calculator marked down from $28.90 to $20.23.

Reasoning: Two ways: One is to find the change and divide by the original amount:

$$\frac{28.9 - 20.23}{28.9} = 0.3 = 30\%.$$

It is sometimes easier to find what percent of the original amount you pay, then subtract:

$$\frac{20.23}{28.9} = 0.7 = 70\%, \text{ which means you save 30\%.}$$

Percents and Percent of Change:
Most competition problems involving percents require that
you compute multiple percents in the same problem.

Example: Lindsey brought five dozen (60) cookies to
school. She gave 40% of the cookies to her teachers, 25% of the remaining cookies to her best friend,
and ate a third of what was left. What percent of
the 5 dozen cookies remain?

Reasoning: Starting with 60 cookies, remove 40% (4 out of
every 10, or 24 cookies), leaving her with 36. Now
remove 25% (1 of every 4, or 9 cookies), leaving her
with 27. She eats one-third (9), leaving her with 18
cookies. 18 out of 60 equals 3/10 or 30%.

Notice that all of the math above could be done in
your head. This is often the case in percent problems. The most common percent change problems
involve a frighteningly common misunderstanding.

Try the following:

Example: Starting with $195, you spend 20%. Your friend
pays you an amount equal to 20% of what you have
left. How much money do you have now?

Reasoning: You do *not* have $195. You have $187.20.
After you spend 20% you have 80% of what you
started with, or $156.00 to be exact. 20% of $156 is
less than 20% of $195 (it is $31.20), so adding 20%
does not get you right back to where you started.

Check for Understanding:
1.730 An $8,000 investment loses 50% of its value on Mon-
day, then gains 50% back on Tuesday, then loses
50% again on Wednesday. If it gains 50% back on
Thursday, how much will the investment be worth?

Practice: Ratios, Proportions, and Percents.

1.040   Two and two-thirds cups of sugar are required to make two-dozen cookies. How many cookies can be made with five cups of sugar?

1.140   The ratio of cherry candies to grape candies in a bag is 3:5. After your friend eats half of the grape flavored candies and only one cherry flavored candy, the ratio of cherry to grape candies is 7:6. How many candies are left in the bag?

1.240   Before a plum is dried to become a prune, it is 92% water. A prune is just 20% water. If only water is evaporated in the drying process, how many pounds of prunes can be made with 100 pounds of plums?

1.340   Keith wants to mark all of the original prices in his store down to half-off. The prices are already marked down by 20%. What additional percent should be discounted? Express your answer as a percent rounded to the tenth.

1.440   On a long hike, Greg forgets to fill his canteen. Fortunately, Harold has 40 ounces of water and Jake has 60 ounces. The three hikers share the water so that each gets an equal amount. At the end of the hike, Greg gives Harold and Jake $5 to split for the water they gave him. How much should Harold get?

1.540   The five interior angles in a pentagon are in the ratio 2:3:4:5:6. What is the measure of the pentagon's largest angle? (See **p.180**).

1.640   Rebecca runs a quarter-mile each week. In each of the last 6 weeks her time has improved (decreased) by 2%, and she can now run a quarter-mile in 66 seconds. What was her time six weeks ago. Round your decimal answer to the tenth of a second.

Review: 1.1 through 1.4

1.050 It takes 6 lumberjacks 7 minutes to saw through 8 trees. How many minutes will it take for 7 lumberjacks to saw through 8 trees?

1.150 A fruit stand sells apples, bananas, and pears. There are 20% more pears than apples, and the ratio of apples to bananas is 3:4. What is the fewest number of pears that could be at the fruit stand.

1.250 If 5% more than a is b, and b is 15% less than c, what is the ratio of a to c?

1.350 Three circles are tangent to each other and have as their centers the vertices of right triangle of side lengths 6, 8, and 10cm. Express the combined area of the three circles in terms of pi.

1.450 Today I am 6 years less than half my father's age. In 6 years, I will be 6 years more than one-third my father's age. How old was my father when I was born?

1.550 Franklin rides his bicycle to the beach averaging 18mph. He rides home along the same route. What speed must he average on the way home if he wants to average 21 miles per hour for the round trip?

1.650 Congruent circles of radius 6 have their centers at C(5, 4) and D(1, 2). The circles intersect at points A and B. What is the slope-intercept form equation of the line which passes through A and B?

1.750 In a cage full of bugs, there are beetles (6 legs) and spiders (8 legs). There are 162 more legs than bugs and 18 more beetles than spiders. How many spiders are there?

1.5: Distribution

Even if you have never heard of it, you have probably been
using the **distributive property** for years. How do
you multiply 7(103) in your head?
When I do it, I compute $7(100) + 7(3) = 700 + 21 = 721$.
This is the distributive property: $7(100 + 3) = 7(100) + 7(3)$.
For any numbers a, b, and c:

$$a(b+c) = ab + ac.$$

The most common mistake that is made occurs when
distributing a negative:

Example: Simplify $4x - 3(x - 2)$.

Reasoning: Treat this as distributing the -3 to the x and to
the -2. Using the definition of subtraction as
adding the opposite, this looks like:
$$4x + (-3)[x + (-2)]$$
This is unnecessarily complicated. With some
practice, you will begin just distributing the negative
more naturally: $4x - 3(x - 2) = 4x - 3x + 6 = x + 6$.

Practice: Distribute the negative and simplify:

1.070 $3a - 4(2 - a)$ **1.170** $8x - (3 + 5x)$

1.270 Subtract $3b - 4a$ from $3a - b$.

Distribution with Polynomials:
It is easiest to explain distribution with polynomials using a
geometric example.

Example: Find the area of the figure below two ways:

Distribution with Polynomials:

In the previous example it is easy to compute:

$$(2+3)(7+5) = (5)(12) = 60.$$

Alternatively, it is possible to find each of the four smaller areas individually and add them together:

$$(2+3)(7+5) = 2(7) + 2(5) + 3(7) + 3(5) = 60$$

This demonstrates the concept of distribution. With variables:

$$(a+b)(c+d) = a(c+d) + b(c+d) = ac + ad + bc + bd.$$

Example: Multiply $(2x-3)(4x-1)$.

Solution: $(2x-3)(4x-1) = 2x(4x) + 2x(-1) - 3(4x) - 3(-1) =$
$8x^2 - 2x - 12x + 3 = 8x^2 - 14x + 3$.

When multiplying by a trinomial or other long polynomial, it is useful to think of distributing each term separately:

$$(2x-3y)(4x-2y-5)$$
$$= 2x(4x-2y+5) - 3y(4x-2y+5)$$
$$= 8x^2 - 4xy + 10x - 12xy + 6y^2 - 15y$$
$$= 8x^2 + 10x - 16xy - 15y + 6y^2$$

Check for Understanding: Distribute and simplify:

1.370 $(3a-4)(2a-3)$ **1.470** $(8x-1)(x+3)$

1.570 $(8a-2b-3)(a+2b)$

Special Products:

Many competition problems revolve around two special cases of distribution, and it is useful to be able to do the distribution for problems like the ones below quickly in your head. Multiply each of the following and look for a shortcut:

1. $(a-5)(a+5)$ **2.** $(x-5)^2$

3. $(6x-7)(6x+7)$ **4.** $(3x+1)^2$

5. $(2a-9)(2a+9)$ **6.** $(xy-4)^2$

Difference of Squares:

Problems 1, 3, and 5 on the previous page each create a difference of squares:

$$(a+b)(a-b) = a^2 - b^2.$$

When multiplying $(6x+5y)(6x-5y)$, you should see quickly that the first term will be $(6x)^2$ and the last term will be $(5y)(-5y)$, with the middle terms $5y(6)$ and $6(-5y)$ cancelling each other:

$$(6x+5y)(6x-5y) = 36x^2 - 25y^2.$$

The solutions to #1, #3, and #5 on the previous page are:

$$a^2 - 25, \ 36x^2 - 49, \text{ and } 4a^2 - 81.$$

Perfect Squares:

Problems 2, 4, and 6 on the previous page are perfect squares, and will always be in the form:

$$(a+b)^2 = a^2 + 2ab + b^2.$$

When multiplying $(6x-5y)^2$, you should see quickly that the first and last terms will be $(6x)^2$ and $(-5y)^2$, with the middle term $2(6x)(-5y)$:

$$(6x-5y)^2 = 36x^2 - 60xy + 25y^2.$$

The solutions to #2, #4, and #6 on the previous page are:

$$x^2 - 10x + 25, \ 9x^2 + 6x + 1, \text{ and } x^2y^2 - 8xy + 16.$$

Check for Understanding: Distribute and simplify each.

1.080 $(a-7)(a+3)$ **1.180** $(y-11)^2$

1.280 $(2x-3)(2x+3)$ **1.380** $(3x+1)(2x-5)$

1.480 $(2a+b)^2$ **1.580** $(a+2)(a+9)(a-2)$

Connection: Sum of the reciprocals.

If you can find the product of two numbers ab, and their sum $a + b$, you can find the sum of their reciprocals:

$$\frac{a+b}{ab} = \frac{a}{ab} + \frac{b}{ab} = \frac{1}{b} + \frac{1}{a}.$$

Example: The product of two positive numbers is 9 and the sum of their squares is 31. What is the sum of their reciprocals?

Reasoning: We are given $ab = 9$ and $a^2 + b^2 = 31$. To find $(a + b)$, we know that $(a + b)^2 = a^2 + 2ab + b^2$. Substituting 31 for $a^2 + b^2$ and 9 for ab gives us $a^2 + 2ab + b^2 = 49$, so $(a + b)^2 = 49$, which makes $a + b = \pm\sqrt{49}$, so $a + b = 7$ (the problem states that both numbers are positive). This is enough to solve:

$$\frac{1}{a} + \frac{1}{b} = \frac{a+b}{ab} = \frac{7}{9}.$$

Practice: Applications.

1.090 A square has an area of 50cm². The length is increased by 4cm and the width is decreased by 4cm. What is the area of the resulting rectangle?

1.190 The sum of two numbers is five and their product is two. What is the sum of the squares of the two numbers?

1.290 If $ab = 7$, $bc = 5$ and $a + c = 4$, what is $a + b + c$?

1.390 The area of the rectangle is 216cm². What is the length of the shorter side of the rectangle?

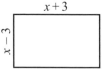

1.490 What is the smallest possible sum of two positive integers whose product is 999,996?

1.6: Quadratics

A trinomial in the form $ax^2 + bx + c$ where $a \neq 0$ is called a **quadratic.**

Factoring:

GCF: The first thing to look for when factoring any polynomial is a GCF. For example, you can factor $4x$ from the polynomial $4x^2 - 16x$ to get $4x(x - 4)$.

Trinomials: A trinomial in the form $ax^2 + bx + c$ is easiest to factor into a product of binomials (if it is factorable) when the value of a is 1. Consider:
$$(x - 3)(x + 5) = x^2 + 2x - 15.$$
Note: $-3 + 5 = 2$ (the b term) and $-3(5) = -15$ (the c term).
When we multiply $(x + j)(x + k)$ we get $x^2 + (j + k)x + jk$.
This makes it easy to factor a trinomial when the coefficient of x^2 is 1.

Example: Factor $x^2 + 7x - 18$.

Reasoning: We are trying to factor $x^2 + 7x - 18$ into $(x + j)(x + k)$, where j and k have a product of -18 and a sum of 7. The pairs of factors of 18 are $1 \cdot 18$, $2 \cdot 9$, and $3 \cdot 6$. We see that $-2 \cdot 9 = -18$ and $-2 + 9 = 7$, so $x^2 + 7x - 18 = (x - 2)(x + 9)$.

Example: Factor $x^2 - 6x + 8$.

Reasoning: We are looking for two numbers whose product is 8 and whose sum is -6. The pairs of factors of 8 are $1 \cdot 8$ and $2 \cdot 4$. We can use $2 \cdot 4$ if both are negative.
$$x^2 - 6x + 8 = (x - 2)(x - 4)$$

Check for Understanding: Factor each:

    1.001 $x^2 - 9x + 20$ **1.101** $x^2 - 25x - 84$

Factoring: Perfect Squares.
If a trinomial in the form $ax^2 + bx + c$ does not have a GCF
and a is not equal to 1, you should look first to see if
it is a perfect square. Recognizing perfect squares
takes some practice.

Example: Factor $4x^2 + 12x + 9$.

Reasoning: If a and c are perfect squares, it is likely that
the trinomial is a perfect square. In this case, we get
$(2x + 3)^2$. Be sure to do a quick check to make sure
that the middle term is correct.

Check for Understanding: Factor each:

     1.201 $9x^2 + 6x + 1$ **1.301** $49x^2 - 126x + 81$

Factoring a Difference of Squares:
Recognizing a difference of squares is easy:

     $a^2 - b^2$ can be factored into $(a + b)(a - b)$.

Example: Factor $4x^2 - 81$.

Reasoning: This is clearly a difference of squares and can
be factored into $(2x + 9)(2x - 9)$.

Practice: Factoring.
Factor each completely.

     1.401 $121x^2 - 1$ **1.501** $25x^2 - 9$

     1.601 $8x^2y - 24xy$ **1.701** $2x^2 - 14x + 24$

     1.801 $4x^2 - 36$ **1.901** $7a^2 - 28a + 28$

     1.011 $x^4 - 81$ **1.111** $x^4 - 5x^2 + 4$

     1.211 $a^2 - 6ab + 9b^2$ **1.311** $30 - 25c + 5c^2$

Harder factoring:

If a trinomial in the form $ax^2 + bx + c$ does not have a GCF
and a is not equal to 1, *and* it is not a perfect square,
the factoring becomes more difficult. If it can be
factored, there is a nice method which will allow you
to factor even difficult trinomials quickly:

First: Learn to **factor by grouping**.

Example: Factor $6x^2 - 3x - 8x + 4$.

Reasoning: The first pair of terms $(6x^2 - 3x)$ can be
factored into $3x(2x - 1)$ and the second pair of terms
$(-8x + 4)$ can be factored into $-4(2x - 1)$, which
means $6x^2 - 3x - 8x + 4 = 3x(2x - 1) - 4(2x - 1)$.
Can you see why this is equal to $(3x - 4)(2x - 1)$?
Try writing-out the distribution of $(3x - 4)(2x - 1)$
to make sure you understand the last step.
$(3x - 4)(2x - 1) = 3x(2x - 1) - 4(2x - 1)$, so
$3x(2x - 1) - 4(2x - 1) = (3x - 4)(2x - 1)$

Now, we add one more step:

Example: Factor $6x^2 - 23x - 18$.

Reasoning: There are many problems which are relatively
easy to guess-and-check, but this is not one of them
(at least not for me). We want to make this problem
look like the previous one by splitting up the $-23x$.

The key is finding a number whose product is equal to ac:
$6(-18) = -108$, and whose sum is b: (-23).
Factors of 108 are $1 \cdot 108$, $2 \cdot 54$, $3 \cdot 36$, **$4 \cdot 27$**, $6 \cdot 18$,
and $9 \cdot 12$. Using 4 and -27, we rewrite the
expression and factor by grouping.

$$6x^2 - 23x - 18 = 6x^2 - 27x + 4x - 18$$
$$= 3x(2x - 9) + 2(2x - 9)$$
$$= (3x + 2)(2x - 9)$$

Practice: Factoring.

1.021 Factor completely: $16x^2 - 38x - 5$.

1.121 The perimeter of a rectangle is 16cm, and the area of the same rectangle is 8cm². What is the diagonal length of the rectangle? (See section **5.3**).

1.221 The difference between the squares of two numbers is 80. If the sum of the two numbers is 16, what is their positive difference?

1.321 Factor completely: $256x^8 - 1$.

1.421 Solve for x: $\dfrac{2x^2 - 5x - 12}{2x + 3} = 9$.

1.521 Two circles are internally tangent at A, with diameter AB intersecting the smaller circle at C. The shaded region has an area of 9π cm², and BC = 4cm. What is the sum of the radii of the two circles?

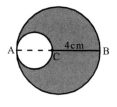

1.621 The diagonal length of a rectangle is $\sqrt{46}$, and its area is 9cm². Find its perimeter. (See section **5.3**).

1.721 The sum of two positive numbers is 6, and the sum of their squares is 22. What is the sum of their reciprocals? Express your answer as a common fraction.

1.821 What is the complete prime factorization of $2^{20} - 1$?

1.921 For positive integers a and b, $(a + \sqrt{b})^2 = 9 + 4\sqrt{5}$, what is $(a + \sqrt{b})^3$? (See section **1.7**).

Solving Quadratics by Factoring:
If $ab = 0$, then either a or b must be 0. Similarly, if
$$(a+b)(c+d) = 0, \text{ then } a+b = 0 \text{ and/or } c+d = 0.$$

Example: Solve for x: $x^2 - 3x - 54 = 0$.

Reasoning: We can factor the left side of the equation to get $(x-9)(x+6) = 0$. This means that either $x - 9 = 0$ or $x + 6 = 0$. Either $x = 9$ or $x = -6$.

Example: Solve for x: $6x^2 = 7x + 3$.

Reasoning: To solve a quadratic by factoring, we want one side of the equation to equal zero, so we subtract $7x + 3$ from both sides of the equation to get $6x^2 - 7x - 3 = 0$. Factoring gives us $(2x-3)(3x+1) = 0$. This means that either $2x - 3 = 0$ or $3x + 1 = 0$.

$$\text{Either } x = \frac{3}{2} \text{ or } x = -\frac{1}{3}.$$

Example: The width of a rectangle is 1cm less than ten times its length. Find the perimeter of the rectangle if the area is 60cm².

Reasoning: The side lengths can be represented by x and $(10x - 1)$. This gives us $x(10x - 1) = 60$, so $10x^2 - x = 60$ and $10x^2 - x - 60 = 0$. Factoring, we get $(5x + 12)(2x - 5) = 0$. This gives two solutions:

$$x = -\frac{12}{5} \text{ and } x = \frac{5}{2}.$$

Only the positive solution makes sense. The longer side is $10 \cdot \frac{5}{2} - 1 = 24$, which makes the perimeter 53cm.

Solving Quadratics: The Quadratic Formula.

The solutions of a quadratic equation $ax^2 + bx + c = 0$ are called the **roots**. Sometimes it will not be possible to solve a quadratic by factoring. When the roots of a quadratic are irrational (and sometimes even when they are rational) it is easiest to solve for the roots using the quadratic formula. The roots of a quadratic are the solutions for x in the equation $ax^2 + bx + c = 0$, given by the **quadratic formula**:

$$x = \frac{-b \pm \sqrt{b^2 - 4ac}}{2a}$$

It is easy to find the derivation of the quadratic formula online and it involves some nice algebra using a method called completing the square. I strongly recommend a thorough review of the derivation. This is one of the few formulas used in this book that absolutely must be committed to memory (along with Heron's formula and a handful of area/volume formulas).

Example: Solve for x: $2x^2 - 4x = 7$.

Reasoning: Begin by subtracting the 7 from both sides to get $2x^2 - 4x - 7 = 0$. Do a quick check to make sure it cannot be factored. Once you recognize that it cannot be factored, use the quadratic formula by plugging-in (2) for a, (–4) for b, and (–7) for c:

$$x = \frac{-(-4) \pm \sqrt{(-4)^2 - 4(2)(-7)}}{2(2)} = \frac{4 \pm \sqrt{16 + 56}}{4}$$

$$= \frac{4 \pm \sqrt{72}}{4} = \frac{4 \pm 6\sqrt{2}}{4} = 1 \pm \frac{3\sqrt{2}}{2}$$

The solutions are $x = 1 + \dfrac{3\sqrt{2}}{2}$ and $x = 1 - \dfrac{3\sqrt{2}}{2}$.

Solving Quadratics: Word Problems.

Many problems which require that you solve a quadratic equation involve a system of equations where the product of two numbers is known along with another relationship between the two numbers (like their sum or difference).

Example: Ryan has forgotten the day and month of his father's birthday. His father gives him the following hints for the numeric date: The day is ten more than twice the month. The month times the day equals the two-digit year he was born, '72. On what date was Ryan's dad born?

Reasoning: (I know, you could probably guess-and-check this one, but we will solve it using a quadratic). We are asked to solve the following system for the day (d) and month (m) of the father's birthday:

$$d = 10 + 2m$$

$$dm = 72$$

As with a linear system of equations, we substitute $10 + 2m$ for d in the second equation:

$$(10 + 2m)m = 72,$$

$$\text{or } 10m + 2m^2 = 72.$$

Divide by 2, rearrange the terms, and subtract to get:

$$m^2 + 5m - 36 = 0$$

Factoring is easiest here: $(m + 9)(m - 4) = 0$
Only the positive solution $m = 4$ makes sense. Plug this back into either of the original equations and solve for d to get $d = 18$. Ryan's father was born on 4/18/72, or April 18, 1972.

It was not necessary in this problem, but the quadratic formula could have been used to find the solutions to the equation $m^2 + 5m - 36 = 0$.

Sum and Product of the Roots:

Look at sum and product of the roots of the following

quadratic: $0 = 10x^2 - 29x - 21 = (5x + 3)(2x - 7)$.

The roots are $x = -\dfrac{3}{5}$ and $x = \dfrac{7}{2}$.

Their **sum** is $-\dfrac{3}{5} + \dfrac{7}{2} = \dfrac{29}{10}$ which is $-\dfrac{b}{a}$ and

their **product** is $-\dfrac{3}{5}\left(\dfrac{7}{2}\right) = -\dfrac{21}{10}$ which is $\dfrac{c}{a}$.

The same is true for any quadratic. This can shorten the work for many problems involving the roots of a quadratic.

Example: The roots of the quadratic $3x^2 - 7x - 18$ are m and n. Find the sum of their reciprocals.

Reasoning: $\dfrac{1}{m} + \dfrac{1}{n} = \dfrac{m + n}{mn}$, so we only need the sum and

the product of the roots. The sum is $-\dfrac{b}{a} = \dfrac{7}{3}$ and the

product is $\dfrac{c}{a} = \dfrac{-18}{3} = -6$, making $\dfrac{m + n}{mn} = \dfrac{7/3}{-6} =$

$\dfrac{7}{3}\left(-\dfrac{1}{6}\right) = -\dfrac{7}{18}$.

Practice: Sum and Product of the Roots.

1.631 What is the sum of the roots of $9x^2 - 7x + 1 = 0$?

1.731 The two solutions of $2x^2 + 1 = 5x$ are j and k. What is the value of $(j - 1)(1 - k)$?

Quadratics: Word Problems.

1.031 The product of two numbers is 9 and their sum is 12. Express their positive difference in simplest radical form.

1.131 The length of a rectangle of area 10cm^2 is one cm greater than three times its width. Express the perimeter of the rectangle as a common fraction in simplest form.

1.231 48 feet of fencing is used to create a pen enclosure which consists of three congruent rectangular pens as shown, with a combined area of 72 ft^2. What is the perimeter of the enclosure?

1.331 48 feet of fencing is used to create a pen enclosure again, but this time the enclosure is against an existing barn. The pens have a combined area of 144 ft^2. What is the length of the side of the barn onto which the enclosure is attached?

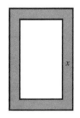

1.431 A photograph is 4.25 inches wide and 7.75 inches tall. It is mounted in a frame with a border x inches wide on all sides. If the area of the shaded border is 45in^2, what is its width x?

1.531 Kendrick rides his bike x miles per hour to school and it takes him $x + 15$ minutes to get there. If Kendrick lives 5.4 miles from school, how many minutes does it take for Kendrick to ride to school?

1.7: Exponents and Radicals

Exponents are used to represent repeated multiplication. For example, 2^3 is used to represent $2 \cdot 2 \cdot 2$.

Multiplication: Simplify $2^3 \cdot 2^4 \cdot 2^2$.

To do this, we can expand and regroup:
$$2^3 \cdot 2^4 \cdot 2^2 = 2 \cdot 2 \cdot 2 \cdot 2 \cdot 2 \cdot 2 \cdot 2 \cdot 2 \cdot 2 = 2^9.$$

Of course, this is not such a good idea when we are trying to simplify $5^{19} \cdot 5^{20}$, but you should see that if we were to write-out the product we would have 39 fives:
$$5^{19} \cdot 5^{20} = 5 \cdot 5 \cdot 5 ... \cdot 5 = 5^{39}.$$

The rule is to add the exponents: $a^x \cdot a^y = a^{x+y}$.

Avoid this common mistake: $7^4 \cdot 7^2$ does *not* equal 49^6.

Division: Simplify $\dfrac{3^6}{3^4}$.

Expand and cancel (3/3 = 1): $\dfrac{\cancel{3} \cdot \cancel{3} \cdot \cancel{3} \cdot \cancel{3} \cdot 3 \cdot 3}{\cancel{3} \cdot \cancel{3} \cdot \cancel{3} \cdot \cancel{3}} = 3^2$.

Once again, this is useful for small exponents, but what about simplifying much larger exponents? You should see that in the case of division, we subtract exponents:
$$\frac{7^{34}}{7^{29}} = 7^{34-29} = 7^5.$$

And if the exponent in the denominator is larger?
$$\frac{7^{29}}{7^{34}} = \frac{\cancel{7} ... \cancel{7} \cdot \cancel{7} \cdot \cancel{7}}{\cancel{7} ... \cancel{7} \cdot \cancel{7} \cdot 7 \cdot 7 \cdot 7 \cdot 7 \cdot 7} = \frac{1}{7^5} = 7^{29-34} = 7^{-5}.$$

This leads us to an understanding of **negative exponents**:
$$a^{-x} = \frac{1}{a^x}, \text{ and } \frac{1}{a^{-x}} = \frac{1}{\left(\dfrac{1}{a^x}\right)} = 1 \cdot \frac{a^x}{1} = a^x$$

Exponents: Rules for exponents.

Using our rules for exponents, it is easy to see why $a^0 = 1$.

Consider $\dfrac{a^x}{a^x} = a^{x-x} = a^0 = 1$. This is true for any value of a, except when $a = 0$ (0^0 is undefined).

Example: Solve for x: $3^x + 4^x = 2$.

Reasoning: This problem is all about recognition. If a problem looks too hard to solve using methods you have learned, there is probably a trick. In this case, understanding that any number to the 0 power is 1 allows you to answer quickly based solely on recognition ($x = 0$).

Raising a Power to a Power: Simplify $\left(2^3\right)^5$.

Expanding again: $\left(2^3\right)^5 = \left(2^3\right)\left(2^3\right)\left(2^3\right)\left(2^3\right)\left(2^3\right) = 2^{3 \cdot 5} = 2^{15}$, which leads us to the rule:

$$\left(a^x\right)^y = a^{xy}$$

Example: Simplify $\left[\left(x^3\right)^3\right]^3$.

Reasoning: Working from the inside out we get:

$$\left(x^{3 \cdot 3}\right)^3 = x^{3 \cdot 3 \cdot 3} = x^{27}$$

When things look weird:

The great thing about math is that the rules are not just made-up. They always work, even when things look more confusing.

Example: Simplify $\left[\left(2x^4\right)^{-4}\right]^{\frac{1}{4}}$.

Reasoning: $\left(2^{1(-4)} x^{4(-4)}\right)^{\frac{1}{4}} = 2^{-4\frac{1}{4}} x^{-16\frac{1}{4}} = 2^{-1} x^{-4} = \dfrac{1}{2x^4}$.

Fractional Exponents: Square Roots and other radicals. Having worked on our rules for exponents, you should be able to see that $9^{\frac{1}{2}} \cdot 9^{\frac{1}{2}} = 9^{\frac{1}{2}+\frac{1}{2}} = 9^1 = 9$, which suggests that: $9^{\frac{1}{2}} = 3$. You are probably more familiar with a different way of writing this:

$$9^{\frac{1}{2}} = \sqrt{9} = 3.$$

Taking the **square root** of a number a asks us to find a number x such that $x^2 = a$. Finding the **cube root** of a number a asks us to find a number x such that $x^3 = a$. You are probably very familiar with square roots like $\sqrt{25} = 5$ or $\sqrt{121} = 11$, and perhaps even cube roots like $\sqrt[3]{125} = 5$ and $\sqrt[3]{216} = 6$. It is useful in competitions to know your perfect squares at least to 20^2 and cubes to 10^3 (see appendix **p. 364**).

Square Roots: Multiplying and Simplifying. It is obvious that $\sqrt{9} \cdot \sqrt{9} = 9$ and $\sqrt{4} \cdot \sqrt{9} = 6$, but slightly less obvious that $\sqrt{2} \cdot \sqrt{8} = \sqrt{2 \cdot 8} = \sqrt{16} = 4$.

The rule: $\sqrt{a} \cdot \sqrt{b} = \sqrt{ab}$.

This is important for simplifying square roots as well:

Example: Simplify $\sqrt{48}$.
Solution: $\sqrt{48} = \sqrt{16 \cdot 3} = \sqrt{16} \cdot \sqrt{3} = 4\sqrt{3}$.

Example: Simplify $\sqrt{1 + 2 + 3 + 4 + ... + 24}$
Solution: $\sqrt{1 + 2 + 3 + 4 + ... + 24} = \sqrt{\dfrac{24 \cdot 25}{2}}$ (see **p.70**)

$= \sqrt{3 \cdot 4 \cdot 25} = \sqrt{4} \cdot \sqrt{25} \cdot \sqrt{3} = 10\sqrt{3}$.

Square Roots: Dividing and Rationalizing.

It is obvious that $\dfrac{\sqrt{9}}{\sqrt{36}} = \dfrac{3}{6} = \dfrac{1}{2}$ and $\dfrac{\sqrt{64}}{\sqrt{81}} = \dfrac{8}{9}$, but slightly less

obvious that $\dfrac{\sqrt{20}}{\sqrt{5}} = \sqrt{\dfrac{20}{5}} = \sqrt{4} = 2$.

The rule: $\dfrac{\sqrt{a}}{\sqrt{b}} = \sqrt{\dfrac{a}{b}}$.

This is also very important for simplifying square roots.

Example: Simplify $\dfrac{\sqrt{48}}{\sqrt{15}}$.

Solution: $\dfrac{\sqrt{48}}{\sqrt{15}} = \sqrt{\dfrac{16}{5}} = \dfrac{\sqrt{16}}{\sqrt{5}} = \dfrac{4}{\sqrt{5}}$, but this is generally

considered incomplete. To complete the simplifica-
tion, it is customary to *rationalize the denominator*
of a fraction.

Examples: Rationalize each denominator.

$$\textbf{1. } \dfrac{4}{\sqrt{5}} \qquad \textbf{2. } \dfrac{5}{2+\sqrt{5}}$$

Solutions:

1. Multiply by $\dfrac{\sqrt{5}}{\sqrt{5}}$ to remove the $\sqrt{5}$ in the denominator:

$$\dfrac{4}{\sqrt{5}} \cdot \dfrac{\sqrt{5}}{\sqrt{5}} = \dfrac{4\sqrt{5}}{5}.$$

2. Multiply by $\dfrac{2-\sqrt{5}}{2-\sqrt{5}}$. $2-\sqrt{5}$ is called the conjugate of

$2+\sqrt{5}$, and creates a difference of squares:

$$\dfrac{5(2-\sqrt{5})}{(2+\sqrt{5})(2-\sqrt{5})} = \dfrac{5(2-\sqrt{5})}{4-5} = \dfrac{10-5\sqrt{5}}{-1} = 5\sqrt{5}-10.$$

Practice: Exponents and Radicals.

1.041 Simplify: $\left[2(n^2)^{-2}\right]^2$.

1.141 Simplify: $\sqrt{\dfrac{13}{56}} \cdot \sqrt{\dfrac{7}{26}}$.

1.241 Solve for x: $\sqrt[6]{x} = \sqrt[3]{5^2}$.

1.341 You can triple the volume of any regular polyhedron by multiplying each of its edge lengths by $\sqrt[3]{3}$. What is the edge length of a polyhedron whose volume is one-third that of a polyhedron of edge length 12cm? Express your answer in simplest radical form.

1.441 Simplify: $\dfrac{1}{\sqrt{1}+\sqrt{2}} + \dfrac{1}{\sqrt{2}+\sqrt{3}} + ... + \dfrac{1}{\sqrt{49}+\sqrt{50}}$.

1.541 Solve for x: $2^x = \left(4^{\frac{1}{3}} \cdot 16^{\frac{3}{4}} \right)^3$.

1.641 Given that n is the least positive integer greater than 1 for which $\sqrt[3]{n}$, and $\sqrt[4]{n}$ are both integers, find $\sqrt{n}$.

1.741 The surfaces of a rectangular prism have areas of 12cm², 16cm², and 27cm². What is the volume of the prism?

1.841 The side lengths of a right triangle are in the ratio $(x):(x+1):(x+3)$. Express the area of the triangle in simplest radical form. (See section **5.3**).

1.941 If $5^n = 2$, what is the value of 25^{2n+1} ?

1.8: Statistics

There are three measures of central tendency (averages)
used in most competition problems: the mean,
median, and mode for a set of data. The range is
also used and is a measure of how spread out a set
of data is.

The **arithmetic mean** is commonly referred to as the
average for a set of values. The mean is the sum
of all values divided by the number of values.

The **median** is the middle number for a set of data. When
the values are arranged from least to greatest, the
median is the value in the middle for an odd number
of values. For an even number of values (where
there is no middle term), the median is the mean of
the two middle terms.

The **mode** is the term which occurs the most. There can
be more than one mode (if more than one value
occurs more than the rest), or no mode at all (if
every value occurs with the same frequency).

The **range** is the difference between the highest and lowest
values in a set.

Example: Find the mean, median, mode, and range for the
following set of values: 16, 20, 13, 21, 24, 30, 21, 7.

Reasoning: First, we order the values from least to
greatest: 7, 13, 16, 20, 21, 21, 24, 30.
Mean: $(7+13+16+20+21+21+24+30)/8 = 19$.
Median: $(20+21)/2 = 20.5$.
Mode: 21.
Range: $30 - 7 = 23$.

There are many other statistical measures, but these are the
ones most commonly used in major competitions.

Statistics: Mean, Median, Mode and Range.

The most commonly used skill required for competition problems involves using the mean to find the sum of the values in a set of data.

Example: Peter averaged a 92 on his first seven quizzes. What score will he need on his 8th quiz to increase his average to a 93?

Reasoning: To average a 92 on seven quizzes, you would need to score $92 \cdot 7 = 644$ points. Make sure you see why: label his first 7 scores $a+b+c+d+e+f+g$.

$$\frac{a+b+c+d+e+f+g}{7} = 92,$$

so $a+b+c+d+e+f+g = 92(7)$.

To average 93 on eight quizzes, he would need to score $93 \cdot 8 = 744$ points. This is a difference of 100 points, so Peter will need to score a 100 on his 8th quiz.

Sometimes it is actually quicker to do the math in your head. It doesn't matter what his first seven scores were, so to make it easy we will just assume he scored seven 92's. Another 92 would keep his average at 92, but we want to add a point to his average. One obvious way to do this would be to add a point to each of the eight scores. We can also add those 8 points to the final score, making it a $92 + 8 = 100$.

Example: The mean for the set of data below is 45. What is the value of x? 35, 40, 42, 42, 46, 47, 50, x.

Reasoning: We could subtract the sum of the seven scores from $45 \cdot 8$ to get 58. There is a method that makes this easy to do in your head. Consider the difference of each number from the mean. The differences must add up to zero, so x is 13 more than the mean.

$-10, -5, -3, -3, +1, +2, +5, +13$ **(58)**.

Practice: Mean, Median, Mode and Range.

1.051 What is the mean of the first ten positive *odd* integers?

1.151 The average for Akhil's first 7 tests this year is 88. What score will he need to average on his next two tests if he wants to improve his test average to 90?

1.251 The mean of a set of seven positive integers is 7, the median is 8, and the distinct mode is 9. What is the greatest possible range for the set of integers?

1.351 Four integers are added to the set {3, 4, 5, 5, 8}, increasing the mean, median, and mode each by 1. What is the greatest integer in the new set?

1.451 Micah scores an 80 on his tenth quiz, increasing his quiz average by 2 points. What is his new quiz average?

1.551 In a set of ten integers, the average of the two smallest integers is 102, the average of the three smallest integers is 103, the four smallest is 104, and so forth until the average of all ten integers is 110. What is the greatest of these integers?

1.651 If Tanya scores 19 points in her last game, she will have averaged exactly 18 points per game for the season. If she can score 35 points, her average will be 20 points per game. How many games are in a season?

1.751 Austin has calculated that if he scores a 95 on his next three tests, it will improve his test average to 93. If Austin has taken six tests so far this year, what is his current average?

1.851 How many distinct sets of three positive integers have a mean of 6, a median of 7, and no mode?

Algebra: Sequences and Series

1.9: Sequences and Series:

A **sequence** is an ordered list of terms, for example: 1, 3, 5, 7, 9 is a sequence of five terms with a common difference of 2. If a sequence is infinite, we usually indicate that the sequence continues forever with three dots: 4, 7, 10, 13,... is an infinite **arithmetic sequence** with a common difference of 3.

A sequence is called an **arithmetic sequence** if the difference between consecutive terms is always the same.

We are often asked to find the nth term of an arithmetic sequence, labeled a_n. You may see an arithmetic sequence labeled: $a_1, a_2, a_3, a_4, ...a_n$. This is just a way of labeling the first term a_1, the second term a_2, and so forth until the nth term is a_n.

Finding an expression which can be used to represent the nth terms is often intuitive, and important for solving most problems involving an arithmetic sequence.

Consider the arithmetic sequence: 4, 11, 18, 25,...
The sequence has a common difference of 7, starting with 4. The 2nd term is $1 \cdot 7 = 7$ more than 4. The 3rd term is $2 \cdot 7 = 14$ more than 4. Following the pattern, the 29th term will be $28 \cdot 7 = 196$ more than 4. The nth term will be $(n-1)7$ more than 4.

The formula for the nth term a_n of an arithmetic sequence an beginning with a_1 with common difference d is:

$$a_n = a_1 + (n-1)d.$$

Like most formulas, the one above is only useful if you understand it. Work to understand how it works rather than simply trying to memorize it.

Arithmetic Sequences:

There are several additional properties of arithmetic sequences which can be useful in solving problems.

If we are looking for the **common difference** given two terms a_x and a_y, subtract a_x from a_y to find the total difference, then subtract x from y to determine how many times the common difference has been added. The common difference d in a sequence is:

$$d = \frac{a_y - a_x}{y - x}.$$

Example: Find the common difference in an arithmetic sequence if the 3rd term is 18 and the 11th term is 44.

Reasoning: The common difference has been added 8 times to get from the 3rd to the 11th term, and the difference between the terms is $44 - 18 = 26$. This gives us a common difference of 26/8 = 3.25.

The median of a finite arithmetic sequence can be found using the first and last terms. This allows us to find some terms quickly. For example, if we are given the 11th and 17th terms of an arithmetic sequence and asked for the 14th term, it will be the average of the 11th and 17th terms (because the 14th term is the median of terms 11 through 17). Note also that **the mean and median of a finite arithmetic sequence are equal**.

Example: The 20th term of an arithmetic sequence is 19 and the 50th term is 44. What is the 35th term of the sequence?

Reasoning: The 35th term is the median of the sequence between the 20th and 50th terms, so we find the mean of 19 and 44:

$$\frac{19 + 44}{2} = 31.5.$$

Arithmetic Series:

An **arithmetic series** is the sum of an arithmetic sequence.
You will learn more about triangular numbers in
chapter **2.3**, but we will introduce them here as they
relate to arithmetic series. Consider the sum of the
first 100 positive integers:

$$1 + 2 + 3 + 4 + ... + 100.$$

Before you reach for your calculator and start
plugging away, consider the mean of the first 100
integers. It is the same as the median:

$$\frac{1 + 100}{2} = 50.5.$$

If you know there are 100 terms, then the sum of the
first 100 terms is just 100 times their average:

$$100 \cdot \frac{1 + 100}{2} = 100 \cdot 50.5 = 5,050.$$

The same is true for any arithmetic series. To find the sum
of the terms, we find the average of the terms and
multiply by the number of terms:

$$a_1 + a_2 + a_3 + ... + a_n = n \cdot \frac{a_1 + a_n}{2}.$$

Sometimes finding the number of terms is tricky.

Example: Solve for x if $x = -9 + 7 + 23 + 39 + ... + 279$.

Reasoning: To find the number of terms, first find the
common difference (16). Add 25 to every term to
make the first term 16 and we get 16+32+...+304.
Dividing this by 16 we get 1+2+...+19, so there are
19 terms (there are many other ways to do this).

The average is: $\frac{-9 + 279}{2} = 135.$

Multiply by 19 terms to get $135 \cdot 19 = 2,565$.

If you prefer to use a formula for this operation, find one on
your own and be sure to check that it works.

Geometric Sequences:

A **geometric sequence** is one in which consecutive terms form a common ratio, for example:

6, 12, 24, 48, ... is a geometric sequence with a common ratio of 12/6 = 2.

$4, 6, 9, \dfrac{27}{2}, \dfrac{81}{4}, ...$ has a common ratio of $\dfrac{6}{4}$, or $\dfrac{3}{2}$.

For a geometric series with first term a and common ratio r:

$a, ar, ar^2, ar^3, ar^4 ...$ the nth term will be ar^{n-1}.

Example: The 10th term of the geometric sequence that begins: 54, 36, 24, 16... can be expressed $\dfrac{2^a}{3^b}$.

Find the positive difference between a and b.

Reasoning: Find the common ratio first: 36/54 = 2/3. The 10th term will be $54(2/3)^9$:

$$54 \cdot \left(\frac{2}{3}\right)^9 = 2 \cdot 3^3 \cdot \frac{2^9}{3^9} = \frac{2^{10}}{3^6}, \text{ so } a - b = 4.$$

The median of a finite geometric sequence of positive numbers is called the **geometric mean**. The geometric mean of two numbers a and b is the square root of their product: $\sqrt{ab}$.

For example, in the sequence a, ar, ar^2, ar^3, ar^4, the median (obviously ar^2 here) can be found by:

$$\sqrt{a \cdot ar^4} = ar^2.$$

Example: A geometric sequence has 99 terms, beginning with 12 and ending with 147. What is the 50th term in the sequence?

Reasoning: In a 99-term sequence, the 50th term is the median or middle number, which is the geometric mean of 12 and 147:

$$\sqrt{12 \cdot 147} = \sqrt{2 \cdot 2 \cdot 3 \cdot 3 \cdot 7 \cdot 7} = 2 \cdot 3 \cdot 7 = 42$$

Geometric Series:
A sum of terms in geometric sequence is called a **geometric series.**

Example: Find the sum: $\dfrac{1}{3} + \dfrac{1}{3^2} + \dfrac{1}{3^3} + \dfrac{1}{3^4} \ldots$

Reasoning: We can multiply $x = \dfrac{1}{3} + \dfrac{1}{3^2} + \dfrac{1}{3^3} + \dfrac{1}{3^4} \ldots$

by $\dfrac{1}{3}$ to get $\dfrac{1}{3}x = \dfrac{1}{3^2} + \dfrac{1}{3^3} + \dfrac{1}{3^4} + \dfrac{1}{3^5} \ldots$ Subtract this

equation from the original to get $\dfrac{2}{3}x = \dfrac{1}{3}$, so $x = \dfrac{1}{2}$.

Try the same process again with variables to find a formula for the sum of terms in a geometric series where a is the first term and r is the common ratio:

$x = a + ar + ar^2 \ldots$	Multiply by the common ratio r.
$rx = ar + ar^2 + ar^3 \ldots$	Subtract the second equation from the first.
$x - rx = a$	Factor out the x.
$x(1 - r) = a$	Divide by $(1 - r)$.
$x = \dfrac{a}{1 - r}$	Now we have a formula!

To find the sum of a geometric series, divide the first term by $(1 - r)$, where r is the common ratio. Do not memorize this formula until you can do the math without it.

Practice: Sequences and Series.

1.061 Find the sum of the first 1,000 positive odd integers.

1.161 The 5th term of an arithmetic sequence is 18 and the 9th term is 24. What is the 99th term?

1.261 The sum of the first three terms of an arithmetic sequence is 20 and the sum of the next three terms is 25. What is the first term in the sequence? Express your answer as a common fraction in simplest terms.

1.361 What is the positive difference between the fifth term of the geometric sequence that begins 16, 24, ... and the fifth term of the arithmetic sequence that begins 16, 24, ...?

1.461 How many geometric sequences of two or more positive integers begin with 1 and end with 1,024?

1.561 Brandy has counted the number of freckles she has each year since she turned 7, when she had only 5 freckles. She turns 17 today and has 245 freckles. If the number of freckles she has can be approximated by a geometric sequence, about how many freckles did she have on her 12th birthday?

1.661 Find the perimeter of the smallest triangle whose integer side lengths form a geometric sequence whose common ratio r is not equal to 1. (See **p.178**).

1.761 Simplify: $\dfrac{1}{2^1} + \dfrac{1}{2^2} + \dfrac{1}{2^3} + \dfrac{1}{2^4} + ... + \dfrac{1}{2^{10}}$.

1.861 Find the sum of $\dfrac{2}{5} + \dfrac{4}{25} + \dfrac{8}{125} + \dfrac{16}{625} ...$

1.10:   More Substitution

There are many uses for substitution outside of solving a
systems of equations.

Example: Nested square roots.

Simplify: $\sqrt{6+\sqrt{6+\sqrt{6+...}}}$.

Reasoning: Let $x = \sqrt{6+\sqrt{6+\sqrt{6+...}}}$, then

$x^2 = 6+\sqrt{6+\sqrt{6+...}}$ we can substitute

$\sqrt{6+\sqrt{6+\sqrt{6+...}}}$ for x to get $x^2 = 6+x$, giving us
the quadratic $x^2 - x - 6 = 0$, which we factor:
$(x-3)(x+2) = 0$. The principal or positive solution
$x = 3$ is assumed. The solution $x = -2$ is extraneous.

Example: Continued Fractions.

Simplify: $\cfrac{1}{2+\cfrac{1}{2+\cfrac{1}{2+...}}}$.

Reasoning: Let $x = \cfrac{1}{2+\cfrac{1}{2+\cfrac{1}{2+...}}}$.

Substituting, we get $x = \cfrac{1}{2+x}$ or $2x + x^2 = 1$.

This gives us the quadratic $x^2 + 2x - 1 = 0$. We use the
quadratic formula **(p.40)** to solve for the roots, which
gives us $x = \sqrt{2} - 1$ (and an extraneous negative
solution).

Practice: Using Substitution.

1.071 Simplify: $0.\overline{9}$.

1.171 Simplify: $\cfrac{5}{6+\cfrac{5}{6+\cfrac{5}{6+...}}}$.

1.271 Simplify: $20+\sqrt{20+\sqrt{20+\sqrt{20+....}}}$.

1.371 Simplify: $3+\cfrac{1}{3+\cfrac{1}{3+\cfrac{1}{3+...}}}$.

1.471 The formula for the sum of the powers of 2 from 2^0 to 2^n is $2^0+2^1+2^2...+2^n=2^{n+1}-1$. Write a formula which could be used to find the sum of the powers of a^0 through a^n in terms of a and n.

1.571 Simplify: $1+\cfrac{3}{2+\cfrac{3}{1+\cfrac{3}{2+\cfrac{3}{1+...}}}}$.

1.671 The cube root of what number can be expressed as the following continued radical: $2\sqrt{3\sqrt{2\sqrt{3\sqrt{2...}}}}$?

1.771 Simplify: $1+\cfrac{1}{1+\cfrac{2}{1+\cfrac{1}{1+\cfrac{2}{1+...}}}}$.

Algebra: Chapter Review

Chapter Review

1.081 The product of two numbers is 30 and their sum is 16. Express their difference in simplest radical form.

1.181 If 3 zoogs are worth 5 moogs, and 7 joogs have the same value as 3 moogs, how many joogs would you expect to get in fair trade for 36 zoogs?

1.281 John is a pilot who regularly flies his small private jet from New York to Chicago. Flying with a 25mph tailwind, the flight takes 3 hours. Flying with a 25mph headwind, the flight takes 4 hours. How far is New York from Chicago?

1.381 What integer n could be included in the set of integers $\{6, 11, 13, 7, 14\}$ so that the mean is equal to $n + 1$?

1.481 If $3x + \dfrac{3}{x} = 5$, find the value of $3x^2 + \dfrac{3}{x^2}$. Express your answer as a common fraction.

1.581 For positive numbers a and b, the positive difference of a and b is divided by the positive difference of their reciprocals and the result is 5. What is the product of a and b?

1.681 If $\sqrt{32 + 10\sqrt{7}} = a + \sqrt{b}$ where a and b are both integers and b has no perfect square factors greater than 1, find $a + b$.

1.781 Tejas begins to paint a fence that is 100 meters long at noon. By 2pm, Tejas has one third of the fence painted and Jason arrives to help. At 3pm, four-fifths of the fence is painted and Tejas leaves Jason to finish painting the remaining fence. What time does Jason finish painting the fence?

1.881 A video camera has a battery pack that will last for 2 hours without charging if you are recording, and 3 hours if you are playing back video that you have already recorded. You want to record a video and then watch the whole thing. What is the greatest length in minutes of video that you can record and play back entirely with your video camera?

1.981 The sum of a and b is 15 and the sum of their squares is 150. What is the positive difference between a and b? Express your answer in simplest radical form.

1.091 Suzy's lemonade uses only sugar and squeezed lemon juice, but the ratio is a secret. One day you overhear Suzy commenting that she accidently doubled the amount of sugar without changing the amount of lemon juice, creating a drink that is 10% sugar. What is the ratio of sugar to lemon juice in Suzy's original recipe?

1.191 What is the greatest prime factor of $3^{12} + 2^2$?

1.291 Chefs Rohan and Lewis are chopping vegetables for a world-record setting stew. Rohan can chop 6 pounds of carrots in 11 minutes, while Lewis takes 13 minutes to chop 6 pounds of carrots. Working together, how many minutes will it take for Rohan and Lewis to chop 144 pounds of carrots?

1.391 A solid rubber ball rebounds to three-fourths the height it is dropped from. What is the total vertical distance traveled by a ball dropped from a height of 24 feet as it bounces to a rest (for example, when it hits the floor for the second time it will have traveled $24 + 18 + 18 = 60$ feet).

1.491 If $ab = 4$, $bc = 5$, and $ac = 10$, find $a^2 + b^2 + c^2$.

Counting
Chapter II

"We all know how to count, I thought this book was supposed
to be about stuff I don't know how to do!?!"

Counting is not always as easy as 1-2-3. There are techniques to be learned which allow for quick counting
of seemingly countless possibilities. Virtually every
probability problem depends on your ability to count
well, and the two chapters go hand-in-hand.

Few formulas are presented in this chapter. Counting
problems at this level rarely require the use of
memorized formulas. If you understand the concepts
behind them you will learn to use the formulas
without ever knowing them. Formulas are generally
easy to find online and there is a short list of useful
formulas in the appendix of this text.

Quite often it is the simplest counting problems which are
easiest to make mistakes on. We begin this chapter
on page 63 and end on page 101. Quick, how many
pages are in this chapter?

2.1: Basics

There are some basic counting techniques that seem obvious, but can cause problems if they are not understood.

Example: Marianne takes a pack of index cards and numbers them starting with 10 and ending with 50. How many cards does she number?

Reasoning: Numbering cards from 10 to 50 is the same as numbering cards from 1 to 41 (subtracting 9 from each number, we get 1 through 41 instead of 10 through 50), so there are 41 cards. Consider a similar problem to convince yourself that this is the case: Problems 10 through 20 were assigned for homework. How many problems is this? (Do you see why there are 11, not 10?)

Practice: Basics.

2.100 How many integers are less than 600 but greater than 500?

2.200 How many even integers are less than 600 but greater than 500?

2.300 Jonathan starts counting at 130 and counts by fives. What is the 13th number that Jonathan says?

2.400 Claire orders new checkbooks. Checks are numbered sequentially. If she orders 400 checks and the last check is number 3474, what number is on the first check?

Try to write a general rule:

How many positive integers are between a and b *exclusive*, where a is less than b?

Between integers a and b, there are $(b-a)-1$ integers. Exclusive means that a and b are excluded.

How many numbers are there from a to b *inclusive* $(a < b)$?

From a to b inclusive there are $(b-a)+1$ integers. Inclusive means that a and b are included.

Here is another easy counting problem to mess up:

Example: Jeremy owns a rectangular plot of land that is 60 yards long and 30 yards wide.

1. If he places a fence post at each corner and posts are placed every three yards, how many fence posts will there be on each side?

2. If he places a fence post at each corner and posts are placed every three yards, how many fence posts will he need to enclose his land?

Reasoning: At first glance, the answers to these problems seem to contradict each other. For the first problem, instead of considering the posts, consider the gaps between the posts. To go 60 yards requires twenty gaps. The first post is placed, and then a post is placed every 3 yards for a total of 21 posts. 30 yards requires 10 gaps, or 11 posts.

If two of the sides have 11 posts, and the other two sides have 21, it would appear that there are 64 posts, but we counted all four corners twice. We must subtract four to get a total of 60 posts.

When calculating the total, I prefer to think of it this way:

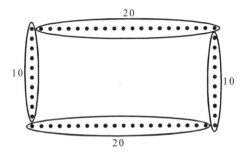

This is especially useful when a problem involves figures with more sides.

Practice: Counting Basics.

2.500 You are assigned even problems from 10 through 40 for tonight's homework. How many problems is this?

2.600 The soccer team has jerseys numbered from 10 to 30. Everyone on the team gets a jersey and there are three left over. How many players are on the team?

2.700 Chopping a carrot into slices (the usual way), how many cuts are required to make 20 pieces?

2.800 How many three digit whole numbers are there?

2.900 Paul is making a ruler. He places a long mark at every whole number, a medium mark every half-inch, and a tiny mark every quarter-inch. How many marks will he need to make a standard six-inch ruler?

2.010 How many even perfect squares are there from 100 to 10,000 inclusive?

2.110 The circumference of a circular table is 30 feet. If a set of silverware is placed every three feet around the circumference of the table. How many place-settings are there?

2.210 How many distinct pairs of consecutive integers have a product less than 10,000?

2.310 How many whole numbers less than 100 are multiples of 3 but not multiples of 5?

2.410 A field in the shape of a regular hexagon is enclosed with a fence using 120 evenly spaced posts. Assuming there is a post at every vertex, how many posts are on each side of the hexagon?

2.2: Venn Diagrams

A **Venn diagram** can be used to organize counting problems
where some items are included in multiple groups
and others are excluded.

Example: In science classroom: 19 students have a brother,
15 students have a sister, 7 students have both a
brother and a sister, and 6 students don't have any
siblings at all. How many students are in the classroom?

Reasoning: When you fill-in a Venn diagram to solve a
problem, work from the inside out. First we fill-in a
7 where the two regions overlap. Then we can fill-
in 12 students who only have a brother (19 minus the
7 we already accounted for) and 8 students who
only have a sister. Six students have no siblings for
a total of $7 + 12 + 8 + 6 = 33$ students.

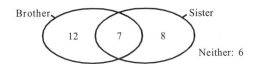

Example:

On a survey of 40 Raleigh students, 14 students responded
that they like Duke, 18 students responded that they
like UNC, and 11 students do not like Duke or UNC.
How many students like both Duke and UNC?

Reasoning:

This problem can be approached with a diagram, but it can
also be solved logically. Drawing the diagram will
help you understand the logic: there are 40 students,
but $14 + 18 + 11 = 43$, so there must be three
students who got counted twice. These are the
three students in the overlapping portion of the Venn
diagram who like both Duke and UNC.

Three-Set Venn Diagrams:
Using more than two sets can be more difficult.

Example: Every student who applied for admission to a
veterinary school has at least one pet: 30 have a cat,
28 have a dog and 26 have fish. If 13 students have
fish and a cat, 15 students have fish and a dog, 11
students have both a cat and a dog, and 4 students
have a cat, a dog, and fish. How many students
applied to veterinary school? Begin at the center of
the diagram below and work your way out to get:

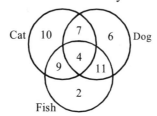

Using a Venn diagram is easy enough (there are 49 students),
but you can also use some basic reasoning. Google
inclusion-exclusion principal for more information
as we only give a general idea of the principal below.

30 have cats + 28 have a dog + 26 have fish = 84 owners.
Students who own two (or more) different animals
were counted multiple times, so we subtract them:
$84 - 13 - 15 - 11 = 45$. This seems right, but it is
different from the answer we got with the diagram.
Notice that when we subtracted students with two
pets, we subtracted the students who have all three
pets three times (we actually wanted to subtract
them twice). Add these 4 students back to get 49.

In a three-set Venn diagram, notice how
many times each group gets
counted when we add the total
members of all three sets:

Practice: Venn Diagrams.

2.020 At the pound there are 40 dogs. If 22 dogs have spots and 30 dogs have short hair, what is the fewest number of dogs that can have short hair and spots?

2.120 Ten friends go out to dinner together: 7 order an appetizer, 5 order a soup, and 4 order a salad. If everyone orders something, but no one orders exactly two things, how many people order all three things?

2.220 How many of the first 729 positive integers are perfect squares, cubes, or both?

2.320 All squares are both rectangles and rhombuses. All rhombuses and rectangles are parallelograms. On a sheet of paper Josh draws 19 rectangles, 15 rhombuses, and 7 squares. How many parallelograms did Josh draw?

2.420 How many of the smallest 1,000 positive integers are divisible by 5, 6, and/or 7?

2.520 Students were surveyed on their preference for tea. Three-fourths of the students surveyed like sweet tea, three-fifths of the students surveyed like unsweetened tea, and one sixth of the students do not like either. What is the fewest number of students surveyed who could like both sweet and unsweetened tea?

2.620 An auto dealership sells expensive foreign automobiles. You are looking for a black convertible Porsche. The lot has 50 cars that meet at least one of your criteria: 18 Porsches, 25 black cars, and 16 convertibles. There are 3 black convertibles, 4 black Porsches, and 5 convertible Porsches. How many black convertible Porsches are there?

2.3: Bowling Pins and Handshakes

How many bowling pins are set up in a
standard bowling lane? Draw the
pattern of pins.

If a fifth row is added, how many total pins will there be?
What if there were 100 rows of pins!?

Lets look for a pattern to see if we can solve this
without adding every row of pins. Several ways to
explain how to count the number of pins in *n* rows of
bowling pins are described below.

Method 1: (See also **p.54**). Find the average number of pins
in each row, then multiply by the number of rows.
Consider 12 rows of pins: There will be:
1 + 2 + ... + 11 + 12 pins. The mean of all of these
numbers is the same as the median. We can find the
mean by adding the first and the last numbers and
dividing by 2.

The mean for the first 12 positive integers is $\dfrac{1+12}{2} = 6.5$.

If we multiply this by the number of terms (12), we get:

$$12 \cdot \frac{1+12}{2} = 12(6.5) = 78.$$

To find the sum of the first *n* positive integers, we can find
their average: $(n+1)/2$ and multiply by the number
of integers *n*. This gives us the general formula for
the sum of the first *n* positive integers:

$$1 + 2 + 3 + ... + (n-1) + n = \frac{n(n+1)}{2}.$$

For your reference, the sum of the first *n* positive integers is
called a **triangular number** (for obvious reasons).

Method 2: Think of it geometrically:

See if you can figure out how this diagram
relates to the previous formula.

To count the number of white pins in the diagram
above, there are 4 pins in each of 5 rows and we
only want to count half of them: $(4 \cdot 5)/2 = 10$.
If there were n pins in each row, there would be
$n + 1$ rows, and we would only want to count half of
them. We get the same general formula as before.

To find the nth triangular number: $T_n = \dfrac{n(n+1)}{2}$.

Method 3: The handshake problem (similar and related).
12 strangers meet to go bowling. If everyone shakes
everyone else's hand exactly once, how many
handshakes have occurred?

Here is one way to look at the problem: The first person
who enters the room shakes no one's hand. The 2nd
person shakes the first person's hand (1). The 3rd
person shakes 2 hands, and so forth until the 12th
person shakes 11 hands. This gives us:

$$1 + 2 + 3 + \dots + 11 = \frac{11(12)}{2} = 66 \text{ handshakes.}$$

Alternatively, each of the twelve people shakes 11
other people's hands. This would appear to be
11(12) handshakes, but we have counted each
handshake twice. Al shaking Bob's hand is the same
as Bob shaking Al's hand, so we must divide by 2.

2.720 Write the general formula for the number of handshakes that occur when n people shake hands, which
is slightly different from the "bowling pin" formula.

Practice: Bowling Pins and Handshakes.

2.920 How many straight lines will it take to connect all five points shown to each of the other 4?

2.030 How many straight lines will it take to connect 30 points if each pair of points is connected by one line and no line passes through more than 2 points?

2.130 A volleyball league has 16 teams. Each season, every team plays every other team exactly once. How many games are played in one season?

2.230 Mark is stacking cans at the paint store. He starts with a row of 20 paint cans and adds rows of 19, 18, 17... until there is just one can atop the giant stack. How many cans will Mark need to complete his stack?

2.330 The first figure below is made of three toothpicks, each one unit long. The second figure is made from 9 of the same toothpicks. How many toothpicks will be needed to create the 16th figure?

2.430 There are 2 diagonals in a square. A pentagon has 5 diagonals. A hexagon has 9 diagonals. How many diagonals there are in a polygon with 15 sides?

2.530 Several couples arrive at a dinner party. Each person at the party shakes the hand of every other person, not including his or her spouse. If there were a total of 112 handshakes, how many couples attended the party?

2.630 What is the largest prime factor of $1+2+3+...+59+60$?

Counting: Outcomes

2.4: Counting Outcomes

Dice, coins, and other outcome counting problems.

Examples:

1. How many possible outcomes are there when:
      One coin is flipped?
      Two coins are flipped?
      Ten coins are flipped?

2. How many possible outcomes are there when:
      One (standard six-faced) die is rolled?
      Two dice are rolled?
      Two coins are flipped and a die is rolled?

The Fundamental Counting Principle states that if there are m ways that one event can happen, and n ways that a second event can happen, then there are mn ways that both events can happen.

Solutions: **#1:** 2, $2^2 = 4$, and $2^{10} = 1,024$.
                #2: 6, $6^2 = 36$, and $2^2 \cdot 6 = 24$.

Example: A bag contains a penny, nickel, a dime, and a quarter. A second bag contains a $1, $5, and $10 bill. If a coin and a bill are selected at random, how many different total values are possible?

Reasoning: There are four different choices for the coin, and three different choices for the bill, which means there are $4 \cdot 3 = 12$ possible values.

Example: At a sub shop you can order your meatball sub in two sizes, with or without cheese, and you get your choice of 5 different types of bread. How many different meatball subs are available?

Reasoning: There are 2 sizes, 2 choices for cheese (with or without), and 5 choices for the type of bread, for a total of $2 \cdot 2 \cdot 5 = 20$ different subs.

Example: A (standard six-faced) die is rolled three times and the results are recorded (in order) to create a three-digit number. How many different numbers greater than 400 are possible?

Reasoning: The first roll can be any one of three numbers: 4, 5, or 6. The next two rolls can be any of the six digits on a die. This makes $3 \cdot 6 \cdot 6 = 108$ different rolls which create a three-digit number greater than 400.

Practice: Counting Outcomes.

2.930 How many outcomes are possible with three rolls of a standard die?

2.040 A company that makes men's jeans offers three styles, eight waist sizes, ten inseam lengths, and two different colors. How many different pairs of men's jeans do they manufacture?

2.140 How many outcomes are possible when a coin is flipped seven times?

2.240 How many four-digit numbers can be formed using only the digits 5, 6, 7, and 8 if digits may be repeated?

2.340 How many ten digit whole numbers use only the digits 1 and 2?

2.440 How many ten digit whole numbers use only the digits 1 and 0?

2.540 Pizzas at Mario's come in three sizes, and you have your choice of 9 toppings to add to the pizza. You may order a pizza with any number of toppings (up to 9), including zero. How many choices of pizza are there at Mario's?

2.5: Casework

Sometimes the most difficult part of counting is keeping
   organized. This is particularly true when working
   with diagrams.

Example: How many triangles (of
   any size) are there in the
   figure?

Reasoning:

If there are no tricks to make the counting easier, the most
   important thing is to keep your counting organized.
   Find a method that works for you.

Work might look like this:

...or more specific, like this:

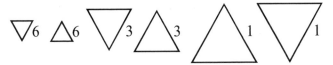

Either way, you get a total of 20 triangles.

Example: How many squares can be formed
   using four of the dots in the unit grid as
   vertices?

Reasoning: The key to this problem is finding all five sizes,
   and being certain that you have counted each of
   them. If you did not find all five sizes, try to find the
   ones you missed before turning the page.

Below are all five sizes:

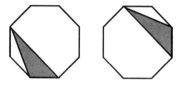

Did you find all 20 squares? I have seen many variations of
this problem in competitions and it is a good one to be
familiar with.

Practice: Casework.

2.640 How many non-congruent triangles can be formed by
connecting three of the vertices of a regular octagon.
For example, the two triangles drawn below are
congruent and should only be counted once.

2.740 Each of the six faces of a cube is painted either black
or white. Two cubes are considered identical if one
cube can be rotated to look like another (for example, there is only one distinct cube that has exactly
one white face). How many distinct cubes are
possible?

2.840 How many right triangles can be
formed by connecting three points
on the unit grid shown?

Note: Many problems that appear to be casework problems
can be solved using shortcuts which allow for much
faster counting. We will learn some of these tricks a
little later in the chapter.

Review: 2.1 to 2.5

2.150 Solve for x if $x = 30 + 29 + 28 + 27 + ... + 3 + 2 + 1$.

2.250 If 99 people stand in a circle, and each shakes the hand of the person on each side, how many handshakes are there all together?

2.350 There are 15 points on a chalkboard numbered 1 through 15. How many lines must be drawn to connect every pair of points whose sum is odd, assuming each line connects just one pair of points?

2.450 Bryan cuts 30 triangles out of a sheet of paper. 22 of the triangles are isosceles and 25 are right triangles. How many are isosceles right triangles?

2.550 How many positive integers less than 1,000 are even and/or divisible by 3?

2.650 To use the copier, teachers must enter three initials (first, middle, last name) on a keypad. How many different three-initial codes are possible?

2.750 How many five-digit positive integers use only the digits 0 through 3 if digits may be repeated?

2.850 How many rectangles (of any size) are there in this figure?

2.950 Sixteen points are placed on the circumference of a circle. How many lines will it take to connect every point to every other point?

2.060 At the salad bar, you can choose between three types of lettuce, six different salad dressings, and there are ten toppings that you can add to your salad. How many combinations of one type of lettuce, one dressing, and any number of toppings are possible?

2.6: Factorials and Permutations

Factorials:

You may have seen an exclamation point in a math problem
at some point and wondered, "What is so exciting
about *that* number?"

No, 4! does not mean **"FOUR!!!"**, that exclamation point is
factorial notation.

The expression *n*! represents the product of all positive
integers less than or equal to *n:*

$$n(n-1)(n-2)(n-3)...(3)(2)(1).$$

Examples make this clear:
$5!= 5 \cdot 4 \cdot 3 \cdot 2 \cdot 1 = 120$.
$10!= 10 \cdot 9 \cdot 8 \cdot 7 \cdot 6 \cdot 5 \cdot 4 \cdot 3 \cdot 2 \cdot 1 = 3,628,800$.
$15!= 15 \cdot 14 \cdot ... \cdot 3 \cdot 2 \cdot 1 = 1,307,674,368,000$.

You can see that factorials can get big fast!
You will rarely be asked to compute large factorials,
but knowing how to simplify division with factorials is
important, particularly when larger numbers are
involved.

Check for Understanding: Simplify.

2.070 $\dfrac{25!}{24!}$ **2.170** $\dfrac{5!}{10}$ **2.270** $\dfrac{20 \cdot 19!}{20!}$

Example: How many different positive integers can be
formed by re-arranging the digits 2, 3, 4, 5, and 6?

Reasoning: There are 5 choices for the first digit. After
selecting the first digit, there are 4 choices left for
the second digit, 3 for the third, 2 for the tens digit,
and the remaining number is used as the units digit.
This gives us 5! = 120 positive integers.

Permutations:

A **permutation** is an arrangement in which order matters.

Example: Five students are running a race. In how many
ways can the three of five students place
1st, 2nd, and 3rd?

Reasoning: 5 students can win, leaving 4 who can place
second and then 3 for third place. This makes
$5 \cdot 4 \cdot 3 = 60$ ways that students can place
1st, 2nd, and 3rd.

Example: An organization is choosing colors for the three
pentagons in its logo. They have narrowed their
choice to 7 colors, and want to have three different
colors in their logo. How many possible logos can
be created by choosing three of the
seven colors and using one for each
pentagon?

Reasoning: The first pentagon can be one of seven different colors, the second can be any one of six, and
there are five colors which remain for the final
pentagon. $7 \cdot 6 \cdot 5 = 210$ ways to color the logo.

There is a formula for **permutations** and some notation
which we must consider. Both $P(n,r)$ and nPr ask
for the number of n things taken r at a time in order.

For example, five people in a race taking three
places is represented by $5P3$ or $P(5,3) = 5 \cdot 4 \cdot 3 = 60$.

The Formula: $nPr = P(n,r) = \dfrac{n!}{(n-r)!}$.

Got that? Now, you can really forget this... apply what you
know, don't memorize a formula. You should,
however, remember what the notation $P(7,2)$ means.

Permutations: Letter Arrangements.

Perhaps the most commonly asked questions requiring the
   use of permutations involve letter arrangements.
   Many more problems can be solved by modeling the
   situation as an arrangement of letters.

Example: How many different five-letter "words" (letter
   arrangements) can be formed by rearranging the
   letters in the word BEAST?

Reasoning: There are 5 letters to choose from for the first
   spot, leaving 4 for the second, 3 for the third, 2 for
   the fourth, and there is 1 remaining for the end of the
   word: $P(5,5) = 5! = 5 \cdot 4 \cdot 3 \cdot 2 \cdot 1 = 120$ "words".

Example:

How many different seven-letter "words" can be formed by
   rearranging the letters in the word ALGEBRA?

Reasoning: This is more difficult. Notice that there are
   two A's. No need to panic, just pretend for a moment that the A's are different. We'll call one of the
   them A_1 and the other A_2.

$P(7,7) = 7! = 7 \cdot 6 \cdot 5 \cdot 4 \cdot 3 \cdot 2 \cdot 1 = 5,040$ "words".

However, we over-counted. A_1LGEBRA$_2$ is the same as
   A_2LGEBRA$_1$, just like A_1A_2LEGBR is the same as
   A_2A_1LEGBR. To eliminate the extra cases, we
   need to divide by the ways that the A's can be
   arranged, which in this case is just $2! = 2$.

$$\frac{P(7,7)}{2} = \frac{7 \cdot 6 \cdot 5 \cdot 4 \cdot 3 \cdot 2 \cdot 1}{2} = 2,520 \text{ "words".}$$

This concept can be applied to a variety of problems,
some of which are discussed later in this chapter.

Practice: Permutations.

2.080 Find $P(10,3)$.   **2.180** Find $8P6$.

2.280 For the pick 3 lottery, six balls numbered 1 through 6 are placed in a hopper and randomly selected one at a time without replacement to create a three-digit number. How many different three-digit numbers can be created?

2.380 How many ways can five different books be ordered on a shelf from left to right?

2.480 The eight members of student council are asked to select a leadership team: president, vice-president, and secretary. How many different leadership teams are possible?

2.580 You are ranking your elective class choices for the upcoming school year. You must rank your top 5 selections in order of preference. How many ways can you rank 5 of the 7 electives that interest you?

2.680 Find the number of arrangements of the letters in the word WORD.

2.780 Find the number of arrangements of the letters in the word LADDER.

2.880 Find the number of arrangements of the letters in the word ICICLE.

2.980 Find the number of arrangements of the letters in the word COOKBOOK.

2.090 Find the number of arrangements of the letters in the word BOOKKEEPER.

Permutations with Restrictions:

Sometimes permutation problems are complicated by restrictions.

Example: How many *even* five-digit numbers contain each of the digits 1 through 5?

Reasoning: The restriction requires that the last digit be either a 2 or a 4. This allows two choices for the units digit. After selecting either a 2 or a 4, there are 4 remaining digits for the tens place, 3 for the hundreds, 2 for the thousands, and 1 for the ten-thousands place:

$$2(4!) = 2 \cdot 4 \cdot 3 \cdot 2 \cdot 1 = 48.$$

Example: How many of the arrangements of the letters in the word COUNTING contain a double-N?

Reasoning: The restriction requires that the N's be grouped together, so we do just that: treat them as a single letter. Now we just count the number of ways to arrange the letters COU N TIG. There are 7 letters, so we get $P(7,7) = 7! = 5,040$.

Example: In how many of the arrangements of the letters in the word EXAMPLE are the letters A and M adjacent to each other?

Reasoning: At first, this appears to be the same situation as the previous problem, however, the letters A and M may appear as AM or MA. Additionally, we have two E's. Group the A and the M. This gives us six "letters" with two E's: EX M PLE. There are 6! ways to arrange these, but we must divide by 2 to account for the two E's. Then we multiply by 2 because the M can be ordered AM or MA. This gets us right back to 6! = 720.

Practice: Permutations with Restrictions.

2.001 How many arrangements of the letters in the word FOOT include a double-O?

2.101 How many arrangements of the letters in the word RECIPE include a double-E?

2.201 How many arrangements of the letters in the word START begin with a T?

2.301 How many arrangements of the letters in the word BEGIN start with a vowel?

2.401 How many arrangements of the letters in the word BEGINNING have an N at the beginning?

2.501 How many of the distinct arrangements of the digits 1 through 6 have the 1 to the left of the 2?

2.601 Seven students line up on stage. If Molly insists on standing next to Katie, how many different ways are there to arrange the students on stage from left to right?

2.701 How many arrangements of the letters in the word ORDERED include the word RED?

2.801 How many arrangements of the letters in the word ORDERED begin and end with the same letter?

2.901 There are nine parking spots in front of the building for six teachers and the principal. If the principal always gets one of the three shady spots, how many ways can all seven cars be parked in the lot?

2.7: Combinations

Consider the following examples:

Example: There are six scrabble letters left in the bag at the end of the game (FHJSU and Y). If you reach in and grab two letters, how many different pairs of letters are possible?

Reasoning: There are six possible letters to choose from. The first letter you pick can be any one of six letters, and the second can be any one of the remaining five. 6 times 5 appears to give us 30 choices, however, the order in which we choose the letters is not important (FH is the same as HF). We divide by the number of ways we can arrange the chosen letters (2! = 2) to get 30/2 = 15 possible pairs of letters.

Example: Remy wants to offer 3 sodas at his snack stand. He has a list of 8 sodas to choose from. How many combinations of 3 sodas are possible?

Reasoning: There are $8 \cdot 7 \cdot 6$ possible ways to select three sodas in order, and $3 \cdot 2 \cdot 1$ possible ways to order the three selected sodas (selecting Coke, Sprite, and Root Beer is the same as Sprite, Root Beer, and Coke). Dividing out the duplicate outcomes gives us:

$$\frac{8 \cdot 7 \cdot 6}{3 \cdot 2 \cdot 1} = 56 \text{ combinations of sodas.}$$

Example: Roger has won a contest at the fair, and gets to choose four *different* prizes from a set of nine. How many combinations of four prizes can he choose from a set of nine?

Reasoning: There are $9 \cdot 8 \cdot 7 \cdot 6$ possible ways to select four prizes in order, and $4 \cdot 3 \cdot 2 \cdot 1$ possible orders. Dividing, we get:

$$\frac{9 \cdot 8 \cdot 7 \cdot 6}{4 \cdot 3 \cdot 2 \cdot 1} = 126 \text{ prize combinations.}$$

Combinations:

The primary difference between **combinations** and permutations is that with combinations, *order does not
matter*. There is a formula for combinations and
some notation which we must consider. C(*n,r*) asks
for the number of ways *n* things can be taken *r* at a
time.

For example, choosing four prizes from a set of nine is
expressed:

$$C(9,4) = \frac{9 \cdot 8 \cdot 7 \cdot 6}{4 \cdot 3 \cdot 2 \cdot 1} = 126.$$

The formula for C(*n,r*): $C(n,r) = \dfrac{n!}{r!(n-r)!}.$

Notation: $C(n,r)$ is also notated $\binom{n}{r}$ or *nCr* and is often

called the "choose" function, for example 9*C*4 is read
"nine choose four". I will use all three notations
interchangeably so that you can become familiar with
each.

Check for Understanding:

2.011 Find 6*C*2.

2.111 Find $C(6,4)$.

2.211 Find the value of $C(85,25)$ subtracted from $C(85,60)$.

2.311 How many different sets of three books can be chosen
from a shelf of 20?

2.411 Eight people are asked to select a leadership team of
three members. How many different leadership
teams are possible?

Paths on a Grid:
Tracing routes across grids is a great way to show how
combinations can arise in less obvious problems.

Example: Tracing the lines starting from point A on the unit
grid below, how many distinct 7-unit paths are there
from A to B?

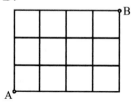

Reasoning (1): Take any path and represent it as series of
moves, either U (up) or R (right). Every unique 7-
unit path consists of four R's and three U's. The
question then becomes: How many ways can we
rearrange the letters RRRRUUU:

$$\frac{7 \cdot 6 \cdot 5 \cdot 4 \cdot 3 \cdot 2 \cdot 1}{(3 \cdot 2 \cdot 1)(4 \cdot 3 \cdot 2 \cdot 1)} = 35.$$

Reasoning (2): We must move up 3 times in 7 moves.
$7C3 = 35$ possible combinations of up moves. Think
of this as choosing where to place the three U's in 7
blanks, then filling the remaining blanks with R's.

Reasoning (3): We can also show this by counting the
number of ways there are to get to each point.

	4	10	20	35
1				
1	3	6	10	15
1	2	3	4	5
1				
1	1	1	1	1

While not recommended for this problem, this
technique is useful for more complex patterns where
the grid is irregular or incomplete.

Combinations: Beyond Casework.
Combinations and the "choose" function offer shortcuts for
  many other seemingly complex problems.

Example: How many distinct rectangles can be formed by
  tracing the lines on the grid below?

Reasoning: This would be a casework nightmare, so we
  look for a better way. Each rectangle requires that
  we choose two horizontal and two vertical lines.
  There are $4C2 = 6$ ways to choose two horizontal
  lines and $7C2 = 21$ ways to choose two vertical lines,
  which gives us $21 \cdot 6 = 126$ rectangles. Good thing
  we didn't need to count them using casework
  techniques!

Example: How many distinct triangles can be formed by
  connecting three of the points below?

Reasoning: It is tempting to say that there are 11 points and
  we can choose any three, so $11C3 = 165$ possible
  triangles. Unfortunately, if we choose three points
  that are on the same row, they will not form a
  triangle. There are $5C3 = 10$ ways to select three
  points on the top row, and $6C3 = 20$ ways to select
  three points on the bottom row. When we subtract
  these from the total, we find that there are 135
  triangles which can be formed.

If a problem looks too difficult for casework, there is likely a
  counting shortcut that can be applied.

Practice: Beyond Casework

2.511 How many distinct triangles can be traced along the lines in the diagram below?

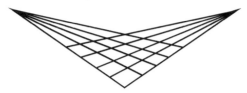

2.611 John walks six blocks on a city grid of sidewalks to his favorite deli for lunch: three blocks north and three blocks west. He never uses the exact same path on his return to work. If John always stays on city sidewalks and goes six blocks each way, how many different ways can John walk to the deli and back?

2.711 Twelve points are arranged into six rows of four points each in the shape of a six-pointed star. How many ways can three of these points be connected to form a triangle?

2.811 How many pentagons can be formed by tracing the lines of the figure below?

2.911 A regular dodecahedron has 12 pentagonal faces, 20 vertices, and 30 edges. How many of the triangles which can be formed by connecting three of its vertices have at least one side within the dodecahedron?

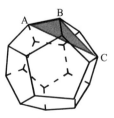

182

Complementary Counting

Complementary counting involves counting what we don't
want and then subtracting it from the total.

Example: Paul flips a fair coin eight times. In how many
ways can he flip at least two heads?

Reasoning: It is possible to figure out how many ways Paul
can flip two, three, four, five, six, seven, or eight
heads:

$$\binom{8}{2}+\binom{8}{3}+\binom{8}{4}+\binom{8}{5}+\binom{8}{6}+\binom{8}{7}+\binom{8}{8} = 247.$$

It is much easier to figure out the total number of
outcomes (2^8) and subtract the number of ways he
can flip zero or one heads: $8C0 = 1$ and $8C1 = 8$.

$$2^8 - 1 - 8 = 247$$

Example: Corey and Tony are friends on the same basket-
ball team. There are eight players on the team.
How many starting lineups of five players include
Corey, Tony, or both?

Reasoning: Again, it requires a bit of computation to figure
out how many teams include just Corey, just Tony, or
both Corey and Tony. Instead, begin by considering
how many starting lineups are possible without
restrictions (choosing 5 from a team of 8: $8C5 = 56$
ways). Subtract lineups that do not include Corey or
Tony (choosing a team of 5 from the remaining 6
players: $6C5 = 6$ ways). Better still, we can choose
one of the 6 remaining players to join Corey and
Tony on the bench in $6C1 = 6$ ways.

$$\binom{8}{5}-\binom{6}{1} = 56 - 6 = 50 \text{ starting lineups.}$$

We are really trying to count what we don't want, which is
often easier to find and subtract from the total.

Practice: Complementary Counting.

2.021 How many positive two-digit integers use two different digits?

2.121 There are seven parking spaces in a row which must be assigned to four co-workers. How many ways can the spaces be assigned if at least two of the assigned spaces must be adjacent?

2.221 How many different ways can six friends stand in line at the movies if Alice and David refuse to stand next to each other?

2.321 How many positive integers less than 50 are *not* divisible by 3 or 5?

2.421 A fair coin is flipped ten times. How many ways are there to flip *more* heads than tails?

2.521 An octahedral die (8 faces) with sides numbered 1 through 8 is rolled twice and the product of the two rolls is computed. How many different rolls produce a product that is composite?

2.621 Five lines are drawn so that each intersects the other four, but no three lines intersect at the same point. Each of the points of intersection is then connected to every other point of intersection. How many triangles are formed which have three of the points of intersection as vertices?

2.721 How many ten-unit paths are there between A and B which *do not* pass through X?

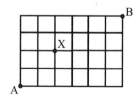

Review: 2.1 through 2.7

2.031 How many ways can gold, silver, and bronze be awarded to the eight finalists in a dog show?

2.131 How many arrangements of the letters in the word PRACTICE are possible?

2.231 Each project in Ms. Rose's class is completed with a partner. Last year, each of her 26 students completed a project with every one of the other students exactly once, and Ms. Rose graded them all. How many projects did Ms. Rose grade last year?

2.331 A mouse is placed as shown in the maze below. If the mouse only moves up or right, how many different paths can the mouse use take to get to the cheese at the end of the maze?

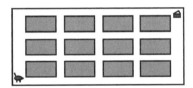

2.431 Find the number of arrangements of the letters of the word MISSISSIPPI.

2.531 Seven students run a race, including Thomas and Raj. How many ways can the seven students finish first through seventh if Raj finishes ahead of Thomas (but not necessarily immediately ahead of Thomas).

2.631 How many distinct *scalene* triangles can be formed by connecting three vertices of a regular nonagon?

2.731 A standard checkerboard has 64 squares alternating black and red on an 8 by 8 grid. How many of the 1,296 rectangles on a checkerboard contain more than one red square?

Review: 2.1 through 2.7

2.041 How many three-digit whole numbers use only odd digits with no digit repeating?

2.141 Homerooms are participating in a 3-on-3 basketball tournament. How many different three-person teams can a homeroom of 15 students select to participate in the tournament?

2.241 Eight 4-inch square posts are placed with three feet of space between them and connected by fencing attached to the outside of the posts to form a small square enclosure. What is the perimeter of the enclosure?

2.341 Zip codes in the United States are five-digits long followed by a four-digit code, for example: 27513-8046. In North Carolina, every zip code begins with either 27 or 28. How many 9-digit zip codes are possible in North Carolina in which each digit is only used once?

2.441 Three identical dominoes are placed on the 3×4 tiled board below to create a complete pathway from the upper-left corner to the lower-right corner of the board (no dominoes may touch only at the corners). How many ways can this be done?

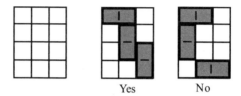

Yes   No

2.541 Lattice points in the form (x, y) are chosen such that $|x| + |y| \leq 2$. How many ways can three of these lattice points be connected to form a triangle?

2.8: Sticks and Stones

Another great counting trick best explained with an example:

Example: Uncle Henry has ten one-dollar bills to distribute among his five youngest nieces and nephews. How many ways are there to distribute his money?

Reasoning:
He could give all of the money to one child (five ways).
He could give two dollars to each child (one way).
He could give $0.00, $1.00, $2.00, $3.00, and $4.00 5! ways.

This is getting us nowhere, there must be a trick!
Consider the following diagram:

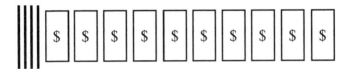

Henry will arrange the dividers on the left with the bills on the right. Money to the left of the first divider goes to the youngest, money between the first and second divider goes to the next child, etc. For example, in the arrangement below, the first child gets $1, the second gets $2, the third gets $1, the fourth gets nothing, and the fifth gets $6.

Using this model, it is simply a matter of choosing the number of arrangements of ten bills and four dividers:

$$\frac{14!}{(10!)(4!)} = 1{,}001, \quad \text{or:} \quad _{14}C_4 = 1{,}001.$$

Think of this as the number of ways to place 4 dividers into 14 blanks, filling the remaining 10 blanks with bills.

Sticks and Stones: Placing dividers (sticks) to separate indistinguishable items (stones) into categories.

Example: You are ordering a half-dozen doughnuts (6), and need to choose from among four flavors: glazed, powdered, cream-filled, and jelly-filled. How many different doughnut orders are possible?

Reasoning: Once again, even with just six doughnuts and four flavors the casework is virtually impossible to do quickly and get right. We will use our divider trick again. This is the same as finding the number of arrangements of dividers and doughnuts below.

The math is the same as finding the number of letter arrangements of AAABBBBBB, or placing 3 dividers (make sure you know why there are 3 not 4 dividers) in 9 blanks (doughnuts fill the other 6):

$$\frac{9!}{(3!)(6!)} = 84 \text{ or } \binom{9}{3} = 84.$$

Practice: Sticks and Stones.

2.051 There are six different choices on the dollar menu at Burgerboy: fries, apple pies, onion rings, chicken nuggets, hamburgers, and cheeseburgers. You decide to purchase four of these items. How many different combinations of four items can you buy from the dollar menu?

2.151 You are purchasing a dozen roses for Valentine's day. The roses come in red, white, and pink and you want at least one of each color. How many different bouquets of one dozen roses are possible?

Sticks and Stones with restrictions.

Sometimes it is useful to use a sticks-and-stones approach in some unexpected situations:

Example: How many ways are there to roll a sum of 7 with three standard six-faced dice?

Reasoning:

This is typically solved using casework: There are $6^3 = 216$ ways to roll three standard die, and we can list the ways to roll a 7 and count the ways to roll each: 5-1-1 (3 ways), 4-2-1 (6 ways), 3-2-2 (3 ways), or 3-3-1 (3 ways) for a total of 15 ways.

Consider the problem with dividers placed between 7 dots. This time, we cannot place 2 dividers adjacent to each other, so there are 6 available gaps between dots in which we can place 2 dividers in $6C2 = 15$ ways to represent rolling a 7 with 3 dice. Below is an example of rolling 4-1-2.

Example: Each of the numbers 1 through 10 is placed in a bag and drawn at random with replacement. How many ways can three numbers be drawn whose sum is 13?

Reasoning:

There are many more ways to do this, and counting cases is not practical. Consider a diagram similar to the one above, only with 13 dots. There are three ways that the dividers *cannot* be placed which are shown below (because you cannot draw an 11):

This leaves $12C2$ minus 3 = 63 ways for the sum to equal 13.

Practice: Sticks and Stones.

2.061 How many ways can a dozen hundred-dollar bills be distributed among five numbered briefcases?

2.161 You are playing a racing video game. To begin, you get to adjust the tuning of your race car by adding a combined total of ten points to three categories. You can adjust your speed, handling, and acceleration by adding anywhere from 0 to 10 points to each category. How many tuning options are there for the car's initial setup?

2.261 Uncle Henry is feeling generous and has decided to distribute four $1 bills, three $5 bills, two $20 bills, and a $100 bill to three nephews. How many different ways can he distribute the money?

2.361 A standard six-faced die is rolled four times. How many different ways are there to roll a 9?

2.461 Three friends: Al, Bill, and Carl, are painting their chests with the word CAVALIERS for a basketball game, with at least two letters painted on each friend's chest. For example, Al might get "CA", Bill "VAL", and Carl "IERS", or Carl could get "CAVA" while Bill gets "LI" and Al gets "ERS". How many ways can the three friends get their chests painted so that when they stand in the correct order, they spell-out the word CAVALIERS?

2.561 An elaborate code consists of left and right arrows which are placed together to represent words. There are spaces between words. For example, the code of three left and four right arrows arranged with two spaces: << >>> <> represents a three-word code phrase. How many different three-word code phrases in this system use 8 letters?

2.9: Pascal's Triangle

Perhaps you already recognize and know how to create
Pascal's triangle. Begin at the top with a 1. Each
row begins with a 1, and each number is the sum of
the two above it:

$$
\begin{array}{c}
1 \qquad \textit{row 0} \\
1 \quad 1 \qquad \textit{row 1} \\
1 \quad 2 \quad 1 \qquad \textit{row 2} \\
1 \quad 3 \quad 3 \quad 1 \qquad \textit{row 3} \\
1 \quad 4 \quad 6 \quad 4 \quad 1 \qquad \textit{row 4} \\
1 \quad 5 \quad 10 \quad 10 \quad 5 \quad 1 \qquad \textit{row 5} \\
1 \quad 6 \quad 15 \quad 20 \quad 15 \quad 6 \quad 1 \qquad \textit{row 6} \\
1 \quad 7 \quad 21 \quad 35 \quad 35 \quad 21 \quad 7 \quad 1 \qquad \textit{row 7}
\end{array}
$$

etc. (see **p. 365**).

There is a nice relationship between combinations and
Pascal's triangle that we will explore.

Let's begin with a problem we have seen before:

How many paths can we trace to each vertex on the grid
below, starting from the top left and moving only
down and to the right?

1	1	1	1	1	1
1	2	3	4	5	6
1	3	6	10	15	21
1	4	10	20	35	56
1	5	15	35	70	126
1	6	21	56	126	252

You should recognize these numbers from Pascal's triangle.

Example: A fair coin is flipped seven times.
How many outcomes show 0, 1, 2, 3, 4, 5, 6, and 7
tails?

Reasoning: There is just one way to flip zero tails, 7 ways
to flip one tails, 21 for three, etc. We are just
computing $7C0$, $7C1$, $7C2$ ... $7C0$. The answers are:
1, 7, 21, 35, 35, 21, 7, and 1. Look familiar?

Pascal's Triangle:

There are some surprising patterns to be found in Pascal's triangle that I encourage you to research. Perhaps the most useful is the relationship between rows and combinations.

Compute the value of each combination below if you have not already recognized this relationship.

$$\binom{0}{0}$$

$$\binom{1}{0} \quad \binom{1}{1}$$

$$\binom{2}{0} \quad \binom{2}{1} \quad \binom{2}{2}$$

$$\binom{3}{0} \quad \binom{3}{1} \quad \binom{3}{2} \quad \binom{3}{3}$$

$$\binom{4}{0} \quad \binom{4}{1} \quad \binom{4}{2} \quad \binom{4}{3} \quad \binom{4}{4}$$

etc.

It is useful to be able to construct Pascal's Triangle quickly for problems like the following:

Example: A fair coin is flipped 7 times. How many ways are there to flip at least five tails?

Reasoning: We need $\binom{7}{5} + \binom{7}{6} + \binom{7}{7}$, which is the sum of the last three (or first three) entries in row 7 of Pascal's triangle: $21 + 7 + 1 = 29$.

Example: Compute $\binom{5}{5} + \binom{5}{4} + \binom{5}{3} + \binom{5}{2} + \binom{5}{1} + \binom{5}{0}$.

Reasoning: This is row 5 of Pascal's triangle. We could add the numbers in the row, but it is more useful to know that the sum of the entries in row n is equal to 2^n. It is the *total* number of possible outcomes for a coin flipped n times.

Practice: Pascal's Triangle.

2.071 Find the sum of $\binom{10}{0} + \binom{10}{1} + \binom{10}{2} + ... + \binom{10}{10}$.

2.171 Jack tosses six fair coins. How many ways are there to flip an odd number of heads?

2.271 Find $a + b$ if $\binom{9}{5} + \binom{9}{6} = \binom{a}{b}$.

2.371 There are 22 ways to flip fewer than 3 heads when n coins are tossed. Find n.

2.471 A delivery special from the local pizza restaurant allows you to choose up to 5 toppings from a list of 9 to add to your pizza. How many combinations of toppings are available if double toppings are not allowed?

2.571 On a game show, you are offered the chance to select up to four of the ten other contestants to be on your team, but they will share the winnings (you don't have to pick anyone if you think you can do well all by yourself). How many combinations of teammates can you select?

2.671 Ten coins are flipped. How many ways can the number of heads showing be a positive multiple of 3?

2.771 Count the number of different ways the word COUNT can be spelled by connecting five letters in the diagram shown, starting with the letter C and always connecting a letter to one of the two below it.

C

O O

U U U

N N N N

T T T T T

Chapter Review

2.081 How many ways can six slices of pepperoni pizza and three slices of cheese pizza be divided among five students if one of the students is a vegetarian?

2.181 How many integers between 1,000,000 and 2,000,000 have at least four fives?

2.281 Standard Wyoming license plates consist of three different letters followed by three different numbers and do not include the letter O or digit 0. How many license plates can be made which begin with the letter A?

2.381 Three standard six-sided dice are rolled: one red, one green, and one white. How many outcomes are possible where the number rolled on the red die is greater than the number rolled on the green die, and the number on the green die is greater than the number rolled on the white die?

2.481 You are ordering an ice-cream sundae. There are 10 flavors of ice cream and 10 toppings. The special of the day allows you to choose two *different* flavored scoops of ice cream and three *different* toppings. How many choices of sundae are available for the daily special?

2.581 Jeffrey has a set of tetrahedral dice. Each has a distinct arrangement of exactly six dots painted on the four faces, and no two dice can be rotated to appear the same. Faces can have any number of dots on each face including zero. How many dice are in a set that has each distinct arrangement of six dots exactly once?

2.681 How many triangles can be formed by connecting three points on the isometric grid shown?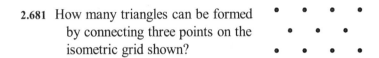

2.781 How many parallelograms can be formed by connecting four of the points on the isometric grid above? (Remember that rectangles and rhombuses are parallelograms.)

2.881 How many positive integers less than 1,000,000 have a digit sum of 5?

2.981 Patricia frequently misspells the word MISSPELL. How many ways are there to misspell the word MISSPELL if all of the correct letters are used, but are placed in the wrong order?

2.091 A mother, her three children, and their spouses are having a photo taken, seated on a long sofa. If each couple must be seated together and grandma prefers to sit between two couples, how many seating arrangements are possible?

2.191 How many ways can eight non-overlapping dominoes be used to cover all 16 squares on the board below?

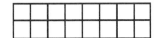

2.291 Seven unique charms are placed on a bracelet. How many distinct arrangements of the charms on the bracelet are possible? Two arrangements are considered distinct if the charms cannot be shown to be in the same order by rotating the bracelet or by turning it over.

Probability
Chapter III

Probability is the study of chance. The probability that an event will occur can be expressed as a ratio of favorable outcomes to possible outcomes. Probabilities range from 0 to 1, or as a percent from 0% to 100%.

When we talk about probability in this chapter we will be talking about theoretical probability (the purely mathematical expectation that an event will occur), not experimental probability (expectation based on observed outcomes of multiple trials).

For example, in theory a fair six-sided die should land on each face with a probability of $1/6$, but it is unlikely that in six rolls the die will land on each face exactly once (see problem **3.410**). Experimental probability approaches theoretical probability as the number of trials increases, so in a billion rolls of a fair six-faced die, you could reasonably expect to see about one-sixth of these rolls land on each face.

If you count well, most probability problems will be easy for you, but there are techniques that must be learned in addition to a solid foundation in counting that will be useful in calculating theoretical probabilities.

3.1 Probability Basics

Probability is **the ratio of favorable outcomes to total possible outcomes**. If we can count outcomes, it is usually easy to express probability as a ratio from 0 (impossible) to 1 (certain).

Example: What is the probability of flipping heads with a fair coin?

Reasoning: Heads is one of two equally likely outcomes, so the probability is 1/2 or 50%.

Example: A positive integer less than 100 is selected at random. What is the probability that the integer is odd?

Reasoning: There are 99 positive integers less than 100 and 50 of them are odd, so the probability of selecting an odd integer is 50/99.

Example: What is the probability of rolling a 6 with a pair of standard six-faced dice?

Reasoning: There are five ways to roll a 6: (1,5)(2,4)(3,3)(4,2), and (5,1). There are $6^2 = 36$ (1,1)(1,2)(1,3)...(6,5)(6,6) possible outcomes when a pair of dice is rolled. The probability of rolling a 6 with a pair of dice is 5/36.

Example: All of the arrangements of the letters in the word ALGEBRA are written on a list, and one of the arrangements is selected at random. What is the probability that the selected arrangement contains a double-A?

Reasoning: There are $(7!)/2 = 2{,}520$ ways to arrange the letters in the word ALGEBRA, and 6! arrangements which include a double-A (see **p.80** for a full explanation). This gives us a probability of:

$$\frac{6 \cdot 5 \cdot 4 \cdot 3 \cdot 2}{7 \cdot 6 \cdot 5 \cdot 4 \cdot 3} = \frac{2}{7}.$$

Probability: Compound Events.
Dependent and Independent Events.
While most probability problems you will encounter can be
solved using counting methods from chapter 2, many
will be easier to solve by calculating the probability of
multiple events.

Two events are **independent** if the result of the first has no
effect on the second. If two events are **dependent**,
then the result of the first affects the outcome of the
second.

If the probability of an event occurring is $P(A)$, and the
probability of a second event occurring is $P(B)$, then
the probability that both events will occur is:

$$P(A \text{ and } B) = P(A) \cdot P(B).$$

If two events are mutually exclusive (meaning that both
cannot happen, for example, the probability of rolling
a 7 *or* an 11 with a pair of standard dice), we
calculate the sum of the probabilities:

$$P(A \text{ or } B) = P(A) + P(B).$$

Many probability problems involve blind selection of objects.
If objects are selected **with replacement**, the
events are treated as independent of one another.
Selections of objects **without replacement** are
dependent events.

If you have not already done so, you should review chapter 2
before beginning this chapter. While many of the
problems can be solved without counting techniques,
the techniques learned in chapter 2 are essential to
many probability problems, and useful in almost all of
them.

Probability: Using Compound Events.

On this page we will use three examples to demonstrate an
approach which involves calculating probability as a
series of multiple events.

Four green blocks and three red blocks are placed in a bag and selected at random.

Example: What is the probability of selecting two red
blocks without replacement?

Reasoning: The probability of selecting a red block is 3/7.
Once a red block is drawn, only 2 of 6 blocks which
remain in the bag are red, making the probability of
the second block being red 2/6:

$$\frac{3}{7} \cdot \frac{2}{6} = \frac{1}{7}.$$

Example: What is the probability of selecting a green block
then a red block with replacement?

Reasoning: The probability of selecting a green block is
4/7. Once it is replaced, the probability of the second
block being red is 3/7, therefore:

$$\frac{4}{7} \cdot \frac{3}{7} = \frac{12}{49}.$$

Example: What is the probability of selecting three blocks
of the same color without replacement?

Reasoning: We must calculate the probability of selecting
three greens $P(GGG)$ or three reds $P(RRR)$ separately, then add these probabilities:

$$P(GGG) = \frac{4}{7} \cdot \frac{3}{6} \cdot \frac{2}{5} = \frac{4}{35} \text{ and } P(RRR) = \frac{3}{7} \cdot \frac{2}{6} \cdot \frac{1}{5} = \frac{1}{35}$$

Therefore, $P(GGG \text{ or } RRR) = \frac{4}{35} + \frac{1}{35} = \frac{5}{35} = \frac{1}{7}.$

Probability: Using Counting Techniques.
On this page we see that counting techniques can be used to
   solve the examples from the previous page. You
   should be able to use both techniques interchangeably, but most students favor one over the other.

Example: What is the probability of selecting two red
   blocks without replacement?
Reasoning: There are $7C2$ ways to select two blocks from
   the bag (without replacement), or 21 combinations of
   two blocks without restrictions. There are $3C2 = 3$
   ways to choose two of the three red blocks:

$$\frac{3}{21} = \frac{1}{7}.$$

Example: What is the probability of selecting a green block
   then a red block with replacement?
Reasoning: There are 7 ways to choose the first block and
   7 ways to choose the second, for a total of $7^2 = 49$
   ways to choose two of the seven blocks (with
   replacement). There are $4C1 = 4$ ways to choose a
   green block first and $3C1 = 3$ ways to choose a red
   block second, which gives us a probability of:

$$\frac{4 \cdot 3}{49} = \frac{12}{49}.$$

Example: What is the probability of selecting three blocks
   of the same color without replacement?
Reasoning: There are $7C3 = 35$ ways to select three blocks
   from the bag (without replacement). There are
   $4C3 = 4$ ways to select three green blocks and
   $3C3 = 1$ way to choose three red blocks:

Therefore, $P(GGG \text{ or } RRR) = \dfrac{4+1}{35} = \dfrac{5}{35} = \dfrac{1}{7}.$

Replacement: Card Problems.

You should be familiar with a standard deck of cards, which
consists of 52 cards in four suits: Spades and Clubs
(black) and Hearts and Diamonds (red), with 13
cards in each suit: Ace, 2, 3, 4, 5, 6, 7, 8, 9, 10, Jack,
Queen, and King.

Example: What is the probability of selecting an Ace from
a standard shuffled deck?

Reasoning: There are 4 Aces out of 52 cards, so the
probability of selecting an Ace is 4/52 or 1/13.

Example: What is the probability of selecting a heart then a
club from a standard shuffled deck with replace-
ment?

Reasoning: The probability of selecting a heart first is
13/52. The heart is returned to the deck, so the
probability of selecting a club second remains 13/52,
therefore P(Heart then Club) is:

$$\frac{13}{52} \cdot \frac{13}{52} = \frac{1}{4} \cdot \frac{1}{4} = \frac{1}{16}.$$

Example: What is the probability of selecting two aces
from a standard shuffled deck without replacement?

Reasoning: The probability of selecting an Ace first is
4/52 or 1/13, after which there will be 3 aces left in a
51-card deck, so the probability of selecting an ace
second is 3/51 or 1/17:

$$\frac{1}{13} \cdot \frac{1}{17} = \frac{1}{221}.$$

I am more comfortable treating *these* problems as compound
events. Learning when to use counting and when to
use compound probability takes practice.

Practice: Card Problems.

For the following problems, assume you are using a standard
deck of cards as described on the previous page.

3.100 What is the probability of selecting a heart from a
shuffled deck of cards?

3.200 What is the probability of selecting three red cards in a
row with replacement?

3.300 What is the probability of selecting two cards from
different suits with replacement?

3.400 What is the probability that the top two cards of a
shuffled deck are both face cards? (Kings, Queens,
and Jacks are all face cards.)

3.500 What is the probability that the top four cards of a
shuffled deck are all of the same suit?

3.600 What is the probability that the top card in a shuffled
deck is a red Ace, and the second card is a spade?

3.700 What is the probability that the top card in a shuffled
deck is an Ace (of any color), and the second card is
a spade? The Ace may be the Ace of spades.

3.800 What is the probability that the top two cards in a
shuffled deck are an Ace (of any suit) and a spade?
The Ace of spades cannot be used to satisfy both
requirements.

3.900 What is the probability that the top two cards in a
shuffled deck are consecutive cards of the same
suit? (The Ace can be high or low).

Practice: More Probability Basics.

3.010 A fair coin is flipped three times, and each flip comes up heads. What is the probability that the next flip will also be heads?

3.110 You roll a pair of dice; one red and the other green. What is the probability of rolling a five on the red die and an even number on the green die?

3.210 For a lottery drawing, a set of balls numbered 1 through 9 is placed in each of three bins. One ball is selected from each bin. What is the probability that all three digits drawn will be odd?

3.310 For a randomly selected phone number, what is the probability that the last three digits are all the same?

3.410 What is the probability of rolling each of the numbers 1 through 6 in any order in six rolls of a standard die?

3.510 A dot is added to each face of two standard dice. What is the probability of rolling an 8 with the modified pair of dice?

3.610 For three randomly selected positive integers, what is the probability that the sum of the units digits is even?

3.710 Six students are randomly seated in the first row of a classroom. What is the probability that from left to right they are in order from oldest to youngest?

3.810 Each spinner below is divided into four equal sectors. Each is spun once, and the product of the spins is calculated. What is the probability that the product is positive?

3.2: Compound Events *and* Counting

Many problems are best solved using a combination of techniques which involve both counting and computing the probability of compound events.

Example: Three fair dice are rolled. What is the probability that exactly two of the rolls show a 1?

Reasoning: First, we compute the probability of rolling 1-1-X, where X can be any number from 2 through 6:

$$\frac{1}{6} \cdot \frac{1}{6} \cdot \frac{5}{6} = \frac{5}{216}.$$

Second, we find the number of ways to arrange the 1-1-X. The probability of rolling 1-1-X is the same as the probability of rolling 1-X-1 or X-1-1 (consider each of the three dice as distinguishable in some way, like being different colors or rolled in order). We triple the probability to get:

$$\frac{5}{216} \cdot 3 = \frac{15}{216} = \frac{5}{72}.$$

Example: Lisa shakes her piggy bank which contains 5 quarters and 5 nickels until 5 coins fall out. Assuming nickels and quarters fall out with equal probability, what is the probability that the sum of the change that has fallen out is $0.85?

Reasoning: The only way for five Nickels (N) and Quarters (Q) to add up to $0.85 is with three Quarters and two Nickels. Begin by computing $P(QQQNN)$:

$$\frac{5}{10} \cdot \frac{4}{9} \cdot \frac{3}{8} \cdot \frac{5}{7} \cdot \frac{4}{6} = \frac{5}{126}.$$

However, there are $5C2 = 10$ ways to arrange $QQQNN$, each has an equal probability of occurring:

$$\frac{5}{126} \cdot 10 = \frac{50}{126} = \frac{25}{63}.$$

Compound Events and Counting:

Example: Hank can hit the bull's eye with a bow-and-arrow one in three times. If Hank fires nine arrows, what is the probability that exactly three of them will land in the bull's eye? Express your answer as a percent rounded to the nearest tenth.

Reasoning: We will use O's to represent successes, and X's to represent misses. He hits the bull's eye with 1/3 probability, and misses with 2/3 probability. First find P(OOOXXXXXX) and then multiply by the number of ways to arrange OOOXXXXXX ($9C3$):

$$\left(\frac{1}{3}\right)^3 \cdot \left(\frac{2}{3}\right)^6 \cdot \frac{9 \cdot 8 \cdot 7}{3 \cdot 2 \cdot 1} = \frac{2^9 \cdot 3^2 \cdot 7}{2 \cdot 3^{10}} = \frac{2^8 \cdot 7}{3^8} = \frac{1792}{6561} \approx 27.3\%.$$

This problem is much more difficult to complete using strictly counting methods because the probability of a hit is different from that of a miss.

Example: There are a dozen eggs in a basket and four have been hard-boiled. You can tell by spinning an egg whether it has been hard-boiled. You select three eggs from the basket. What is the probability that only one of the three is hard-boiled?

Reasoning: The probability of selecting a hard-boiled egg followed by two raw eggs is given by:

$$P(HRR) = \frac{4}{12} \cdot \frac{8}{11} \cdot \frac{7}{10} = \frac{28}{165}.$$

There are two other equally likely possibilities: P(RHR) and P(RRH), so we triple the probability above to get:

$$3 \cdot \frac{28}{165} = \frac{28}{55}.$$

Practice: Compound Events and Counting.

3.020 Hriday attempts five free-throws at practice. If Hriday has a 40% chance of making each free-throw, what is the probability that he will make exactly three of the five shots?

3.120 A homeroom has 7 boys and 5 girls. The homeroom teacher randomly selects two representatives to serve on student council. What is the probability that the teacher selects one boy and one girl?

3.220 Jeremy has found a way to flip a coin so that tails lands face up twice as often as heads. What is the probability of Jeremy flipping more tails than heads in three coin flips using this method?

3.320 The school cafeteria has chocolate chip cookies and oatmeal cookies for dessert. What is the probability that exactly 3 of the next 5 students in line will select chocolate chip cookies if everyone selects a cookie, and students prefer chocolate to oatmeal 2 to 1?

3.420 If the probability of rain on any given day in February is 40%, what is the probability that for a given week in February there will be exactly three rainy days? Express your answer to the nearest percent.

3.520 A drawer contains 7 blue socks and 5 black socks. Four socks are randomly selected from the drawer. What is the probability that a pair of blue socks and a pair of black socks can be made from the 4 socks drawn?

3.620 In six rolls of a standard die, what is the probability that the same number will be rolled exactly five times?

3.3: Casework and Probability

Most of the problems we have done so far could be completed in one of two different ways: by computing the probability of compound events, or by counting favorable and total outcomes.

For example, in the piggy bank example (**p.111**), we could have computed the number of ways to choose five coins from a bank of ten: $10C5 = 252$. There are $5C2 = 10$ ways to choose two nickels and $5C3 = 10$ ways to choose three quarters for a total of $10 \cdot 10 = 100$ ways to choose two nickels and three quarters. This gives us the same probability we calculated before:

$$\frac{5C2 \cdot 5C3}{10C5} = \frac{10 \cdot 10}{252} = \frac{100}{252} = \frac{25}{63}.$$

Sometimes, computing compound probabilities is not useful, and counting methods must be used. This is most often true in problems which involve **casework** (see section **2.5**).

Example: Oleg rolls a standard die three times. What is the probability that the third roll is greater than the sum of the first two rolls?

Reasoning: We know that there are $6^3 = 216$ possible outcomes for three rolls of a standard die. Now we must count the number of ways in which the third roll would be greater than the sum of the first two. Remember to keep organized:

If the last roll is a six, the first two rolls could be:
(1,1) (1,2) (1,3) (1,4) (2,1) (2,2) (2,3) (3,1) (3,2) (4,1)
If the last roll is a five, the first two rolls could be:
(1,1) (1,2) (1,3) (2,1) (2,2) (3,1)
If the last roll is a four we have: (1,1) (1,2) (2,1)
And for three we have: (1,1)
This gives us a total of 20 out of 216 rolls, or $\frac{5}{54}$.

Practice: Casework and Probability.

3.030 Three numbers are selected at random and without replacement from a bag containing each of the numbers 1 through 9. What is the probability that the three numbers are consecutive integers?

3.130 Four of the vertices of a regular octagon are selected at random and connected to form a quadrilateral. What is the probability that the quadrilateral will be a rectangle?

3.230 An organization is choosing colors for the stripes on its flag. The flag has three horizontal stripes and a vertical stripe as shown. If the color of each of the four stripes is selected at random from the colors red, blue, and green. What is the probability that no two stripes of the same color share an edge?

3.330 Three numbers are selected at random and without replacement from a bag containing each of the numbers 1 through 9. What is the probability that all three share a common factor greater than 1?

3.430 Three of the vertices of a regular heptagon are connected to form a triangle. What is the probability that the triangle formed is isosceles?

3.530 Each of the 6 faces of a cube is painted either white or black with equal probability. What is the probability that no two black faces share an edge?

3.4: Probability and Combinations

Probability problems often require careful counting of combinations. In the case where objects are grouped, it is often easiest to divide the number of ways to form a group using the given restrictions by the total number of groups that can be formed without restrictions.

Example: Five boys and seven girls, are randomly assigned to three groups of four students each. What is the probability that one of the three groups will be all girls?

Reasoning: There are $12C4 = 495$ ways to select 4 students from a group of 12. There are $7C4 = 35$ ways to select 4 of the 7 girls. The probability of a randomly formed group consisting of all girls is therefore $35/495 = 7/99$. Because there are 3 groups formed, the probability of any one of those groups consisting of all girls is:

$$3 \cdot \frac{7}{99} = \frac{21}{99} = \frac{7}{33}.$$

This problem could have also been solved using compound probability by finding the probability of one group having four girls and then multiplying by three:

$$\frac{7}{12} \cdot \frac{6}{11} \cdot \frac{5}{10} \cdot \frac{4}{9} \cdot 3 = \frac{7}{99} \cdot 3 = \frac{7}{33}.$$

Example: The 26 letters of the alphabet are placed on tiles and randomly separated into two equal piles. What is the probability that the word MATH can be found in one of the two piles?

Reasoning: First, we consider the number of 13-letter piles selected from 26 letters: $26C13=10,400,600$. Then we consider the number of those piles that contain the letters MATH. This leaves room in the group for 9 more letters selected from a set of 22, or $22C9 =$

497,420. Dividing and simplifying gives us 11/230. There are two piles of letters, so the probability of MATH being in one of the two piles is twice that:

$$2 \cdot \frac{11}{230} = \frac{11}{115}.$$

Using compound probability is more difficult here and I would not recommend it. The math looks like this when we use compound probability:

$$_{13}C_4 \cdot \frac{4}{26} \cdot \frac{3}{25} \cdot \frac{2}{24} \cdot \frac{1}{23} \cdot 2 = \frac{11}{115}.$$

Practice: Counting Combinations.

3.040 The thirteen diamonds are separated from a standard deck of cards. What is the probability that all three face cards (KQJ) are in a set of five randomly selected cards from this set?

3.140 Three students are randomly selected from a group of twelve that includes twins Billy and Adam. What is the probability that Adam is selected but Billy is not?

3.240 A youth basketball team consists of 12 players. If they are randomly divided into 4 groups of 3 players each for passing drills, what is the probability that the 2 girls on the team will be placed in the same group?

3.340 The digits 1 through 9 are divided into three sets of three digits. What is the probability that the product of one of the sets is odd?

3.440 There are 3 vegetarians in a class of 20 students. If 3 students are chosen at random, what is the probability that exactly one of the 3 is a vegetarian?

3.5: Complementary Counting and Probability

It is often easiest to compute the probability of what we do not want. Subtracting this from 1 gives us the probability of what we do want.

Example: The chance of rain for each of the next five days is 25%. What is the probability that it will rain at least once in the next five days? Express your answer to the nearest tenth of a percent.

Reasoning: We only need to calculate the probability that it will not rain at all. If there is a 25% chance of rain for each of the next five days, there is a 75% chance that it will not rain, or 3/4 for each of five days:

$$\left(\frac{3}{4}\right)^5 = \frac{243}{1024} \approx 23.7\% \quad \text{or} \quad (0.75)^5 = 0.2373... \approx 23.7\%$$

Example: You hold the Q in a game of Scrabble, and need a U to be able to make a word. There are 9 letters left in the bag and two are U's. If you select four letters at random, what is the probability that you will get at least one U?

Reasoning: It is easier to compute the probability that you will not get a U. Beginning with two U's and seven letters which are not U's, we get the probability of not drawing a U as:

$$\frac{7}{9} \cdot \frac{6}{8} \cdot \frac{5}{7} \cdot \frac{4}{6} = \frac{5}{18}$$

This means: $1 - \frac{5}{18} = \frac{13}{18}$ of the time you *would* draw a U.

With counting techniques: there are a total of $9C4 = 126$ combinations of four letters and $7C4 = 35$ combinations which do not include a U, which means the probability of not drawing a U is $35/126 = 5/18$. This leaves a 13/18 probability of drawing the U.

Complementary Counting and Probability:

3.050 You are rolling a pair of dice to see who goes first in a board game. You only need to beat a 4 to win the chance to go first. What is the probability that you will roll greater than a 4?

3.150 The digits 1 through 4 are randomly arranged to create a four-digit number. What is the probability that the number formed is not divisible by 4?

3.250 Three coins are flipped. What is the probability of flipping at least one heads and at least one tails?

3.350 A pair of standard dice is rolled, and the product of the digits is calculated. What is the probability that the product is even?

3.450 For any date in history, Luke can quickly tell you what day of the week it was. You choose three dates at random and Luke tells you the day of the week for each. What is the probability that at least two of the dates occurred on the same day of the week?

3.550 There are nine blocks in a bag: three red, three white, and three blue. Three blocks are selected at random and without replacement. What is the probability that at least two of the blocks will be different colored?

3.650 The first nine letters of the alphabet are randomly placed into three equal piles of three letters each. What is the probability that the letters A and B end up in different piles?

3.750 If the digits 1 through 5 are randomly arranged so that one digit fills each of the five circles, what is the probability that at least two consecutive integers will be connected by a line segment?

Review: 3.1 through 3.5

3.060 A bag contains 10 black blocks and 4 white blocks. What is the probability of selecting 3 black blocks from the bag without replacement?

3.160 Four of the vertices of a cube are selected at random. What is the probability that all four selected points will be coplanar?

3.260 When you drop a piece of buttered toast, your mother suggests that it will land buttered-side down twice as often as buttered-side up. If this is true, what is the probability that at least one out of three dropped slices of toast will land buttered-side up?

3.360 Three of the vertices of a cube are connected to form a triangle. What is the probability that all three vertices are on the same face of the cube?

3.460 The weatherman has predicted a 30% chance of snow for each of the next three days. Your younger brother shows off his addition skills, suggesting that there is a 90% chance of snow. What is the actual probability that it will snow on at least one of the next three days? Express your answer as a percent rounded to the tenth.

3.560 You are dealt three cards from a standard deck of 52 cards. What is the probability that exactly two cards are from the same suit?

3.660 3 digits are selected from the set {2, 3, 4, 5, 6, 7, 8} without replacement. What is the probability that the sum of the three digits is prime?

3.760 Twenty-seven students each flip a fair coin. What is the probability that there are more heads showing than tails?

3.6 Geometric Probability

Most of the problems in this unit require that you know how to compute lengths, areas, and even volumes of figures in space. If you are not familiar with at least most of the area formulas, review section **5.4** first and come back to this section later.

Geometric probability involves counting outcomes that are different from the outcomes we have counted so far. Instead of objects or events, the "favorable outcomes" consist of lengths or areas.

Example: A point is selected at random on line segment AB. What is the probability that the point will be closer to the midpoint of AB than to either A or B?

Reasoning: Divide segment AB into fourths.

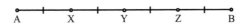

Any point on AX or ZB is closer to an endpoint, while any point on XZ is closer to the midpoint. Since XZ is half the length of AB, the probability of a randomly selected point being closer to the midpoint is 1/2.

Example: A point is selected at random within a circle of radius 6cm. What is the probability that the point lies in the shaded area outside of the small circle of radius 4cm?

Reasoning: We only need to calculate the areas of the two circles, leaving the areas in terms of pi we have the small circle of area 16π, and the large circle of area 36π, which makes the shaded area $36\pi - 16\pi = 20\pi$. The probability that the point is selected within this region is:

$$\frac{20\pi}{36\pi} = \frac{5}{9}.$$

Geometric Probability.

Some word problems are not easily recognized as geometric
   probability problems. When a problem appears to
   have countless possible outcomes, graphing can be a
   useful tool for solving probability problems.

Example: The bus comes to a stop near your house every
   day at a random time between 6:45 and 6:50. You
   arrive at the bus stop at a random time between 6:40
   and 6:45 every day and wait until the bus comes.
   What is the probability that you wait less than 4
   minutes for the bus to arrive? Express your answer
   as a percent.

Reasoning: Set up a graph with your arrival time graphed
   against the arrival time of the bus. Shade the area
   where your wait time is less than 4 minutes.

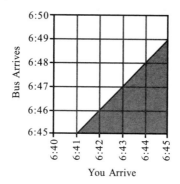

The whole graph has an area of 25 units², and the shaded
   triangle is 8 units². Your probability of waiting less
   than 4 minutes is 8/25 or 32%.

Example: What is the probability that two (not necessarily
   integer) numbers selected at random between 1 and
   4 have a sum greater than 4? Express your answer
   as a common fraction in simplest form.

Reasoning: Set up a graph again, shading the area in which
$x + y > 4$.

The shaded area represents 7/9 of the whole so the
probability is 7/9.

Practice: Geometric Probability.

3.070 In rectangle ABCD, AB = 1 and BC = 2. Point X is
selected at random within the rectangle. What is the
probability that the area of triangle ABX is more than
twice the area of triangle BCX?

3.170 Concentric circles have radii of 3, 4, 5,
and 6cm. What is the probability that a
random point selected within the large
circle is in one of the shaded regions?

3.270 A point is randomly selected inside the
right triangle ABC. What is the
probability that it will fall within the
shaded region if AX = 3 and CX = 2.

3.370 Point X is selected at random within square ABCD of
side length 3. What is the probability that quadrilateral ABXD has an area greater than 4 square units?

3.470 One side of a triangle is 5cm long. Two (not necessarily integer) numbers are randomly selected between
0 and 10. What is the probability that the two
numbers can be the other two sides of the triangle
(see **p.178**).

3.7: Expected Value

Expected value is easiest to think of as the average outcome.
It is not necessarily (as its name may suggest) the
outcome that is expected to occur. If we think in
terms of experimental probability, the expected value
of an event is the long-term average.

Example: What is the expected value of one roll of a
standard six-faced die?

Reasoning: There are six possible outcomes, each equally
likely: 1, 2, 3, 4, 5, or 6. In a perfect world, six rolls
would yield one of each for a total of $1+2+...+6 = 21$.
The expected value (average outcome) is:

$$\frac{1+2+3+4+5+6}{6} = \frac{21}{6} = 3.5$$

No one ever expects to roll a 3.5 on a single roll of a die, but
the average value of a roll on a standard die is 3.5.

Expected value problems often involve money.

Example: A change machine is broken. If you put in a
penny, it spits out a coin at random: either a penny,
nickel, dime, or quarter, each with equal probability.
How much profit can you expect to make by inserting 100 pennies?

Reasoning: Consider again a perfect scenario in which you
put in four pennies and get back four different coins:
a penny, a nickel, a dime, and a quarter, for a total of
$0.41. You put $0.04 in, so your profit on four
pennies is $0.37 and your expected profit on 100
pennies is $25(0.37) = 9.25$, or $9.25.

Challenge:

3.570 Find the expected value for a penny inserted into the
machine if you have unlimited pennies and are
allowed to re-insert pennies (pennies only) that you
get back from the machine.

Practice: Expected Value.

3.080 A multiple choice test has 20 questions, each with 5 answer choices. Correct answers are worth 6 points, blank answers are worth 1.5 points, and incorrect answers are worth 0 points. What is the expected value of a random guess?

3.180 Eight cash prizes assigned to briefcases: $0, $2, $10, $50, $100, $250, $500, and $1000. What is the expected value of a randomly selected briefcase?

3.280 A row or column of three numbers is selected on a standard calculator with the numbers 1 through 9 arranged as shown. What is the expected value for the sum of the three selected numbers?

7	8	9
4	5	6
1	2	3

3.380 There are $1 and $5 bills in a bag. The expected value for a randomly selected bill is $1.20. What is the fewest number of bills that could be in the bag?

3.480 What is the expected value for the sum of the digits on a standard digital (12-hour) clock?

3.580 Three white, four red, and five blue blocks are placed in a bag and two blocks are selected at random without replacement. If the blocks selected are the same color, you win $3 if they are both red or both blue, and $6 if they are both white. What is the expected value for a draw of two blocks?

3.680 A bag contains $1, $2, and $5 tokens. The number of $1 tokens in the bag is equal to the number of $2 tokens, and there are eighteen $5 tokens. The expected value for the draw of a token at random is $2.25. How many tokens are in the bag altogether?

Chapter 3 Review

3.090 The expiration date on a credit card is given as two digits for the month and two digits for the year. What is the expected value for the sum of the digits in the expiration date for a credit card that expires between 01/10 and 12/15 inclusive? Assume that each month and year occur with equal frequency.

3.190 Alice and Ben take turns rolling a standard six-sided die. The first person to roll a six wins. If Alice goes first, what is the probability that she will win the game?

3.290 A rectangular prism has edges of length 3cm, 4cm, and 5cm. What is the probability that a randomly selected point on the surface of the prism will be on one of its two smallest faces?

3.390 In five rolls of a standard die, what is the probability of rolling a "full house", that is, two of one number and three of a different number?

3.490 The probability that two randomly selected integers from a set have a product that is odd is 1/5. If the set includes three odd integers, how many integers are in the set altogether?

3.590 Point X is randomly selected within square ABCD. What is the probability that angle AXB is acute? Express your answer as a percent rounded to the tenth (see p. 186).

3.690 Circles of integral diameter are arranged so that each is entirely within the next larger circle, and the probability of a randomly selected point being within the shaded region is exactly 1/2. What is the smallest possible area of the shaded region?

3.790 Two distinct pairs of vertices are randomly selected on a cube and each pair is connected by a line segment. What is the probability that the two line segments intersect?

3.890 Scientists predict that an active volcano has a 75% chance of erupting at least once in the next 5 years. If the probability that the volcano will erupt is the same for each year, what is the probability that the volcano will erupt within the next year? Express your answer to the nearest tenth of a percent.

3.990 Staring at point A on the map below, Jennifer needs to walk to point B using the grid of city streets shown. At each intersection, Jennifer flips a coin to decide whether to go north or east (at intersections where she has a choice). What is the probability that she will pass the intersection marked with an X on her way from A to B?

Number Theory
Chapter IV

Number Theory is the study of how numbers work, specifi-
cally how integers work. In this chapter we will deal
almost exclusively with positive integers, also called
natural numbers or counting numbers.

Most of the problems we will examine in this chapter revolve
around a number's unique prime factorization. There
are many clever problem solving strategies which
require the use of a number's prime factorization.

We will also look into the use of different number bases,
patterns involving the units digit, some interesting
relationships between decimals and fractions, and we
will introduce modular arithmetic.

Because so much of what we do relies on finding the prime
factorization of a number, we will begin with a look
at prime numbers and some divisibility rules.

4.1: Primes and Divisibility

A **Prime Number** is a whole number whose only factors are 1 and itself. Numbers which have more than two factors are composite. To find all of the prime numbers between 1 and 100, complete the following exercise:

The **Sieve of Eratosthenes** is an ancient algorithm used to identify prime numbers. We will use a sieve to find all of the primes numbers less than 100.

Create or copy the diagram on the opposite page and perform the following operations:

1: Cross out 1 by **Shading** in the box completely. One is neither prime nor composite.

2: Use a forward **Slash** \ to cross out all multiples of 2, starting with 4. Two is the first prime number.

3: Use a backward **Slash** / to cross out all multiples of 3 starting with 6. Three is prime.

4: Multiples of 4 have been crossed out already when we did #2, all multiples of 4 are multiples of 2.

5: Draw a **Square** on all multiples of 5 starting with 10. Five is prime.

6: Multiples of 6 should be X'd already (from #2 and #3).

7: **Circle** all multiples of 7 starting with 14. Seven is prime.

8: Multiples of 8 were crossed out already when we did #2.

9: Multiples of 9 were crossed out already when we did #3.

10: Multiples of 10 were done when we did #2 and #5.

All of the remaining numbers are prime.

How many primes did you discover between 1 and 100?

A list of the smallest 50 primes can be found on page 364 in the appendix of this text.

Sieve of Eratosthenes

1	2	3	4	5	6	7	8	9	10
11	12	13	14	15	16	17	18	19	20
21	22	23	24	25	26	27	28	29	30
31	32	33	34	35	36	37	38	39	40
41	42	43	44	45	46	47	48	49	50
51	52	53	54	55	56	57	58	59	60
61	62	63	64	65	66	67	68	69	70
71	72	73	74	75	76	77	78	79	80
81	82	83	84	85	86	87	88	89	90
91	92	93	94	95	96	97	98	99	100

Primes less than 100:
2 3 5 7 11 13 17 19 23 29 31 37 41 43 47 53 59 61 67 71 73 79 83 89 97

Divisibility Rules:

There are some easy tricks you can use to determine if a number is divisible by 2, 3, 4, 5, 6, 8, 9 and 10.

A number is divisible by:

2: If it is even.
3: If the sum of its digits is divisible by 3.
4: If the number formed by the last 2 digits is divisible by 4.
5: If the ones digit is 5 or 0.
6: If it is divisible by 2 *and* 3 (all even multiples of 3).
7: There is no *good* trick for 7, just do the division.
8: If the number formed by the last 3 digits is divisible by 8.
9: If the sum of the digits is divisible by 9.
10: If the last digit is a 0.
11: We will learn this trick on **p.134**. It is more complicated.

Most of the proofs for the divisibility rules above are available online, and I encourage you to look them up.

The divisibility rules for 4 and 8 deserve clarification:

Four divides 100 evenly, so four divides large numbers like 87,300 and 65,498,200. This makes it easy to understand why you only need to look to the last two digits to determine divisibility by four.

Eight divides 1,000 evenly. For the same reason as four, you only need to look at the last three digits to determine divisibility by 8. In fact, 8 divides 200, so the rule is even simpler. When determining if 98,656 is divisible by 8, it is easy to see that 98,600 is divisible by 8, so in the case where the hundreds digit is even, you only need to look at the last two digits.

Check for Understanding:

4.100 Which of the following are factors of 3,435,864?
        2   3   4   5   6   8   9   10

4.200 Which of the following are factors of 123,456,780?
        2   3   4   5   6   8   9   10

More Difficult Divisibility Problems:

Example: What is the smallest 4-digit number that is divisible by 2, 3, 4, 5, 6, 8, 9, and 10?

Reasoning: The number must end in a zero. Let's assume that to be the smallest it should start with a 1. Since the digits must add up to 9, the last three digits must add up to 8. 1,080 is the smallest four-digit integer divisible by 2, 3, 4, 5, 6, 8, 9, and 10.

Alternate Solution: Consider the prime factorization of the result. You need a 2 for divisibility by 2 (2), a 3 for divisibility by 3 ($2 \cdot 3$), another 2 for divisibility by 4 ($2^2 \cdot 3$), and a 5 for divisibility by 5 ($2^2 \cdot 3 \cdot 5$). This number is already divisible by 6. Another 2 must be included for divisibility by 8 ($2^3 \cdot 3 \cdot 5$), and another 3 for divisibility by 9. The resulting number is divisible by 2, 3, 4, 5, 6, 8, 9, and 10 ($2^3 \cdot 3^2 \cdot 5 = 360$). We were asked for a four-digit integer, so we need to multiply 360 by 3 to get 1,080.

Example: Using only 1's and 2's, what is the smallest integer you can create which is divisible by both 3 and 8?

Reasoning: The units digit must be a 2. Since 12 and 22 don't work, we need a 3-digit number that is divisible by 8. $112/8 = 14$, but it is not divisible by 3. Unfortunately, 122, 212, and 222 are not divisible by 8. We must go to a 4-digit number that ends in 112 and whose digit sum is a multiple of 3. The only 4-digit number that works is 2,112 (we want the sum of the digits to be 6), so it is the smallest.

Answer before turning the page:

The digits of a number are all 8's, and it is divisible by 9. What is the least positive integer that fits this description?

Solution:

The divisibility rule for nine is that the sum of the digits must
be divisible by 9. If the integer consists only of 8's,
there must be nine of them for the sum to be divisible by 9. 888,888,888 is the smallest integer consisting entirely of 8's which is divisible by 9.

Practice: Divisibility.

4.500 What is the smallest positive integer that is divisible by
2 and 3 that consists entirely of 2's and 3's, with at
least one of each?

4.600 What is the smallest five-digit integer divisible both by
8 *and* by 9?

Divisibility Rule: Eleven.

The divisibility rule for 11 is seldom taught in regular classes.

Practice:

First, take a moment to multiply several numbers by 11:

504	1723	ABCD
x 11	x 11	x 11

You should see some patterns with the digits.
In the final example, the digits become:

A   A+B   B+C   C+D   D

ten-thousands   *thousands*   *hundreds*   *tens*   *ones*

If you add the alternating digits you get the same result.

$$A+(B+C)+D \text{ and } (A+B)+(C+D)$$

The proof of the divisibility rule for 11 (and many others)
uses modular arithmetic, which we will introduce
later in this chapter (see **p.170**).

To find out if a number is divisible by eleven:
Sum the alternating digits. Subtract these two sums.
If the result is zero **or** is divisible by 11, the number is
    divisible by 11.

Examples: Determine if each number is divisible by 11
    without a calculator:

1. 495   **2.** 9,835   **3.** 14,806   **4.** 918,291

Reasoning:

495 is divisible by 11 because $(4+5)-9=0$.

9,835 is not divisible by 11 because $(9+3)-(8+5)=-1$.

14,806 is divisible by 11 because $(1+8+6)-(4+0)=11$.

918,291 is divisible by 11 because $(9+8+9)-(1+2+1)=22$.

Practice: Divisibility by 11.

4.010 Which of the following is/are divisible by 11?
       3,951   907,654   14,256

4.110 What digit could fill-in the blank to make 89,_43
       divisible by 11?

4.210 What five-digit multiple of 11 consists entirely of 2's
       and 3's?

4.310 What is the largest five-digit multiple of 11?

4.410 How many three-digit multiples of 11 end in a 2?

4.510 Find the remainder when 1,234,567 is divided by 11?

4.610   Find the smallest positive integer greater than 90,000
       that is divisible by 11.

Practice: Divisibility and Primes.

4.020 What digit could be used to fill in the blank to make 45,2_8 divisible by both 3 and 8?

4.120 How many positive multiples of 3 less than 1,000 use only the digits 2 and/or 4?

4.220 360 is divisible by both 8 and 9. How many positive integers less than 360 are also divisible by both 8 and 9?

4.320 Using only the digits 1, 2, and 3 with at least one of each, what is the smallest integer that can be created which is divisible by 8 and 9?

4.420 Using only the digit 2, *how many* 2's must be used to create an integer that is divisible by both 9 and 11?

4.520 What is the sum of all 4-digit multiples of 8 which use each of the digits 1, 2, 3, and 4 exactly once.

4.620 For the number ABC, each distinct letter represents a *different* digit. If ABC, CAB, and BCA are all divisible by 6 and 9, find the value of ABC + CAB + BCA.

4.720 Each of the digits 0 through 9 is used exactly once to create a ten-digit integer. Find the greatest ten-digit number which uses each digit once and is divisible by 8, 9, 10, and 11.

4.820 What is the remainder when 456,564,465,645 is divided by 6?

4.920 Using two 5's and two 6's, it is possible to create four 4-digit numbers which are divisible by 11. What is the sum of these four numbers?

4.2: Factors

Finding the prime factorization of a number is key to many
number theory problems.

Testing to see if a number is prime: If we want to know
if 401 is prime, do we need to test to see if the
following numbers are factors: 4? 7? 10? 13? 23?

When we are checking to determine whether a number is
prime or not, we only need to check prime factors.
There is no need to check for divisibility by composite numbers like 4 and 10 because if 4 were a factor,
2 would be a factor. If 10 were a factor, 2 and 5
would both also be factors.

We don't need to check all primes, only those which are less
than the square root of the number we are checking.
For example, when testing to determine whether or
not 401 is prime, we only need to test primes up to
19. If 23 were a factor, it would have to be multiplied by a number less than 20.

To determine whether a number *n* is prime:

Check for divisibility by primes less than $\sqrt{n}$ starting from
least to greatest.

Example: Is 181 prime?
Check in your head using divisibility rules: 2, 3, 5, and 11.
Check 7 and 13 on paper if you need to. Make sure
you understand why you do not need to check
numbers like 4 and 17 as factors. (181 is prime).

Check for Understanding:
4.030 Which of the following are primes? If a number is not
prime, name its prime factors: 287, 391, 503.

4.130 The number 13 is prime, and when its digits are
reversed, 31 is also prime. Besides13 and 31, how
many other 2-digit primes also satisfy this condition?

The Fundamental Theorem of Arithmetic:

The fundamental theorem of arithmetic states that every positive integer has a unique prime factorization. For example: $5,544 = 2^3 \cdot 3^2 \cdot 7 \cdot 11$. There is no other way to factor 5,544 into a product of primes.

To find the prime factorization of a number, it is often easiest to create a factor tree. If you remember your divisibility rules this should be easy:

Examples: Use a factor tree to find the prime factorization of each:

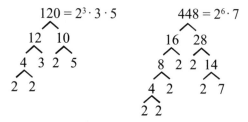

Check for Understanding:

4.530 Write the prime factorization of each number below using exponents and placing the prime factors in order from least to greatest.

440   432   209

4.630 Write the prime factorization of each number below. These three numbers all have something in common. Can you tell what it is?

441   256   576

With practice, you will no longer need to construct a factor tree to find the prime factorization of most numbers. Try writing the factors down as you do the division in your head.

Perfect Squares:

441, 256, and 576 (from the previous practice problem **4.630**) are all perfect squares. If a number is a perfect square, each of the prime factors will have an even exponent in its prime factorization.

Example: What perfect square is represented by $3^4 \cdot 5^2$?

Reasoning: $3^4 \cdot 5^2 = (3^2 \cdot 5)^2 = 45^2$.

Check for Understanding:

What perfect squares are represented below?

4.730 5^4 **4.830** $2^4 \cdot 3^2$ **4.930** $2^2 \cdot 3^6 \cdot 5^2$

Counting Factors:

One way to count the number of **factors (divisors)** that a number has is to list them.

Examples:

40:	96:	196:
1 x 40	1 x 96	1 x 196
2 x 20	2 x 48	2 x 98
4 x 10	3 x 32	4 x 49
5 x 8	4 x 24	7 x 28
	6 x 16	14^2
	8 x 12	

When you list factors, list them in pairs and go from least to greatest. There is a nice relationship between the prime factorization of a number and its number of factors (also called divisors). For example, look at the prime factorization of 40: $40 = 2^3 \cdot 5$.

Every factor of 40 can be written as a product of 2's and 5's.

$1 = 2^0 \cdot 5^0$ $2 = 2^1 \cdot 5^0$ $4 = 2^2 \cdot 5^0$ $8 = 2^3 \cdot 5^0$

$5 = 2^0 \cdot 5^1$ $10 = 2^1 \cdot 5^1$ $20 = 2^2 \cdot 5^1$ $40 = 2^3 \cdot 5^1$

Note that each factor of 40 can be formed by pairing 0, 1, 2, or 3 twos with 0 or 1 five.

Factor Counting: If you are only asked *how many* factors a number has, there is an easy shortcut.

Example: How many factors does 56 have?
Reasoning: First find the prime factorization: $56 = 2^3 \cdot 7^1$.
Each factor can have either 0, 1, 2, or 3 twos.
Each factor can have 0 or 1 seven.
This means that 56 has 4 choices for the number of twos and 2 choices for the number of sevens in each of its factors, for a total of $4 \cdot 2 = 8$ factors.

Example: How many factors does $240 = 2^4 \cdot 3^1 \cdot 5^1$ have?
Reasoning: Add 1 to each exponent in the prime factorization and multiply: $(4 + 1)(1 + 1)(1 + 1) = 20$ factors.

Practice: Factor Counting.
4.040 How many factors (divisors) does each number have?

$72 = 2^3 \cdot 3^2$ $\qquad$ $180 = 2^2 \cdot 3^2 \cdot 5^1$

$210 = 2^1 \cdot 3^1 \cdot 5^1 \cdot 7^1$ $\qquad$ $112 = 2^4 \cdot 7^1$

4.140 What is the smallest positive integer that has exactly 6 factors?

4.240 What is the smallest positive integer that has exactly 10 factors?

4.340 How many positive integers are less than 100 and have an odd number of factors?

4.440 If a and b represent distinct positive integers which have exactly 3 factors each, how many different products ab are less than 1,000?

4.540 What is the prime factorization of the smallest positive integer that has exactly 31 factors?

4.640 Find all five 2-digit positive integers which have exactly 12 factors.

Trickier Factor Counting: Odds, Evens, and Squares.

Example: How many odd numbers are factors of 240?

Reasoning: We will begin by looking at the prime factorization of 240:

$$240 = 2^4 \cdot 3^1 \cdot 5^1$$

Any number multiplied by 2 is even, so the odd factors are the ones that have no 2's in their prime factorization. We can only use the 3's and 5's as factors for a total of $2 \cdot 2 = 4$ factors: 1, 3, 5, and 15.

Example: How many even numbers are factors of 240?

Reasoning: This is a case where complementary counting makes the most sense. Count the total number of factors (20) and subtract the number of odd factors (4) from above for a total of 16 even factors. This is much easier than counting all of the factors that include a two.

Example: How many perfect squares are factors of 360?

Reasoning: Again, look at the prime factorization:

$$360 = 2^3 \cdot 3^2 \cdot 5^1$$

We need to find factors that include only even powers of 2, 3, and 5: 2^0 or 2^2 and 3^0 or 3^2. 5^1 cannot be part of the prime factorization of a perfect square. This gives us $2 \cdot 2 = 4$ perfect square factors:

$$2^0 = 1, \ 2^2 = 4, \ 3^2 = 9, \text{ and } 2^2 \cdot 3^2 = 36.$$

Notice that this is simply a matter of multiplying the number of choices for 2's and 3's in the prime factorization of a perfect square factor. Do not forget to include 1 when counting perfect squares.

Practice: Factors.

4.050 How many of the factors of 480 are even?

4.150 How many of the factors of 900 are odd?

4.250 How many of the factors of 440 are even?

4.350 How many of the factors of 1,296 are perfect squares?

4.450 If a number n has exactly 7 factors, how many factors does n^2 have?

4.550 How many 3-digit integers have exactly 3 factors?

4.650 The number n is a multiple of 7 and has 5 factors. How many factors does $3n$ have?

4.750 The number p is a multiple of 6 and has 9 factors. How many factors does $10p$ have?

4.850 How many perfect squares less than 400 have more than three factors?

4.950 What is the smallest positive integer that has exactly 18 factors?

4.060 What is the smallest positive integer that has exactly 16 factors and is not divisible by 6?

4.160 What is the least positive *odd* integer that has exactly 12 factors?

4.260 Distinct positive integers a and b have 5 and 6 factors respectively. What is the smallest possible product ab if a and b are relatively prime? (Being relatively prime means that they do not have any factors in common other than 1.)

4.3: More Factor Tricks

Product of the Factors:

Now that you can count the number of factors of any natural
number (positive integer) quickly, lets find a quick
way to find the product of those factors.

Begin again by making a list of all factors of 96, and 196:

96:	196:
1 x 96	1 x 196
2 x 48	2 x 98
3 x 32	4 x 49
4 x 24	7 x 28
6 x 16	14^2
8 x 12	

It is easy to see that the factors come in pairs (except for
perfect squares, we will discuss this in a moment).

Fill in the blanks to complete the sentences below:

4.070 96 has _____ factors, which can be divided
into _____ pairs, and the product of each pair is
_____. Therefore, the product of all of the *pairs*
is _____ to the _____ power.

4.170 196 has ____ factors. Since each pair of factors has a
product of _____, we can replace every factor
with the number _____ without changing the
product. Therefore, the product of the factors of 196
is _____ to the _____ power.

If you have learned to use fractional exponents (section **1.7**),
the products of the factors can be written as:

$$96^{\frac{12}{2}} = 96^6 = (2^5 \cdot 3)^6 = 2^{30} \cdot 3^6$$

$$196^{\frac{9}{2}} = \left(196^{\frac{1}{2}}\right)^9 = \sqrt{196}^{\,9} = 14^9 = 2^9 \cdot 7^9$$

Try to come up with a general formula before you continue.

The **product of the factors** for a number n with x factors can be expressed as:

$$n^{\left(\frac{x}{2}\right)}$$

Try not to memorize a formula without understanding it. Continue to use logical reasoning like the statements on the previous page until you understand the formula. Once you understand it, there is no need to memorize.

Example: Find the product of the factors of 40, then 225.

Reasoning: 40 is not a perfect square. Its prime factorization is $2^3 \cdot 5$, so 40 has 8 factors. The product of each pair of factors is 40, so the product of the four pairs is 40^4 which equals $(2^3 \cdot 5)^4 = 2^{12} \cdot 5^4$.

225 is a perfect square. Its prime factorization is $3^2 \cdot 5^2$, so it has 9 factors. Think of each of these factors as the square root of 225 (15) so the product of the factors of 225 is 15^9, which equals $3^9 \cdot 5^9$.

Practice: Product of the Factors.

4.080 Write the prime factorization of the product of the factors of 45.

4.180 A number a has $2b$ factors. What is the product of the factors of a in terms of a and b?

4.280 The product of the factors of 30 is equal to $2^x \cdot 3^x \cdot 5^x$. Find x.

4.380 The product of what number's factors can be expressed as 3^3?

4.480 The product of the factors of 54 is divided by the product of the factors of 36. Write the result as a common fraction in simplest form.

Sum of the Factors:

One of my favorite number theory tricks involves finding the
sum of the factors of a number. The explanation
requires that you understand the distributive property.
If you do not already understand distribution, I
suggest you read the unit on distribution (section **1.5**)
in the Algebra chapter of this book.

Example: What is the sum of the factors of 20? (This one
is easy to check by listing them all out.)

Reasoning: First, as usual, we need the prime factorization:
$$20 = 2^2 \cdot 5$$

Take a look at what happens when we distribute the sum of
the powers of 2 to the sum of the powers of 5:

$$(2^0 + 2^1 + 2^2)(5^0 + 5^1) =$$
$$(1 + 2 + 4)(1 + 5) =$$
$$1(1 + 5) + 2(1 + 5) + 4(1 + 5) =$$
$$1 + 5 + 2 + 10 + 4 + 20 = 42$$

Distribution gives us every factor!

Of course, we don't need to distribute to find the sum of the
factors. Skip the distribution:

$$(1 + 2 + 4)(1 + 5) = (7)(6) = 42.$$

This is much more important with bigger numbers.

Examples: Find the sum of the factors of each.

1. $108 = 2^2 \cdot 3^3$ **2.** $378 = 2 \cdot 3^3 \cdot 7$ **3.** $408 = 2^3 \cdot 3 \cdot 17$

108: $(1 + 2 + 4)(1 + 3 + 9 + 27) = (7)(40) = 280$

378: $(1 + 2)(1 + 3 + 9 + 27)(1+7) = (3)(40)(8) = 960$

408: $(1 + 2 + 4 + 8)(1 + 3)(1 + 17) = 1{,}080$

Practice: Sum of the Factors.

4.090 Find the sum of the factors for each: 50, 405, and 210.

4.190 Which single-digit integer has a greater factor sum: 6, 8, or 9?

4.290 Find the sum of the factors of each number below and look for a pattern to determine the sum of the factors of 2^{30}. **a.** 64   **b.** 128   **c.** 256   **d.** 2^{30}

4.390 The sum of the factors of what perfect cube is 400?

4.490 What is the average of all the factors of 48? Express your answer as a decimal rounded to the nearest tenth.

4.590 What is the least positive integer whose factor sum exceeds 100?

4.690 The sum of the factors of $2 \cdot 3 \cdot 5 \cdot 7 \cdot 11$ is divided by the number of factors in $2^{11} \cdot 3^7 \cdot 5^5 \cdot 7^3 \cdot 11^2$. What is the result?

4.790 What is the sum of the factors of 496?

Perfect/Abundant/Deficient:

The terms perfect, abundant, and deficient refer to the factor sum of a number.

The numbers 6 and 28 are the two smallest *perfect* numbers. Try to discover the property that makes these numbers perfect. Is 496 also a perfect number?

There are very few perfect numbers. Most numbers are either *abundant* or *deficient*. If 30 is abundant and 35 is deficient, do you think that 100 is abundant or deficient? Try to find out on your own before reading ahead.

A **perfect number** is one whose factor sum is equal to twice the number. Another way of saying this is that the sum of a number's proper divisors (factors other than itself) is equal to the number.

The number 6 is perfect because the sum of its factors is 12, 28 is the second smallest perfect number and 496 is the third smallest perfect number. There are some very cool properties of perfect numbers which are beyond the scope of this text, but I would encourage you to do some research on perfect numbers and Mersenne primes.

You can probably guess what abundant and deficient mean.

An **abundant** is a number whose factor sum is greater than twice the number.

A **deficient number** is a number whose factor sum is less than twice the number.

The number 100 is abundant because its factor sum (217) is greater than 200.

Practice: Perfect/Abundant/Deficient.

4.001 Is 40 perfect, abundant, or deficient?

4.101 Are all prime numbers abundant or deficient?

4.201 Are all powers of 2 abundant or deficient?

4.301 Are all multiples of 6 (greater than 6) abundant or deficient?

4.401 The prime factorization of 8,128 is $2^6 \cdot 127$. Is 8,128 perfect, abundant, or deficient?

GCF and LCM:

GCF stands for Greatest Common Factor.
The Greatest Common Factor (also called Greatest Common
   Divisor or GCD) for a pair or set of integers is the
   largest number that is a factor of each.

LCM stands for Least Common Multiple.
The Least Common Multiple for a pair or set of integers is
   the smallest integer for which each number is a
   factor.

GCF and LCM should be taught extensively in your regular
   math class, so I only include a brief explanation of
   GCF and LCM and a technique that I have rarely
   seen taught.

Sometimes the GCF and LCM are obvious:

Example: What is the GCF for the following pairs?
   a. 15 and 35   **b.** 40 and 50   **c.** 36 and 54

The GCFs are 5, 10, and 18. If you missed the third GCF,
   make sure you understand why you missed it.

Example: What is the LCM for the following pairs?
   a. 4 and 6   **b.** 10 and 12   **c.** 24 and 40

The LCMs are 12, 60, and 120. If you missed any of these,
   you probably just haven't worked with numbers long
   enough to have the number sense required to do
   these in your head.

It is not always this easy. What if you were asked to find the
   GCF and LCM of 84 and 140? You may not be able
   to get the answer to this one in your head, even with
   excellent number sense.

GCF and LCM: Venn Diagrams

Venn Diagrams (section 2.2) are a great way to solve GCF and LCM problems.

Example: Use a Venn diagram to find the GCF and LCM between 84 and 140.

$84 = 2 \cdot 2 \cdot 3 \cdot 7$
$140 = 2 \cdot 2 \cdot 5 \cdot 7$

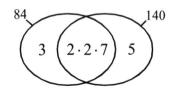

GCF

Factors of both numbers are placed in the overlapping area. These represent all of the common factors of 84 and 140. The product of these numbers is the GCF. It should be clear to you from the diagram that no number larger than $2 \cdot 2 \cdot 7 = 28$ is a factor of both 84 and 140.

LCM

The product of all the numbers in the diagram gives us the LCM (420). Again from the diagram it is clear that 140 goes into 420 three times and that 84 goes into 420 five times.

Example: Use a Venn diagram to find the GCF and LCM for 36, 48, and 90.

$36 = 2 \cdot 2 \cdot 3 \cdot 3$
$48 = 2 \cdot 2 \cdot 2 \cdot 2 \cdot 3$
$90 = 2 \cdot 3 \cdot 3 \cdot 5$

The GCF is 6.
The LCM is 720.

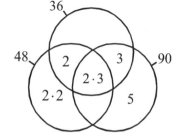

With a little practice this becomes very quick and easy.

Practice: Use a Venn diagram to find the GCF and LCM for each pair or set of numbers.

4.011 45 and 60
4.111 80 and 112
4.211 28, 42, and 105

The product of the GCF and the LCM:

Example: Find the GCF and LCM for 45 and 105.
Now, multiply the GCF by the LCM.
Finally, multiply $45 \cdot 105$.
What do you notice?

Consider why this works before reading ahead. Looking at the Venn diagram may help.

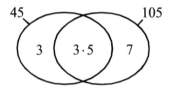

The product of a *pair* of numbers is equal to the product of their GCF and LCM. This is not the case for more than two numbers.

Practice: GCF and LCM.
4.311 The product of two numbers is 315 and their GCF is 3. What is their LCM?

4.411 The GCF for a pair of numbers is 18, and the LCM is 180. If one of the numbers is 90, what is the other number?

4.511 The GCF of two distinct perfect squares is 4, and their product is 3,600. What is the least positive difference between the two perfect squares?

Practice: GCF and LCM.

4.021 You are buying cups, plates, and napkins for a school picnic. Cups come in packs of 24, plates come in packs of 30, and napkins come in packs of 100. What is the least number of packs of napkins will you need to buy if you want to buy the exact same number of cups, plates, and napkins?

4.121 Janice and Kiera begin jogging around a track, starting at the finish line and going the same direction. Janice completes a lap every 78 seconds, while Kiera takes 90 seconds to complete each lap. At the end of their workout, they cross the finish line together in a whole number of minutes for the first time. How many more laps did Janice run than Kiera?

4.221 Ken gets his hair cut every 20 days. Larry gets his cut every 26 days. Ken and Larry get their hair cut on the same Tuesday. What day of the week is it the next time they get their hair cut on the same day?

4.321 Positive integers a, b, and c, satisfy the following conditions:
$GCF(a,b,c) = 1$.
$GCF(a,b) = 3$.
$GCF(a,c) = 4$.
$GCF(b,c) = 5$.
What is the least possible value of $LCM(a,b,c)$?

4.421 Kinsie has 80 chocolate chips, 112 pecans, and 128 M&Ms. She wants to bake a batch of giant cookies using all of the toppings she has. What is the greatest number of identical cookies she can make?

4.521 Including the endpoints, how many lattice points (points on the coordinate plane whose x and y coordinates are both integers) are on the line segment which connects (126, 162) to the origin?

Factorials and Factor Tricks:

Many of the same skills we have been using apply to problems which involve factorials. If you are not already
familiar with factorial notation, refer to section **2.6** of
this text and come back to this section.

Example: Find the sum of the factors of (5!).

Reasoning: Begin with the prime factorization of (5!):
$5! = 5 \cdot 4 \cdot 3 \cdot 2 = 2^3 \cdot 3 \cdot 5$, so the sum of the factors is
$(1 + 2 + 4 + 8)(1 + 3)(1 + 5) = 360$.

Often, problems involving factorials will require that you find
the power of a particular factor.

Example: Find the largest power of 3 that divides (9!).

Reasoning: We are looking for the power of 3 in the prime
factorization of (9!). Instead of trying to write-out
the entire prime factorization, we only need to look
for powers of 3: There are three numbers in
$9 \cdot 8 \cdot 7 \cdot 6 \cdot 5 \cdot 4 \cdot 3 \cdot 2$ which contribute 3 as a factor:
3, 6, and 9. 3 and 6 each contribute one 3, while 9
contributes two 3's for a total of four 3's. Our
answer is therefore 3^4.

Example: Find the largest power of 3 that divides (99!).

Reasoning: This is a little harder: Every multiple of 3
contributes one three, but every multiple of 9 contributes two 3's, every multiple of 27 contributes three
3's, and 81 contributes four 3's. The counting is
easier than it looks. There are 33 multiples of 3
(that's thirty-three 3's). There are 11 multiples of 9.
This adds 11 *more* threes. Do you see why this is
not 22 more? We have already counted one of the
3's in each multiple of 9. There are three multiples
of 27 (three more 3's) and one multiple of 81 (one
more 3) for a total of 33+11+3+1= 48 threes or 3^{48}.

Practice: Factorials.

4.031 Simplify: $\dfrac{12!}{11!} + \dfrac{10!}{9!} + \dfrac{8!}{7!} + \dfrac{6!}{5!} + \dfrac{4!}{3!} + \dfrac{2!}{1!}$

4.131 How many positive integers are factors of $(7!)$?

4.231 Find the sum of the factors of $(7!)$.

4.331 What is the LCM of $6!$ and 600?

4.431 What is the largest prime factor of $(100!)$?

4.531 Find the largest power of 6 that divides $(18!)$.

4.631 What is the LCM of $6!$, 216, and 300?

4.731 In the prime factorization of $2,500!$, what is the power of 7?

4.831 Find the smallest positive integer value of n for which 2^{15} divides $(n!)$.

4.931 Find the smallest positive integer value of n for which 3^{15} divides $(n!)$.

4.041 When $125!$ is written as an integer, how many zeros does it end with?

4.141 Find the largest integer n where n^2 is a factor of $(10!)$.

4.241 Find the largest prime factor of $(17!+18!)$.

4.341 If $n!$ ends in exactly 100 zeros, what is the greatest possible value of n?

4.441 In a non leap year, the number of minutes in February is equal to $n!$, what is n?

Review: 4.1 through 4.3

4.051 What is the product of the digits which could be used to fill-in the blanks which would make the integer 4_,_13 divisible by 99?

4.151 What is the smallest prime factor of 1,517?

4.251 How many of the factors of 12,321 are perfect squares?

4.351 What is the sum of all three-digit multiples of 11 which have exactly 10 factors?

4.451 What is the greatest number of factors that any three-digit number has?

4.551 The year 1849 was the last calendar year that had exactly 3 factors. What is the next calendar year which will have exactly 3 factors?

4.651 For how many integer values of n is $\dfrac{900}{n}$ a positive integer?

4.751 Find the power of 7 in the prime factorization of (343!).

4.851 What is the largest possible value of n for which $n!$ is *not* divisible by 1,024?

4.951 The GCF(a,b) is 6, and LCM(a,b) is 72, find the sum of a and b if $a > b > 6$.

4.061 Melody makes a list of all the proper fractions $\dfrac{n}{496}$ which have a numerator of 1 when written in simplest terms. What is the sum of all the positive fractions on Melody's list?

4.4: Different Bases

We have ten fingers and ten toes, which is probably why we
have a number system which uses ten digits.

With our ten-digit numbering system:
The first digit left of the decimal point is the *ones* place (10^0).
The second digit is the *tens* place (10^1).
The third digit is the *hundreds* place (10^2).
etc.

In our base ten system:

$$352 = 3(10^2) + 5(10^1) + 2(10^0) \text{ or } 300 + 50 + 2.$$

Example: Suppose we were born with 6 fingers and toes,
and we based our numbering system on six digits.
What would our numbers look like then?

1. How many digits would we use? What would the largest
   digit be?
2. What would the first three digits in a 3-digit number
   represent?
3. Try to write the number 12 in base 6. Try 37.

Reasoning:

1. With ten fingers and toes, we use ten digits (0 through 9).
   If humans had six fingers and toes, we would
   probably use six digits (0 through 5).
2. Instead of ones, tens, and hundreds, the digits would
   represent *ones*, *sixes*, and *thirty-sixes*.
3. In base 6, the number twelve would require a two in the
   sixes place. Two sixes equals 12, so the representation of twelve in base 6 would be "20". To write 37,
   we need a one in the *thirty-sixes* place, a 0 in the
   sixes place, and a 1 in the *ones* place. The number
   represented as 37 in base-10 would be written as 101
   using a base-6 numbering system.

Notation of different bases:

To represent a number in a different base, a subscript is used. For example, 123_4 means "123 base 4", or $1(4^2) + 2(4^1) + 3(4^0)$. 123_4 is equal to 27_{10}.

If there is no subscript, it is assumed that you are using base 10 notation.

Example: What base 10 integer is represented by 415_6?

Reasoning: The easiest way to think about the conversion is to convert "ones, tens, hundreds, thousands..." into "ones, sixes, thirty-sixes, etc." (for base 6).

415_6 means $4(36) + 1(6) + 5(1) = 144 + 6 + 5 = 155$.

Practice: Different Bases.

4.071 How would you represent $5 \cdot 8^6 + 2 \cdot 8^2$ as a base 8 numeral?

4.171 In base 2, what is the place value of the 1 in $10,000_2$?

4.271 Find the base 10 value of each:
   a. 215_6 **b.** 101_2 **c.** 777_8

4.371 What is the largest base 10 number that can be represented as a 3-digit number in base-6?

4.471 How many digits would it take to represent 242_{10} in base 3?

4.571 Convert 222_8 to base 4.

4.671 How would you represent 9^6 as a base-3 numeral?

4.771 What is the base-10 decimal representation of 0.24_5?

Simple arithmetic in different number bases:

Part of the reason why it is good to study other number bases is that it helps us to understand some of the simple things we have taken for granted in our own number system.

Example: Complete the following exercises to find an easy way to multiply a base 5 number by 5:

a. Convert 14 and 70 to base 5.

b. Convert 21 and 105 to base 5.

c. What do you notice?

d. Solve in base 5: $10_5 \cdot 43_5$

e. Will the same method work in any base?

f. Try $100_6 \cdot 13_6$.

In base ten, we can multiply by ten just by adding a zero. The same principle applies in any (positive integer) base. Multiplying a base-5 number by 5 can be done by simply adding a zero. Multiplying a base-5 number by 25 (100_5) will add two zeros, multiplying by 125 (1000_5) will add three, etc.

Example: Complete the following exercises to find an easy way to add numerals in different bases.

a. Convert 112_6 and 23_6 to base 10 and add them.

b. Convert the sum back to base 6.

c. Add: 112_6
          $+ 23_6$

d. Add: 145_6 What makes this problem harder?
          $+ 42_6$

The **addition algorithm** (method) in different number bases works the same. In the example above, you must remember that there is no "7" in base 6. "7" is written as 11 in base 6, so you write a 1 and carry a 1.

$$\begin{array}{r} {}^{1\ 1}145_6 \\ +\ 42_6 \\ \hline 231_6 \end{array}$$

Example: Complete the following exercises to find an easy way to subtract numerals in different bases.

   a. Convert 154_6 and 23_6 to base 10 and subtract.

   b. Convert the difference back to base 6.

   d. Subtract $\begin{array}{r} 154_6 \\ -\ 23_6 \\ \hline \end{array}$

   d. Subtract: $\begin{array}{r} 212_6 \\ -\ 34_6 \\ \hline \end{array}$ What makes this harder?

The **subtraction algorithm** (method) in different number bases works the same. In the example above, you must remember that when you "borrow", you are not borrowing 10, you are borrowing 6. As in base 10, we can check our subtraction with addition.

$$\begin{array}{r} {\scriptstyle 1\ 6\ 8} \\ \cancel{2}\cancel{1}\cancel{1}_6 \\ -\ 34_6 \\ \hline 134_6 \end{array}$$

Check with addition:

$$\begin{array}{r} {\scriptstyle 1\ 1} \\ 134_6 \\ +\ 34_6 \\ \hline 212_6 \end{array}$$

When I borrow for subtraction, notice that I cheat a little and write 8 instead of 12_6.

Practice: Different Bases.

Answer each in the number base used.

4.081 $25_8 \cdot 10_8$ **4.181** $436_8 \cdot 1{,}000_8$

4.281 $333_8 + 333_8$ **4.381** $333_6 + 333_6$

4.481 $333_4 + 333_4$ **4.581** $567_8 - 456_8$

4.681 $213_6 - 144_6$ **4.781** $100_6(113_6 - 45_6)$

4.881 $10000_2 - 1011_2$ (try it without converting to base 10).

4.981   Subtract: $444_9 - 11111_3$. Write your answer in base 9.

4.5: The Units Digit

Your teacher hands out the following multiple choice questions and gives you one minute to complete all three with no calculator. Can you find a way to solve each without actually knowing the answer?

1: What is $6{,}437 \cdot 7{,}654$?
A. 49,268,796   **B.** 49,268,797   **C.** 49,268,798

2: What is $65{,}656^2$?
A. 4,310,710,334   **B.** 4,310,710,336   **C.** 4,310,710,338

3: Which of the following integers is a perfect square?
A. 7,921   **B.** 7,922   **C.** 7,923

The answer to each of these multiple-choice questions is easy when you understand some simple properties of a number's units digit. (1.C   2. B   3. A)

Addition: The units digit of the sum of two numbers is easy to figure out by simply adding the units digits.
Example: What is the units digit of $1{,}067 + 23{,}908$?
Hopefully you see that adding only the units digits gives us 5 without completing the addition.

Multiplication: The units digit of a product is also easy.
Example: What is the units digit of $1{,}023 \cdot 21{,}098$?
We only need to multiply the units digits to see that the result will end in a 4.

Perfect Squares: The units digit of a perfect square is simple as well, using the same technique as above.
Example: What is the units digit of $947{,}864^2$?
Squaring only the 4 gives us the units digit (6).

Here is a trickier example:

Example: How you can tell that 595,378,263,068,723,132 is not a perfect square (without a calculator)?

Reasoning: The units digit is a 2. Are there any digits which, when squared, end in a 2? There is no number n for which n^2 ends in a 2, so the number above cannot possibly be a perfect square.

Example:

Which of the ten digits can be the units digit of a perfect square: 0, 1, 2, 3, 4, 5, 6, 7, 8, 9 ?

Reasoning:
$$0^2 = 0 \quad 1^2 = 1 \quad 2^2 = 4 \quad 3^2 = 9 \quad 4^2 = 16$$
$$5^2 = 25 \quad 6^2 = 36 \quad 7^2 = 49 \quad 8^2 = 64 \quad 9^2 = 81$$
The units digit of a perfect square can only be a 0, 1, 4, 5, 6, or a 9. There are no perfect squares which end in 2, 3, 7, or 8.

Practice: Units Digit.
No cheating! Calculators are off-limits.

4.091 Is $9,089^2 + 765^2$ equal to 83,195,146 or 83,195,140?

4.191 What is the units digit of $(346^2 + 364^2)^2$?

4.291 Given that 4,624 is a perfect square, what is $\sqrt{4,624}$?

4.391 What is the units digit of $(1+2+3+4+ \ldots +29+30)^2$?

4.491 Three-digit integer n is divisible by 2 but not by 5. What is the units digit of $(n^2)^2$?

4.591 Peter multiplies four consecutive integers and divides the result by 10, leaving a remainder. What is the remainder?

The Units Digit and Exponents:

At first it seems impossible to know the units digits of a number like 1079^{87}, but when we find a pattern, the problem becomes trivial:

$1,079^1$ ends in a 9.

$1,079^2$ ends in a 1.

$1,079^3$ ends in a ___.

$1,079^4$ ends in a ___.

$1,079^{87}$ ends in a ___.

We are only looking for the units digit, and we can quickly see that all odd powers of 9 end in a 9. There are similar patterns for every units digit which we will explore below:

Examples: Find the units digit of each.

Set 1: These are the easiest ones:

    a. $1,355^{94}$ **b.** $81,001^{31}$ **c.** $465,376^{308}$

Each of these ends in the same units digit no matter what power is used. (a.5 b.1 c.6)

Set 2: These are a little harder (but still easy):

    a. $987,654^{35}$ **b.** $81,069^{52}$

These repeat every-other digit.

Odd powers of a number ending in 4 end in a 4, while even powers end in a 6.

Odd powers of a number ending in 9 end in a 9, while even powers end in a 1. (Set 2 answers are a.4 b.1)

Set 3: These actually require a little thought. Find the pattern of repeating units digits for each integer below before turning the page:

    a. 652^{39} **b.** 983^{61}

    c. 777^{102} **d.** 588^{777}

For a number ending in 2, 3, 7, or 8, the units digits cycle in sets of four.

$2^1 = 2$, $2^2 = 4$, $2^3 = 8$, $2^4 = 16$, multiplying by 2 again we get $2^5 = 32$, and the cycle of units digits repeats. The cycle for 2's is 2 - 4 - 8 - 6 - 2 - 4 - 8 - 6...

$3^1 = 3$, $3^2 = 9$, $3^3 = 27$, $3^4 = 81$, multiplying by 3 again we get $3^5 = 243$, and the cycle of units digits repeats. The cycle for 3's is 3 - 9 - 7 - 1 - 3 - 9 - 7 - 1 ...

The cycle for 7's is 7 - 9 - 3 - 1 - 7 - 9 - 3 - 1 ...

The cycle for 8's is 8 - 4 - 2 - 6 - 8 - 4 - 2 - 6 ...

Reasoning: Set 3
To find the units digit for a number like 588^{777}, we know that the 4th, 8th, 12th, ... 772nd, and 776th powers of 588 will end in a 6 (because of the pattern described above), so the 777th power must end in an 8.

You can solve this by finding the remainder when 777 is divided by 4. The remainder is 1, so the units digit will be the first in the cycle. If the remainder were 3, the units digit would be a 2, the same as the units digit for 8^3. (Set 3 answers: a.8, b.3, c.9, and d.8)

We are beginning to introduce something called modular arithmetic, which will be discussed more later in this chapter (section **4.7**).

Practice:
4.002 What is the units digit of $(1976^{61})(2007^{61})$?

4.102 What is the units digit of $3^{91} + 3^{92} + 3^{93} + 3^{94}$?

4.202 What is the units digit of $9^n + 9^{n+1}$?

4.6: Fractions and Decimals

There are some patterns that you should recognize when using fractions and decimals.

There is an easy way to determine whether a fraction represents a **repeating** or a **terminating** decimal. First, let's use our calculators to determine the decimal expansion of some common fractions. Use bar notation for decimals that repeat.

$$\frac{1}{2} = \qquad \frac{1}{3} = \qquad \frac{1}{4} = \qquad \frac{1}{5} = \qquad \frac{1}{6} =$$

$$\frac{5}{9} = \qquad \frac{24}{99} = \qquad \frac{817}{999} = \qquad \frac{2}{999} = \qquad \frac{71}{999} =$$

$$\frac{2}{7} = \qquad \frac{3}{7} = \qquad \frac{4}{7} = \qquad \frac{5}{7} = \qquad \frac{6}{7} =$$

Converting by hand:

The most common method used to convert a fraction into a decimal by hand is to divide the denominator into the numerator:

$$\frac{1}{2} = 2\overline{)1.0}^{\;.5} \qquad \frac{2}{3} = 3\overline{)2.0}^{\;.\overline{6}} \qquad \frac{4}{13} = 13\overline{)4.000000}^{\;0.\overline{307692}}$$

Terminating/Repeating Decimals:

The decimal expansion of a fraction in simplest form will terminate only if the denominator contains no prime factors other than 2 or 5.

Examples: Figure out which of the following can be represented by terminating decimals before checking your answers with a calculator:

$$\frac{1}{30} \qquad \frac{7}{8} \qquad \frac{3}{125} \qquad \frac{5}{24} \qquad \frac{7}{128} \qquad \frac{3}{48}$$

Ninths, Ninety-Ninths, etc.:
The repeating block of a fraction whose denominator is 9, 99,
   999, etc. in the denominator will be the numerator.
   Use leading zeros where necessary.

$$\frac{5}{9} = 0.\overline{5} \qquad\qquad \frac{24}{99} = 0.\overline{24}$$

$$\frac{817}{999} = 0.\overline{817} \qquad\qquad \frac{1}{999} = 0.\overline{001}$$

$$\frac{7}{11} = \frac{63}{99} = 0.\overline{63} \qquad\qquad \frac{4}{33} = \frac{12}{99} = 0.\overline{12}$$

Practice: Express as a decimal (without using a calculator):

4.012 $\dfrac{41}{99} =$ **4.112** $\dfrac{2}{99} =$ **4.212** $\dfrac{71}{999} =$

4.312 $\dfrac{2}{33} =$ **4.412** $\dfrac{5}{111} =$ **4.512** $\dfrac{2}{37} =$

Converting a repeating decimal into a fraction requires
   some basic algebra. Here is an easy conversion of a
   decimal that you may already recognize. (See also
   problem **1.071**).

$$x = 0.\overline{5}$$
$$10x = 5.\overline{5}$$
$$10x - x = 5.\overline{5} - 0.\overline{5}$$
$$9x = 5$$
$$x = \frac{5}{9}$$

Examples: Convert the following to common fractions:

1. $x = 0.\overline{24}$ **2.** $x = 0.1\overline{25}$ **3.** $x = 0.01\overline{3}$

Try each of these on your own before continuing.

Reasoning:

1. You should recognize $x = 0.\overline{24}$ as $\dfrac{24}{99} = \dfrac{8}{33}$.

2. If $x = 0.1\overline{25}$ then $10x = 1.\overline{25}$ and $1000x = 125.\overline{25}$.

$1000x - 10x = 125.\overline{25} - 1.\overline{25}$.

$990x = 124$, so $x = \dfrac{124}{990} = \dfrac{62}{495}$.

3. There is a nice shortcut I will use for the third example:

If $x = 0.01\overline{3}$, then $100x = 1.\overline{3}$, which means that $100x = 1\dfrac{1}{3}$. Since $100x = \dfrac{4}{3}$, dividing by 100 gives us $x = \dfrac{4}{300} = \dfrac{1}{75}$.

With practice, you can use this method to quickly convert just about any repeating decimal into a common fraction.

Sevenths:

There is a nice pattern to the repeating block of the sevenths. Over the years I have seen several competition problems which are much simpler if you can remember this property.

$\dfrac{1}{7} = 0.\overline{142857} \qquad \dfrac{2}{7} = 0.\overline{285714} \qquad \dfrac{3}{7} = 0.\overline{428571}$

$\dfrac{4}{7} = 0.\overline{571428} \qquad \dfrac{5}{7} = 0.\overline{714285} \qquad \dfrac{6}{7} = 0.\overline{857142}$

There are web pages dedicated to 142,857, which is called a cyclic number. I encourage you to do some research on the properties of 142,857 and other cyclic numbers.

Practice: Fractions and Decimals.
Solve each *without a calculator.*

4.022 What is the last digit in the decimal expansion of $\dfrac{1}{256}$?

4.122 What is the 59th digit in the decimal expansion of $\dfrac{5}{33}$?

4.222 Add $0.\overline{07} + 0.0\overline{07}$. Express the result as a fraction in simplest form.

4.322 What is the least positive value of n that will make the decimal expansion of $\dfrac{n}{168}$ a terminating decimal?

4.422 Add $\dfrac{1}{37} + \dfrac{1}{9} + \dfrac{1}{3}$. Express the result as a decimal using bar notation.

4.522 How many digits long is the repeating block of the decimal expansion of $\dfrac{110}{111}$?

You *may* use a calculator for the following problems.

4.622 A six-digit integer is formed by placing two 3-digit integers side-by-side. If the larger of the two integers is placed ahead of the smaller integer, the number formed is six times greater than if the smaller integer is placed ahead of the larger one. What is the sum of the two 3-digit integers?

4.722 Kelsey writes a 6-digit integer. Michael copies the integer but places the units digits first, maintaining the order of the remaining five digits (for example, 123,456 becomes 612,345). If Michael's integer is fives times Kelsey's, what is Michael's integer?

4.7: Modular Arithmetic

We have already learned to use the concepts behind modular
    arithmetic to solve several types of problems.

Example: What is the units digit of 468^{357} ?

Reasoning:

The units digit repeats in blocks of 4 (8-4-2-6). Any number
    ending in 8 which is raised to the 4th, 8th, 12th, 16th,
    20th, ... 352nd, and 356th power will always end in the
    same digit (6).

Since 468^{356} ends in a 6 then, 468^{357} must end in an
    8, which is the next digit in the repeating pattern.

Example: In the decimal expansion of two-sevenths, what
    is the hundredth digit to the right of the decimal
    point?

Reasoning: The decimal repeats in blocks of six.
    The 6th, 12th, 18th, 24th, 30th, ... 90th, and 96th digits
    are all the same.

Since two-sevenths is just $0.\overline{285714}$, we can see
    that if the 96th digit is a 4, the hundredth digit must be
    a 7 (four decimal places later).

Example: It is currently 5 o'clock. What time will it be
    1,000 hours from now?

Reasoning: The pattern repeats every 12 hours. You know
    that in 12 hours it will be 5 o'clock.
    In 24, 36, 48, 60, ... 984, and 996 hours it will be 5
    o'clock again. Therefore, in 1,000 hours it will be 4
    hours later or 9 o'clock. All we needed was the
    remainder of 1,000 divided by 12. Asking for the
    time 1,000 hours from now is equivalent to asking for
    the time 4 hours from now.

Modular Arithmetic:

What we have been doing in problems like these is called
modular arithmetic, and revolves around the use of
remainders.

The **modulus** is the length of the repeating block (abbrevi-
ated mod). Two numbers are considered congruent
if they leave the same remainder when divided by
the modulus.

Notation: 13 is congruent to 1 modulo 12 (because both 1
and 13 leave a remainder of 1 when divided by 12).
The notation looks like this: $13 \equiv 1 (\mod 12)$. For
modulus 12, only the numbers 0 through 11 are used,
because $12 \equiv 0 (\mod 12)$.

The symbol $\equiv$ means "is congruent to" not "is equal to",
because the numbers $-12, 0, 12, 24, 36$, etc. are all
congruent when we use modulus 12 (not equal).
Two numbers a and b are congruent modulo m if
their difference $(a - b)$ is divisible by m.

Example: What are the five smallest positive integers
greater than 5 which are congruent to 3 modulo 5?

Reasoning: All we need to do is add multiples of 5 to the
smallest integer greater than 5 which is congruent to
3 modulo 5: 8, 13, 18, 23, and 28 are all congruent to
$3 (\mod 5)$. We can see that the remainder of each of
the numbers above when divided by 5 is 3.

Consider the clock problem from the previous page. On a
standard clock, the time will be the same every 12
hours. This means that in 1,000 hours, the time will
be the same as it is in 4 hours, or 58,732 hours. Each
leaves a remainder of 4 when divided by 12:
$58,732 \equiv 1,000 \equiv 4 (\mod 12)$

Check for understanding:
Find the value of each modulo 12:
      1. 100   **2.** 1,100   **3.** 3,300

There are a few properties in modular arithmetic which can make solving problems easier. Hopefully you found that that $100 \equiv 4(\bmod 12)$, meaning 100 leaves a remainder of 4 when divided by 12. We can use this to solve for $1,100(\bmod 12)$. 1,100 is just 11 hundreds, so there will be 11 remainders of 4, or a remainder of 44. Of course, we cannot have a remainder of 44 when dividing by 12. Dividing out the remaining 12's leaves a remainder of 8.

We can see that 3,300 is just 3(1,100) and creates three remainders of 8, or 24: If $1,100 \equiv 8(\bmod 12)$, then $3(1,100) \equiv 3 \cdot 8(\bmod 12) \equiv 24(\bmod 12) \equiv 0(\bmod 12)$.

Two important general formulas:
For $a \equiv x(\bmod N)$ and $b \equiv y(\bmod N)$, $a + b \equiv x + y(\bmod N)$.
For $a \equiv x(\bmod N)$ and $b \equiv y(\bmod N)$, $ab \equiv xy(\bmod N)$.

Example: Every 12 hours, Parker's standard clock advances 19 hours. If Parker's clock is correct at 6am on the morning of June 1st, what time will his clock read at 6am on the morning of July 1st?

Reasoning: There are 30 days in June, for a total of 60 twelve-hour periods. $19 \equiv 7(\bmod 12)$ and $60 \equiv 0(\bmod 12)$. We can see then that $19 \cdot 60 \equiv 7 \cdot 0(\bmod 12) \equiv 0(\bmod 12)$. At the beginning of July, Parker's clock will be correct and will read 6 o'clock again.

In a 31-day month: The math looks like this:
$19 \equiv 7(\bmod 12)$ and $62 \equiv 2(\bmod 12)$, which gives us: $19 \cdot 62 \equiv 7 \cdot 2(\bmod 12) \equiv 14(\bmod 12) \equiv 2(\bmod 12)$. Parker's clock would be two hours fast, reading 8 o'clock.

Modular Arithmetic Applications:

Modular arithmetic helps explain some of the complex
   patterns we find in more difficult problems.

Example: What is the remainder when $3^1 + 3^3 + 3^5 + ... + 3^{29}$
   is divided by 8?

Reasoning: We will look at some remainders using mod 8:

$$3^1 \equiv 3 (\text{mod} 8)$$

$$3^2 = 3 \cdot 3 = 9 \equiv 1 (\text{mod } 8)$$

$$3^3 = 3 \cdot 3^2 \equiv 3 \cdot 1 (\text{mod } 8) \equiv 3 (\text{mod } 8)$$

$$3^5 = 3^2 \cdot 3^3 \equiv 1 \cdot 3 (\text{mod} 8) \equiv 3 (\text{mod} 8)$$

We can continue in this way to show that every odd
power of 3 is congruent to $3 (\text{mod} 8)$. Adding the
first 15 odd powers of 3 gives us:
$3^1 + 3^3 + 3^5 + ... + 3^{29} \equiv 3 \cdot 15 (\text{mod } 8) \equiv 5 (\text{mod } 8)$.
The remainder is therefore 5.

Example: Prove the divisibility rule for 11 (**p.134**).

Reasoning: Look at the first few place values in mod 11:

$$10^0 = 1 \equiv 1 (\text{mod } 11)$$
$$10^1 = 10 \equiv -1 (\text{mod } 11)$$
$$10^2 = 100 \equiv 1 (\text{mod } 11)$$
$$10^3 = 10^1 \cdot 10^2 \equiv -1 \cdot 1 (\text{mod } 11) \equiv -1 (\text{mod } 11)$$

We can continue in this way to show that every odd power of
10 is congruent to $-1 (\text{mod } 11)$, and even powers are
congruent to $1 (\text{mod } 11)$, or: $10^n \equiv (-1)^n (\text{mod } 11)$. A
number written in base-10 which is divisible by 11 is
congruent to $0 (\text{mod } 11)$. For a base-10 multiple of
11 with digits a_0 through a_n we have:

$$a_0 (10^0) + a_1 (10^1) ... + a_{n-1} (10^{n-1}) + a_n (10^n) \equiv 0 (\text{mod } 11)$$
$$a_0 (-1)^0 + a_1 (-1)^1 ... + a_{n-1} (-1)^{n-1} + a_n (-1)^n \equiv 0 (\text{mod } 11)$$
$$a_0 - a_1 + a_2 - a_3 + a_4 - a_5 ... + a_n (-1)^n \equiv 0 (\text{mod } 11)$$

Therefore, for any number divisible by 11: if we add
all of the even digits and subtract all of the odd digits,
the result is divisible by 11. This is a good demon-
stration of the power of modular arithmetic.

Practice: Modular Arithmetic.

4.032 What is the 1,896,253rd digit in the decimal expansion of $\frac{1}{41} = .\overline{02439}$?

4.132 During her history class, Priyanka writes her name over and over again on a sheet of paper. She completes 955 letters before the paper is taken away by her teacher and she is reminded to pay attention in class. What is the last letter she writes?

4.232 The 350 sixth graders at Ligon Middle School stand in a big circle. They count off to form groups, starting with Katy and working to the left. They count off from 1 to 8 and then repeat until everyone has a number, and students who share the same number form a group. If Meera wants to be in the same group as Katy, what is the fewest number of places to Katy's right that she should stand?

4.332 What is the remainder when $(1 + 2 + 3... + 48)^{49}$ is divided by 50?

4.432 What is the smallest positive integer multiple of 31 that leaves a remainder of 1 when divided by 13?

4.532 Your digital clock is broken. To set the minutes, when you push the $>$ button the minute value jumps ahead by 7 minutes, and when you push $<$, the minutes value goes back by 7 minutes. The time says 6:56 and when you push $>$, the time says 6:03. From 6:03, what is the fewest number of times you can push either button to get the clock to read 6:04?

4.632 Craig is planting rows of trees in an orchard. If he plants all of his trees in 14 equal rows there will be 1 tree leftover. Planting them in 15 equal rows leaves 2 extra trees. Given that Craig has over 200 trees, what is the fewest number of trees he could have?

Chapter Review

4.042 What is the product of all the positive integer factors of 199?

4.142 How many of the *factors* of 900 have exactly 18 factors?

4.242 The digits of a 5-digit positive integer are 1's, 2's, and 3's with at least one of each. What is the smallest such integer that is divisible by both 8 and 9?

4.342 What is the remainder when $(2^0 + 2^1 + 2^2 + ... + 2^{99})$ is divided by 9?

4.442 How many positive integers less than 10,000 are divisible by *all* of the following: 2, 3, 4, 5, 6, 8, 9, 10, *and* 11?

4.542 What is the base-10 value of the greatest five-digit base-4 integer?

4.642 Five-hundred people stand in a circle. Starting with Roy and working to his left, each person counts off a number from 1 through 6 and then starting over again (1, 2, 3, 4, 5, 6, 1, 2, 3, ...) until everyone has counted a number. What number is counted off by the person standing to Roy's right?

4.742 The number 222 is raised to the 222nd power and then multiplied by 9. What is the units digit of the result?

4.842 Convert $0.1\overline{4}$ to a fraction in simplest form.

4.942 In the prime factorizations of integers a, b, and c: a and b have exactly 4 (not necessarily distinct) prime factors in common, a and c have exactly 5 prime factors in common, while b and c share 6. What is the least positive product abc for three positive integers which satisfy these conditions?

4.052 For how many positive values of *n* where $n \leq 100$ is $\frac{1}{n}$ represented by a terminating decimal?

4.152 What base-10 fraction is represented by the base-5 decimal $0.\overline{2}_5$?

4.252 Add $0.\overline{2} + 0.0\overline{2} + 0.00\overline{2}$. Express the result as a fraction in simplest form.

4.352 What is the greatest possible product for a set of positive integers whose sum is 25?

4.452 What is the units digit of 10! in base 9?

4.552 For graduation the senior class is divided into 38 equal groups to be seated in an auditorium in which each row has 35 seats. Seniors fill all but the last seat in the last row. If there are less than 1,000 graduating seniors, how many students are in each of the 38 groups?

4.652 The tires on an antique car have wheels with five spokes, but the tires are slightly different sizes: The larger tire in back has a diameter of 30 inches, while the smaller tire in front has a diameter of 27 inches. A photographer wants to photograph the car while the wheels are in a position identical to the one above (with both stars up-side down). How many times will this occur during the course of a quarter-mile parade if the wheels begin the parade in the position shown?

4.752 What is the smallest positive integer *a* for which both *a* and *a* + 1 each have exactly 6 factors?

Geometry
Chapter V

Geometry is the study of figures in space. What you will find
in the pages ahead are the geometry topics that I
have found most interesting, most useful, and used
most frequently in math competition at the middle
school level. As in each of the previous chapters,
many topics have been left out due to space limita-
tions.

Most students will not take Geometry in middle school,
however, I will begin this chapter with the assump-
tion that readers are familiar with some basic terms
and definitions, most of which can be learned from
watching several episodes of *Sesame Street*. You
will also need to be familiar with some basic notation
used for naming points, lines, circles, etc.

Many problems in this chapter rely on a solid foundation in
algebra. It is recommended that you complete a full
review of the algebra chapter before moving on to
geometry. The solutions and explanations assume a
solid foundation in algebra including exponents,
radicals, and quadratics.

5.1: Geometry Basics

Lines and Angles:

When two lines intersect, four angles are
> formed.

Angles 1 and 2 are called **linear angles**.
> Linear angles are **supplementary**,
> meaning the sum of their measures
> is 180 degrees.

Angles 1 and 4 are called **vertical angles**.
> Vertical angles are congruent.

Parallel Lines are in the same plane but never intersect.
When a line intersects a pair of parallel lines, it is called a
> *transversal.* When the parallel lines below are
> crossed by a transversal, three types of angles are
> created:

Angles 1 and 5 are
Corresponding Angles (CA).
Other pairs of corresponding angles:
2 & 6, 3 & 7, 4 & 8.

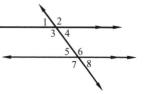

Angles 5 and 4 are **Alternate Interior Angles (AIA).**
Interior because they are between the parallel lines, and
> alternate because they are on opposite sides of the
> transversal. Angles 3 and 6 are also alternate
> interior angles.

Angles 1 and 8 are **Alternate Exterior Angles (AEA).**
Exterior because they are outside the parallel lines, and
> alternate because they are on opposite sides of the
> transversal. Angles 2 and 7 are also alternate
> exterior angles.

All three types of angles above form congruent pairs. Using
> corresponding angles and vertical angles helps us
> determine:
> $\angle 1 \cong \angle 4 \cong \angle 5 \cong \angle 8$, and $\angle 2 \cong \angle 3 \cong \angle 6 \cong \angle 7$.

Triangles: Triangles are classified by their sides and their angles.

A triangle with three congruent sides is called **equilateral**. A triangle with two or more congruent sides is called **isosceles**. A triangle with no congruent sides is called **scalene**.

A triangle in which all of the angles are less than 90° is called **acute**. A triangle in which one angle is 90° is called a **right** triangle. A triangle in which one angle measure is greater than 90° is called **obtuse**.

In an equilateral triangle, all of the angle measures are congruent (60°). An isosceles triangle has two congruent **base angles** which are opposite the congruent sides.

In any triangle, the largest angle will always be opposite the longest side, and the smallest angle will be opposite the shortest side. The marks below are used to indicate congruent sides and a right angle.

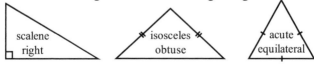

Triangle Angle Sum: We can use what we know about parallel lines to prove that the sum of the angles in a triangle is 180 degrees.

If we construct a line through a vertex of any triangle, parallel to the opposite base, it becomes clear that the sum of the interior angles in a triangle must equal 180 degrees. Because $\angle 1 \cong \angle 5$ and $\angle 3 \cong \angle 4$ (by AIA), $\angle 5 + \angle 2 + \angle 4 = \angle 1 + \angle 2 + \angle 3 = 180°$

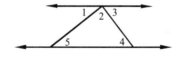

The Triangle Inequality:

There is a property of triangles which seems almost too obvious to mention, but many competition problems have stumped even the smartest students who overlooked the following:

The sum of the length of any two sides of a triangle must be greater than the length of the third side:

$a+b>c.$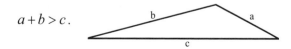

Consequently, the difference between the lengths of any two sides of a triangle must be less than the length of the third side: $a>c-b$.

This seems trivial until you are stumped by a problem which requires the use of this property.

Example: What is the area of a triangle of integral side lengths and perimeter of 8cm?

Reasoning: At first, it seems that we have not been given enough information to solve the problem. Consider the combinations of three integers that add up to 8: 1+1+6, 1+2+5, 1+3+4, 2+2+4, and 2+3+3. Only one of these sets of integers can be the lengths of the sides of a triangle: 2, 3, and 3.

The area of a triangle is equal to half its base times its height. The altitude of an isosceles triangle meets the base at a right angle, so we can use the Pythagorean theorem to find the height: $3^2 - 1^2 = h^2$, so $h = \sqrt{8} = 2\sqrt{2}$ and the area is $1 \cdot 2\sqrt{2} = 2\sqrt{2}$ cm².

Triangle Exterior Angles:

There is a nice property of the
exterior angles in a triangle
that can create some
shortcuts.

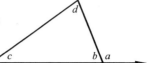

The measure of an exterior angle is equal to the sum of the
measures of its remote interior angles. This is just a
fancy way of saying that $a = c + d$ in the diagram.

Notice that $a + b = b + c + d = 180°$. Therefore, $a = c + d$.

Example:

Determine the measure of each labeled angle a through e.
The extra arrows are there to represent lines that are
parallel.

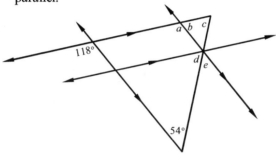

Reasoning:

Angle a and the angle labeled 118° are corresponding angles,
so the measure of angle a is 118°. Angle a and b
form a linear pair and are supplementary, so the
measure of angle b is 62°. The 118° angle is an
exterior angle of the large triangle, so 118° is equal to
54° plus angle c. This makes the measure of angle c
64°. Angles c and d are corresponding, making angle
$d = 64°$. Finally, angle a corresponds to the angle
formed by $d + e$, which means that $e = a - d = 54°$.

There are many other ways to find each of these angles. If
you found each angle in a different way, great!

Polygons:

A polygon is a closed plane figure. **Diagonals** in a polygon
connect non-adjacent pairs of vertices.

Polygons may be convex or concave. In a **convex** polygon,
all of the diagonals are contained entirely within the
polygon. If a polygon is not convex, it is **concave**.
An **equilateral** polygon has all sides of equal length.
An **equiangular** polygon has (you guessed it) all
angles of equal measure. A **regular** polygon is
equilateral and equiangular.

Polygon Angle Sum:

We have shown that the sum of the angle measures in a
triangle is 180°. We can use this to find a way to
determine the sum of the angle measures in any
polygon:

If a polygon has n sides, we can always divide it into
$(n-2)$ triangles by drawing $(n-3)$ diagonals. The
example below shows a concave heptagon being
divided into 5 triangles.

The sum of the angle measures in
each triangle is 180 degrees, so the
sum of the angles in a polygon with
n sides is $180(n-2)$.

Perhaps even more useful is the sum of the
exterior angles in a polygon. In
any polygon, the sum of its exterior
angles will always equal 360°.

Practice: Triangles and Polygons.

5.100 In isosceles triangle ABC, the measure of angle A is 96 degrees. What is the measure of angle B?

5.200 The angle measures of a scalene triangle are x, $2x$, and $2x + 15$ degrees. What is the measure of the smallest angle?

5.300 What is the interior angle measure of a regular 15-gon?

5.400 In regular decagon ABCDEFGHIJ, what is the measure of angle ACB?

5.500 Four angles in a quadrilateral form an arithmetic sequence whose common difference is 28. What is the measure of the largest angle? (See **p.53**).

5.600 A regular polygon has interior angles measuring 179° and a side length of 2cm.   Find its perimeter.

5.700 A polygon has 11 sides and 10 congruent 150° interior angles. What is the measure of its largest exterior angle?

5.800 A star is a decagon with five acute interior angles. What is the greatest number of acute interior angles in any decagon?

5.900 Parallelogram ABCD has side lengths 9cm and 13cm. Find the shortest integral length of diagonal AC.

5.010 What is the maximum number of diagonals in a concave nonagon (9 sides) which can be drawn entirely outside of the interior of the polygon?

5.110 How many scalene triangles of integral side length have a perimeter less than or equal to 12 units?

Trapezoids and Parallelograms:

There are some useful properties of quadrilaterals which we will use to solve a variety of problems. I encourage you to take the time to investigate the proofs of the properties below on your own.

Trapezoids have exactly one pair of parallel sides, called its bases. A **midsegment** of a trapezoid connects the midpoints of the non-parallel sides. The midsegment will always be parallel to the bases, and its length is the average of the bases (in a triangle, a midsegment is half the length of the parallel base). An **isosceles trapezoid** has congruent non-parallel sides and congruent base angles.

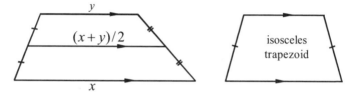

Parallelograms have two pairs of parallel sides. The parallel sides are congruent. Diagonals of a parallelogram bisect each other. If a parallelogram is equilateral, it is called a **rhombus**. The diagonals of a rhombus have the additional property that they are perpendicular to each other. If a parallelogram is equiangular it is called a **rectangle**. The diagonals of a rectangle have the additional property that they are congruent. A regular quadrilateral is a **square.**

Properties of the diagonals of parallelograms:

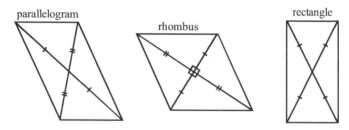

Kites:

A kite is a quadrilateral with two distinct pairs of congruent
sides which are adjacent. The angles where congruent sides meet are called vertex angles. The angles where non-congruent sides meet are called nonvertex angles. Non-vertex angles are congruent. The diagonals of a kite are perpendicular. The diagonal connecting the vertex angles bisects the other diagonal as well as both vertex angles.

Diagonal properties
of a kite:

Example: In parallelogram ABCD, diagonals AC and BD
intersect at E. If $AE = 2x + 9$ and $CE = 5x$, what is
the length of diagonal AC?

Reasoning: The diagonals of a parallelogram bisect each
other, so the lengths of AE and CE must be equal.
Solving for $2x + 9 = 5x$, we get $x = 3$, so AE=CE=15
and AC=30.

Example: The midsegment of an isosceles trapezoid is 4cm
longer than the shorter of the two bases. The long
base is three times the length of the short base. Find
the length of the trapezoid's midsegment.

Reasoning: If we call the short base x, the midsegment
$x + 4$, and the long base $3x$, then the average of the
bases ($2x$) is equal to the length of the midsegment
($x + 4$): $2x = x + 4$ gives us $x = 4$ and the
midsegment is therefore 8cm long.

Practice: Geometry Basics.

5.020 In regular octagon ABCDEFGH, what is the measure of angle ACH?

5.120 In parallelogram ABCD, diagonal AC is twice the length of diagonal BD.   The perimeter of triangle ABC is 21cm and the perimeter of triangle BCD is 17cm, what is the perimeter of parallelogram ABCD?

5.220 The sides of a regular polygon are 2cm long and the interior angles of the polygon measure 171 degrees. What is the perimeter of the polygon?

5.320 The midpoints of quadrilateral ABCD are connected to form quadrilateral WXYZ. If diagonals AC=10cm and BD=8cm, what is the perimeter of quadrilateral WXYZ?

5.420 What is the smallest angle which can be created by connecting three vertices of a regular 36-gon?

5.520 How many regular polygons have interior angles of integral measure?

5.620 In the section of regular polygon below, the measure of angle ACB is 5 degrees. What is the perimeter of the polygon?

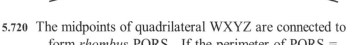

5.720 The midpoints of quadrilateral WXYZ are connected to form *rhombus* PQRS. If the perimeter of PQRS = 18cm, what is the length of diagonal WY?

5.820 The long diagonal of a rhombus is 3 times the length of the short diagonal. The perimeter of the rhombus is 40cm, what is its area? (See section **5.3**).

5.2: Circles

We begin with some vocabulary. Aside from the more commonly known parts of a circle (radius, circumference, and diameter), you should also know the terms chord, secant, and tangent. As with many terms in geometry, these are easiest to define with a diagram:

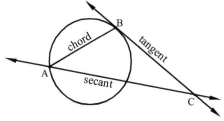

$\overline{AB}$ is a **chord**. The endpoints of a chord lie on the circle. A diameter is a chord which passes through the center of a circle.

$\overline{AC}$ is a **secant**. A secant is a line which passes through the circle.

$\overline{BC}$ is a **tangent**. A tangent is a line which intersects a circle at exactly one point. Note that tangent can also be used as an adjective, describing two figures which touch at one point.

An **arc** is a portion of a circle's circumference. Arcs are measured in degrees and the measure of an arc is the same as the corresponding central angle (arc AC in the diagram below has the same degree measure as central angle ABC).

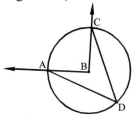

An **inscribed angle** is an angle with its vertex and endpoints on the circumference of a circle. In the above diagram, angle ADC is an inscribed angle.

A tangent will be perpendicular to the radius drawn to the point of tangency. Conversely, a line drawn through the point of tangency perpendicular to a tangent will pass through the center of the circle.

If a radius bisects a chord, the chord and radius are perpendicular. The converse is also true. If a chord and radius are perpendicular, then the radius bisects the chord.

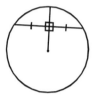

The measure of an inscribed angle is equal to half the measure of the intercepted arc. This is extremely useful, and we will prove the easiest case below.

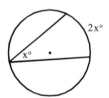

Proof (when XZ is a diameter): In the diagram shown, central angle measure c is equal to the arc measure d. It is also apparent that c is an exterior angle measure for triangle WXY, which means $c = a + e$.

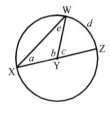

Triangle WXY is isosceles (two sides are radii), so angle measures a and e are equal. Substituting, we get $c = 2a$, $d = 2a$, or:

$$a = \frac{1}{2}d$$

Note that **an angle inscribed in a semicircle will always be a right angle**.

Finally, **arcs intercepted by congruent chords are congruent.**

More Useful Properties:

Try to determine a relationship between the variables in the
  diagrams below.

Example 1: Chord/Tangent.

What is the relationship between
  angle measure a and arc
  measure b?

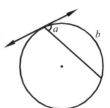

Example 2: Secants.

What is the relationship
  between angle
  measure a and arc
  measures b and c?

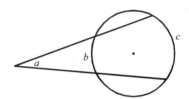

Example 3: Secant/Tangent.

Does the same relationship
  apply if one of the
  secants is a tangent?

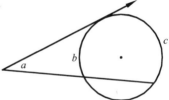

Reasoning:

The reasoning for these is easier to demonstrate with diagrams.

Example 1: Chord/Tangent.

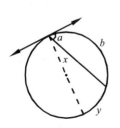

$y = 180 - b$, $a = 90 - x$, and $x = \dfrac{y}{2}$.

This makes $x = \dfrac{180 - b}{2} = 90 - \dfrac{1}{2}b$.

Therefore $a = 90 - \left(90 - \dfrac{1}{2}b\right) = \dfrac{1}{2}b$.

This gives us: $a = \dfrac{1}{2}b$.

Example 2: Secants.

$x = \dfrac{c}{2}$ and $y = \dfrac{b}{2}$. Because $x = a + y$, $\dfrac{c}{2} = a + \dfrac{b}{2}$.

Therefore $a = \dfrac{c}{2} - \dfrac{b}{2} = \dfrac{c - b}{2}$.

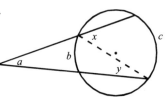

$a = \dfrac{c - b}{2} = \dfrac{1}{2}(c - b)$

If you can remember how you got the formula above, you do not need to memorize it.

Example 3 works very similarly to example 2, combining what we learned from example 1. The formula remains the same even if both secants are tangents. I will leave the proof for you to discover.

Example 4: Intersecting Chords.

What is the relationship between the vertical angles formed by inter-secting chords and the measures of the intercepted arcs?

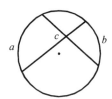

Example 5: Parallel Lines.

What is the relationship between the measures of arcs intercepted by parallel lines?

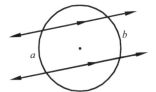

Example 6: Cyclic Quadrilaterals.

A quadrilateral that can be inscribed in a circle is called a cyclic quadrilat-eral. What is the relationship between the measures of opposite angles in a cyclic quadrilateral?

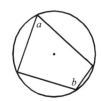

Example 4: Intersecting Chords.

When chords intersect inside a circle, the measure of the angles formed will be the average of the intercepted arcs. In the diagram, c is the average of a and b.

Proof: Angle WYZ = $a/2$, and angle XZY = $b/2$ (inscribed angles). Triangle VZY has exterior angle measure c and remote interior angles $b/2$ and $c/2$. Therefore:

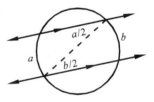

$$c = \frac{a}{2} + \frac{b}{2} = \frac{a+b}{2}.$$

Example 5: Parallel Lines.

When parallel lines intercept a circle, the measure of the intercepted arcs will be congruent.
In the diagram, $a = b$.

Proof: Add a transversal to create congruent alternate interior angles:

$$\frac{a}{2} = \frac{b}{2}, \text{ therefore } a = b.$$

Example 6: Cyclic Quadrilaterals.

Opposite angles in a cyclic quadrilateral are supplementary:
$$a + b = 180.$$

Proof: Angle measure a is half the measure of arc XYZ and angle measure b is half arc XWZ. Added together they are half the degree measure of the entire circle:

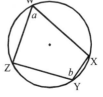

$$a + b = \frac{1}{2}\,\widehat{XYZ} + \frac{1}{2}\,\widehat{XWZ} = \frac{1}{2}(360) = 180$$

Practice: Circle Properties.

Find each arc or angle measure *x* in the diagrams below.
Diagrams are not to scale.

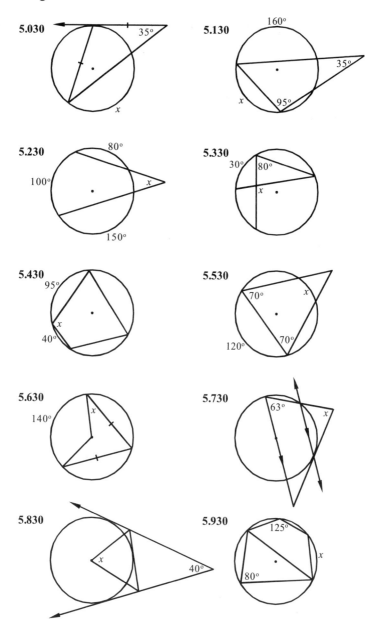

Circumference and Arc Length:

Pi (π) is the ratio of a circle's circumference (C) to its diameter (d), which gives us the formula for the circumference of a circle in terms of the diameter or radius (r):

$$\frac{C}{d} = \pi, \text{ so } C = \pi d \text{ or } C = 2\pi r.$$

The **length of an arc** is generally found using its degree measure. For example, an arc with a measure of 36° will be one tenth the circumference of the circle. Many problems involving arc measure involve multiples of 60° or 90°.

Example: What is the perimeter of the figure to the right which consists of three congruent tangent circles of radius 6cm?

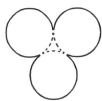

Reasoning: If we connect the centers of all three circles, we create an equilateral triangle. Each circle is missing 60° from its circumference, leaving five-sixths of three circles around the perimeter:

$$3 \cdot \frac{5}{6} \cdot 12\pi = 30\pi \text{ cm}$$

Example: A regular pentagon of side length 5cm has a circle with a 5cm radius centered on one vertex. Find the perimeter of the figure.

Reasoning: The interior angle of a pentagon is 108°, or 3/10 of the circle, leaving 7/10 of the circle's circumference: $10\pi(7/10) = 7\pi$. Add this to the three 5cm sides of the pentagon to get $15 + 7\pi$ cm.

Practice: Circumference and Arc Length.
Assume figures are as they appear in the diagrams.
Find the perimeter of each figure.

5.040 Concentric semicircles of
radius 6cm and 10cm.

5.140 The square has a perimeter of
16cm and vertices at the
centers of congruent circles.

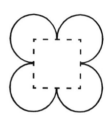

5.240 Congruent circles A and B
share 3cm radius AB.

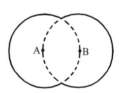

5.340 The dashed regular hexagon
has side length 3cm.

5.440 A dog is tethered by a 9-foot leash
to the center of the side of a
shed which is shaped like a
regular hexagon with 6-foot
sides. What is the length of the
dashed path that the dog can
patrol at the end of its leash?

5.3: The Pythagorean Theorem

Perhaps the most useful (and most often used) tool in Geometry is the Pythagorean theorem. An entire book could be filled with problems involving the Pythagorean theorem (many have). The sum of the squares of the legs of a right triangle is equal to the square of the hypotenuse, or, as you probably know it:

$$a^2 + b^2 = c^2$$

There are hundreds of proofs of the Pythagorean theorem which I encourage you to research on your own. Below is one that you may be able to discover on your own:

5.540 Use the diagram to the right to write a proof of the Pythagorean theorem. Hint: Find the area of the figure in two different ways.

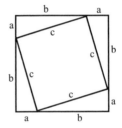

The **converse of the Pythagorean theorem** is also true. If the three sides of a triangle satisfy $a^2 + b^2 = c^2$, then the triangle is a right triangle. A set of three integers which satisfy the Pythagorean theorem is called a Pythagorean triple.

Knowing the most common **Pythagorean triples** is very helpful in recognizing and solving problems (see appendix). It is possible to generate a complete list of Pythagorean triples.

Choose any two positive integers a and b ($a > b$) and plug them into the following diagram to find the sides of the right triangle. Use some algebra to figure out why this always works before looking ahead.

Pythagorean Triples:

$$(2ab)^2 + (a^2 - b^2)^2 = (a^2 + b^2)^2$$

$$4a^2b^2 + a^4 - 2a^2b^2 + b^4 = a^4 + 2a^2b^2 + b^4$$

$$a^4 + 2a^2b^2 + b^4 = a^4 + 2a^2b^2 + b^4$$

The sum of the squares of the legs in the diagram above will always equal the square of the hypotenuse, no matter what numbers are selected for *a* and *b*.

There are some patterns which make many of the Pythagorean triples easy to remember.

Of course, the easiest triples to remember are multiples of the common ones like 3-4-5, 6-8-10, and 15-20-25.

When the short leg is an odd integer:
3-4-5, 5-12-13, 7-24-25, 9-40-41, 11-60-61, ...
Let's use 5-12-13 as our example. The difference between consecutive squares (12^2 and 13^2) is the same as the sum of the numbers being squared. Consider this: to get from 12^2 to 13^2, you need to add a 12 and a 13 (see diagram), therefore $13^2 - 12^2 = 13 + 12 = 5^2$.

$5 + 4 = 3^2$, so $5^2 - 4^2 = 3^2$.

$13 + 12 = 5^2$, so $13^2 - 12^2 = 5^2$.

$25 + 24 = 7^2$, so $25^2 - 24^2 = 7^2$.

$41 + 40 = 9^2$, so $41^2 - 40^2 = 9^2$.

$61 + 60 = 11^2$, so $61^2 - 60^2 = 11^2$. etc.

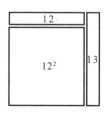

8-15-17 (and 12-35-37): Notice the difference between the long sides is two this time. The difference of squares whose difference is two is twice their sum.
$2(17 + 15) = 8^2$, so $17^2 - 15^2 = 8^2$.
$2(37 + 35) = 12^2$, so $37^2 - 35^2 = 12^2$.

20-21-29. Remember this one, it is an oddball that comes up in a lot of problems.

Example: On a map, Salem is 28 miles due south of
Springfield and 45 miles due west of Richmond.
How many miles is Richmond from Springfield?

Reasoning: Sketching a quick
diagram we find that this is
a simple Pythagorean
theorem problem:
$28^2 + 45^2 = c^2$, so c = 53.

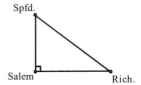

Example: Chord AB is 18cm long and tangent to the
smaller of two concentric circles. What is the area
between the two circles?

Reasoning: With concentric
circles, designate r for the
smaller radius and R for
the larger radius. We are
trying to find $\pi(R^2 - r^2)$.

If AB is 18 inches, AX = 9. AC = R and XC = r.
By the Pythagorean theorem, $9^2 + r^2 = R^2$, so
$81 = R^2 - r^2$, making $\pi(R^2 - r^2)$ equal to 81π.

Example: Semicircles have their diameters on the sides of
right triangle ABC, The area of the small semicircle
is 5π cm^2, and the medium semicircle has an area of
7π cm^2. What is the area of the large semicircle?

Reasoning: We *could* find the lengths of the
sides of the triangle by finding the radii
of the semicircles, use the Pythagorean
theorem to find the missing side length,
then use it to find the area of the
largest semicircle. We could also recognize that by
the Pythagorean theorem, the sum of the areas of
two smaller circles (of radius a and b) is equal to the
area of the larger circle (of radius c):
$\pi a^2 + \pi b^2 = \pi c^2$ gives us 12π cm^2.

Practice: The Pythagorean theorem.

5.050 Parker rides his bicycle 5 miles south, then 5 miles west, then 7 more miles south. How far is he from where he started?

5.150 Express the distance between opposite corners of a cube of edge length 2cm in simplest radical form.

5.250 An ant is crawling along the outside of the box below. What is the shortest distance he can walk from A to B along the path shown?

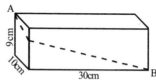

5.350 There is a shorter path from A to B in the diagram above. What is the shortest distance along the outside of the box from A to B? Express your answer as a decimal rounded to the nearest tenth.

5.450 A 50-foot ladder rests against a wall so that the top of the ladder is 48 feet from the ground. As you start to climb the ladder it slips. If the top of the ladder drops 8 feet, how many feet does the bottom of the ladder slide from its original position?

5.550 Write an expression to represent the distance between opposite corners of a right rectangular prism whose edge lengths are a, b, and c.

5.650 A cylinder with a 4cm diameter is 4cm tall. What is the length of the shortest path from the base to a point at the top of the cylinder on the opposite side? Express your answer in centimeters as a decimal rounded to the tenth.

Special Right Triangles:

There are two right triangles which occur quite frequently. Knowing the relationship between their sides is key to solving many competition problems which involve the Pythagorean theorem.

Example: What is the diagonal measure of a square whose sides measure 3cm?

Reasoning: Drawing the diagonal of a square divides it into two congruent right triangles, each of which has angles measuring 45, 45, and 90 degrees.

Using the Pythagorean theorem, we discover that the diagonal length of a 3cm square is $3\sqrt{2}$ cm.

For a square of side length 7, the diagonal measure would be $7\sqrt{2}$.

A square of side length x, has diagonal measure $x\sqrt{2}$.

Example: What is the altitude of an equilateral triangle whose sides measure 4cm?

Reasoning: Drawing the altitude of an equilateral triangle divides it into two congruent right triangles, each of which has angles measuring 30, 60, and 90 degrees.

Using the Pythagorean theorem, we discover that the altitude of a 4cm equilateral triangle is $2\sqrt{3}$.

The altitude of a 14cm equilateral triangle is $7\sqrt{3}$.

The altitude of an equilateral triangle of side length x is $\dfrac{x\sqrt{3}}{2}$.

Special Right Triangles:

The 45-45-90 right triangle:
(One-half of a square).

Given leg length a, the hypotenuse is $a\sqrt{2}$.

Given the hypotenuse length a, divide by $\sqrt{2}$ to find the

length of the legs: $\dfrac{a}{\sqrt{2}} = \dfrac{a\sqrt{2}}{2}$

 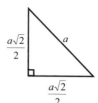

The 30-60-90 right triangle:
(One-half of an equilateral triangle).
The hypotenuse of a 30-60-90 right triangle is twice the
length of the short leg. The long leg of a 30-60-90
right triangle is equal to the product of the short leg
and $\sqrt{3}$. If you remember the first case, you should
be able to apply it to get the other two cases below:

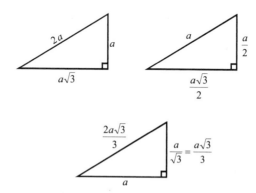

Example: What is the area of a regular hexagon whose
  sides measure 2cm?

Reasoning: A hexagon can be formed by
  joining six equilateral triangles. Each
  triangle has sides equal in length to
  the sides of the hexagon (2cm) and
  an altitude of $\sqrt{3}$ cm. Each triangle
  therefore has an area of $\sqrt{3}$ cm², making the area of
  the hexagon $6\sqrt{3}$ cm².

Example: What is the height of the stack of three
  congruent circles of radius 12cm?

Reasoning: Connect the centers of the circles to form an
  equilateral triangle. The triangle has an altitude of
  $12\sqrt{3}$ cm. We need to add the radius (12cm) twice
  to get the height of the stack: $(12\sqrt{3} + 24)$ cm.

Example: What is the radius of the inscribed circle in an
  equilateral triangle of edge length 6cm?

Reasoning: If we draw all three
  altitudes of an equilateral triangle,
  the triangle is divided into six
  congruent 30-60-90 triangles.
  The altitude is $3\sqrt{3}$ cm. Notice
  the relationship between a and b
  in the diagram: $b = 2a$. This makes a equal to one-
  third of the altitude, or $\sqrt{3}$ cm.

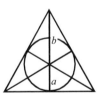

You can only use these relationships for the specific
triangles. Do not try to apply the properties of a
30-60-90 triangle to a triangle that you are not sure is
a 30-60-90 triangle.

Practice: Special Right Triangles.

Irrational answers should be left in radical form.

5.060 Riding your bicycle, you roll over a piece of gum which sticks to the bottom of your 24-inch diameter tire. You roll forward and the tire makes a 120° rotation. How high above the ground is the gum on the tire?

5.160 Equilateral triangle XYZ is inscribed in equilateral triangle ABC as shown. What is the ratio of the area of triangle XYZ to the area of triangle ABC?

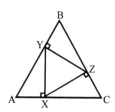

5.260 The vertices of a cube of side length 2cm are connected to form a triangle as shown. What is the area of the triangle?

5.360 What is the height of a STOP sign (regular octagon) whose sides are one foot long?

5.460 Find the length AC in regular hexagon ABCDEF if the perimeter of the hexagon is 24cm.

5.560 The midpoints of a hexagon are connected to form a smaller hexagon. What is the ratio of the perimeter of the small hexagon to the perimeter of the large hexagon?

5.660 What is the area of the smaller of the two concentric circles if the side length of the equilateral triangle is 8cm?

5.760 An isosceles right triangle has hypotenuse length x. What is the area of the triangle in terms of x?

The Distance Formula:

The distance between coordinates on the plane can be found using the Pythagorean theorem.

Example: Find the distance between $(5,-4)$ and $(-3,2)$ on the coordinate plane.

Reasoning: If we connect the points on the plane, we can create a right triangle in which the distance between the points is the hypotenuse.

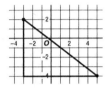

To find the width of the triangle, we subtract the x-coordinates. To find the height of the right triangle, we subtract the y-coordinates.

This gives us a distance $d = \sqrt{(2+4)^2 + (-3-5)^2} = 10$ units.

The distance d between any two points on the coordinate plane (x_1, y_1) and (x_2, y_2) is given by the formula:

$$d^2 = (x_2 - x_1)^2 + (y_2 - y_1)^2$$
$$\text{or}$$
$$d = \sqrt{(x_2 - x_1)^2 + (y_2 - y_1)^2}$$

This is the same as finding the hypotenuse of a right triangle whose width is given by $(x_2 - x_1)$, and whose height is given by $(y_2 - y_1)$.

Check for Understanding:

Find the distance between each pair of points below. Leave your answer in simplest radical form.

5.860 $(-1,4)$ and $(2,-5)$ **5.960** $(-7,-1)$ and $(2,-10)$

Algebra and the Pythagorean Theorem:
There are many geometry problems which require defining
variables and using algebra.

Example:
In rectangle ABDE, AB=12 and
BD=16. Find the side length
of rhombus ACDF.

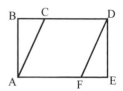

Reasoning:
Label the length of side AC $= x$. This makes CD $= x$ as well
and BC $= 16 - x$. This gives us all three sides of
right triangle ABC. Use the Pythagorean theorem to
solve for x:

$$(16 - x)^2 + 12^2 = x^2$$
$$256 - 32x + x^2 + 144 = x^2$$
$$400 = 32x$$
$$x = 12.5$$

Practice: Algebra Problems.

5.070 Square ABCD has side length 12cm.
What is the length of congruent
segments BX, CX, and EX?

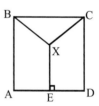

5.170 Congruent squares of side length
16 are inscribed in a circle as
shown. Find the area of the
circle in terms of pi.

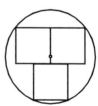

5.270 Segment AB is trisected at its
points of intersection with
concentric circles of radius 7cm
and 9cm. Find the length of
segment AB.

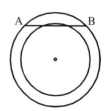

Review: The Pythagorean Theorem.

5.080 The radius of the large semicircle is 2cm. What is the radius of the small semicircle?

5.180 Square ABCD has vertices A(1,−2) and C(4, 5). What is the area of the square?

5.280 Circle C passes through points X, Y, and Z on congruent squares. Find the area of each of the three squares if the radius of the circle is 15cm.

5.380 A metal band is wrapped tightly around pipes of radius 3cm and 9cm. What is the length of the band? Express your answer in simplest radical form.

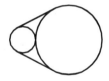

5.480 The top right corner of a standard 8.5 by 11 sheet of paper is folded down and left to align with the left edge, and the bottom right corner is folded up and left so that the fold lines look like the diagram below. What is the area of triangle ABC formed by the right edge and the fold lines?

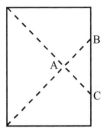

5.580 Regular hexagon ABCDEF has sides measuring 6cm. What is the area of triangle ACE?

5.4: Area

You should know most of these area formulas already. Just in case, here are the most important ones:

Any parallelogram: $A = bh$

Triangle: $A = \dfrac{1}{2}bh$

Trapezoid: $A = \dfrac{1}{2}h(b_1 + b_2)$

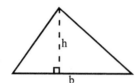

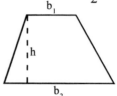

Kite: $A = \dfrac{1}{2}ab$, where a and b are the diagonal lengths.

Circle: $A = \pi r^2$, where r is the radius.

You should also be familiar with **Heron's formula** for the area of a triangle, given side lengths a, b, and c along with the semiperimeter s (half the perimeter):

$$A = \sqrt{s(s-a)(s-b)(s-c)}$$

There are dozens of other area formulas which involve trigonometry or more complex operations. I have a terrible memory and have found that just knowing the formulas above is usually sufficient.

If your memory is better than mine, you may try memorizing the formulas for the area of a regular hexagon or octagon, given the length of the sides.

Regular Hexagon: $A = \dfrac{3s^2\sqrt{3}}{2}$

Regular Octagon: $A = 2s^2\sqrt{2} + 2s^2$

Use your knowledge of special right triangles and the diagrams above to discover the derivation of these
formulas on your own (if you have not already).

Many interesting area problems involve addition and subtraction of overlapping regions and/or various applications of the Pythagorean theorem.

Example: The shaded areas below are called lunes.
ABC, AXB, and BYC are all semicircles.
AB = 8cm, BC = 12cm. Find the combined area of
the shaded lunes.

Reasoning: It is useful for me
to create a diagram like
the following:

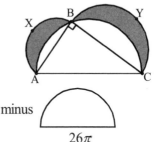

minus

$8\pi + 48 + 18\pi$ 26π

Notice that the combined area of the lunes (48cm²)
is equal to the area of the triangle. This is always
true, and was proven by Hippocrates about 2,500
years ago! See if you can figure out how this is
related to the Pythagorean theorem (see the related
example at the bottom of page **195**).

Area: Working backwards.

Finding the area of a figure can often be useful when you are looking for additional information about a figure.

Example: Find the length of the altitude to the hypotenuse of a 5-12-13 right triangle.

Reasoning: The area of a right triangle is usually easiest to find using the legs as the triangle's base and height, but the hypotenuse and the altitude to the hypotenuse can also be used as the triangle's base and height. Therefore, the product of 5 and 12 must equal the product of 13 and the altitude:

$$13a = 5 \cdot 12$$
$$a = \frac{60}{13}$$

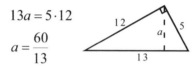

Example: What is the area of the circle inscribed within a triangle of area 30cm² and perimeter 30cm?

Reasoning: For this problem it is useful to recognize the relationship between the inradius of any triangle and its area.

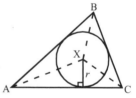

The three triangles AXB, AXC, and BXC share the same altitude, which is the radius r of the inscribed circle. The sum of the areas of these three triangles is obviously the same as the area of the larger triangle:

$$\frac{1}{2}(AB + AC + BC)r = 30, \text{ so } \frac{1}{2}(30)r = 30.$$

Solving for r, we find that the radius is 2cm, and the area of the circle is therefore 4π cm².

Practice: Area.

5.090   The large square has a side length of 8cm. What is the area of the smaller square?

5.190   Triangle ABC has its vertices at $A(-7,2)$, $B(-1,10)$ and $C(14,2)$. Find its area.

5.290   Find the combined area of the shaded regions in the quarter-circle, which has overlapping semi-circles centered on each radius.

20ft

5.390   A hexagon of side length 4cm has both an inscribed and a circumscribed circle. What is the area of the region (called an annulus) between the two circles?

5.490   Regular octagon ABCDEFGH has a side length of 2cm. Find the area of square ACEG.

5.590   The ratio of AB to BC is 1:3. What is the ratio of the shaded area to the unshaded area in the figure?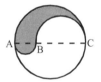

5.690   What is the area of a rhombus of side length 17cm which has a short diagonal of length of 16cm?

5.790   The distance between the centers of the circles is 1cm. Find the area of the shaded region.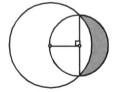

5.890   What is the smallest possible area for a triangle of integral side lengths whose perimeter is 15cm? Round your decimal answer to the hundredth.

5.990   Find the altitude to the side of a rhombus with diagonals measuring 6cm and 8cm.

5.5: Three-Dimensional Geometry

A **polyhedron** is a geometric shape made up of polygon **faces** which meet at straight-line **edges** that come together at **vertices.**

Like polygons, polyhedra are named with prefixes to indicate the number of faces, for example, an **octa**hedron has 8 faces and a **hexa**hedron has 6 faces. One exception is the **tetrahedron**, which has four faces.

A regular polyhedron has congruent regular polygon faces. There are five convex regular polyhedra called **Platonic solids:**

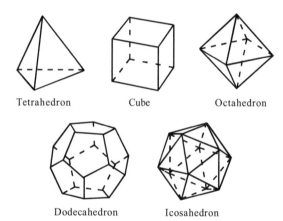

Tetrahedron   Cube   Octahedron

Dodecahedron   Icosahedron

There is a relationship between the number of **faces, vertices, and edges** on any polyhedron. See if you can discover this relationship by looking at the table below which lists the faces, vertices, and edges for each of the Platonic solids:

Polyhedron	Faces	Vertices	Edges
Tetrahedron	4	4	6
Cube	6	8	12
Octahedron	8	6	12
Dodecahadron	12	20	30
Icosahedron	20	12	30

Faces, Vertices, and Edges:

The number of edges on a polyhedron is always two less than the sum of its faces and vertices:

$$f + v = e + 2 \quad \text{or} \quad f + v - e = 2$$

You do not need to remember the formula above if you can remember that there *is* a relationship, and that a formula exists. If I am concerned that I have the formula mixed up, I consider a simple polyhedron like a cube. I know there are 6 faces, 8 vertices, and 12 edges on a cube and I can use this information to figure out the formula above if I have forgotten.

This is a strategy I often use and recommend instead of trying to commit dozens of formulas to memory.

Aside from the Platonic solids, one particular polyhedron comes up frequently enough that it should be mentioned: the truncated icosahedron, more commonly recognized as a soccer ball.

Example: A soccer ball is made by stitching together 20 regular hexagons and 12 regular pentagons, each with a side length of one inch. What is the combined length of the seams required to stitch together a soccer ball?

Reasoning: We are looking for the number of edges. There are 20 hexagons for a total of 120 edges, and 12 pentagons with 60 edges, but each edge is shared by two faces: $(120 + 60)/2 = 90$ edges, or 90 inches of seams.

The reasoning above also allows us to find the number of vertices using $f + v - e = 2$. This gives us: $32 + v - 90 = 2$, so there are a total of 60 vertices.

Prisms and Cylinders:

A **prism** is a polyhedron with two congruent polygons (called the bases) connected by parallelograms (called the lateral faces). We will deal primarily with right prisms, in which the lateral faces are rectangles (in an oblique prism, the lateral faces are non-rectangular parallelograms). Prisms are named based on their bases, for example:

Triangular Prism   Pentagonal Prism   Heptagonal Prism

A **cylinder** is similar to a prism with a circular base. The line which connects the center of the circular bases is called the axis. If the axis is perpendicular to the bases, the cylinder is called a right cylinder (otherwise, it is called oblique).

Right Cylinder

The **volume** of a prism or cylinder (right or oblique) can be found by multiplying the area of its base times its height.

The **surface area** of a prism is the sum of the areas of its faces. The surface area of a cylinder is the sum of the area of its bases and its lateral surface. In a right cylinder the lateral surface is a rectangle. The width of this rectangle is equal to the circumference of the circle. The height is the same as that of the cylinder. Try to write the formula for the surface area of a cylinder before reading ahead.

The formula for the surface area of a cylinder:

$$A = 2\pi r^2 + 2\pi rh.$$

Once again, do not memorize the formula above. If you understand its derivation it is much more useful.

Pyramids and Cones:
A **pyramid** is a polyhedron with a polygonal base whose other faces are all triangles which meet at a point called the **apex**. Like a prism, a pyramid is named by the shape of its base.

A **cone** is similar to a pyramid whose base is a circle.

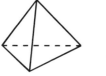

Triangular Prism   Pentagonal Prism   Cone

The **volume** of a pyramid or cone is one-third the area of its base times its height.

The **surface area** of a pyramid is the sum of the area of its faces. The surface area of a cone is the sum of its circular base and the lateral surface area. The lateral surface area (when unrolled) is a sector of a circle of radius s (the slant height of the cone).

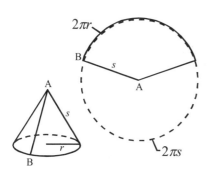

The sector is a fraction of the whole circle: $(2\pi r)/(2\pi s) = r/s$. The area of the whole circle is πs^2, so the **lateral surface area** (sector) is:

$$\frac{r}{s}(\pi s^2) = \pi rs.$$

Spheres:

A sphere is the set of all points in three-dimensional space
that are equidistant from a given center.

You will need to remember the formulas for volume
and surface area of a sphere (I encourage you to
look up the derivations of these formulas).

Volume: $V = \dfrac{4}{3}\pi r^3$ **Surface Area:** $A = 4\pi r^2$

Example: A hemisphere has a surface area (including its
base) of 36π cm². What is its volume?

Reasoning: First, we must recognize that the surface area
of a hemisphere is equal to half the surface of a
sphere of equal radius plus the area of the circular
base: $2\pi r^2 + \pi r^2 = 3\pi r^2$, which equals 36π cm².
Solving for r we get:

$$3\pi r^2 = 36\pi$$
$$r = 2\sqrt{3}$$

Substituting $r = 2\sqrt{3}$ into the formula for the volume
of a hemisphere (half the volume of a sphere):

$$V = \frac{2}{3}\pi(2\sqrt{3})^3 = 16\pi\sqrt{3}\,\text{cm}^3.$$

Example: Find the height of a cylinder whose volume and
radius are equal to that of a sphere of radius 6cm.

Reasoning: We could find the volume of the sphere and
solve an equation to find the height of the cylinder,
but it is easier to use both equations at once, cancelling out common factors:

$$\pi(6)^2 h = \frac{4}{3}\pi(6)^3, \quad \text{so} \quad h = \frac{4}{3}(6) = 8\,\text{cm}.$$

Practice: Three-Dimensional Geometry.

5.001 A semicircle with diameter AD = 12cm is rolled to form a cone by connecting A to D. What is the volume of the cone?

5.101 A cannonball with a 4-inch radius sinks to the bottom of a barrel full of water, raising the water level by 1/3 of an inch. What is the radius of the cylindrical barrel?

5.201 The number of square centimeters in the surface area of a hemisphere (including the base) is equal to the number of cubic centimeters in its volume. What is its radius?

5.301 Two cylinders are partially filled with water, each to a depth of 24feet. The smaller cylinder has a radius of 3feet and the larger has a radius of 4feet. Water is emptied from the larger cylinder into the smaller cylinder until each holds an equal volume of water. What is the difference between the depths of the two cylinders in feet and inches?

5.401 A cone and a hemisphere of equal surface area each have a 3-inch radius. What is the height of the cone?

5.501 A cube is inscribed within a hemisphere. The cube has 2-inch edges. What is the surface area of the hemisphere?

5.601 A snub cube has 6 squares faces and 32 triangular faces. What is the total number of vertices and edges on a snub cube?

Practice: Three-Dimensional Geometry.

5.011 A cylinder with a 6-inch radius is laid on its side and filled to a depth of 9 inches. The cylinder is 24 inches long. What is the volume of water contained in the cylinder?

5.111 The radius of a cylinder is increased by 40%, but the height is cut in half. What is the percent change in the volume of the cylinder?

5.211 A decagonal trapezohedron has 20 faces, each of which is a kite. How many vertices are there on a decagonal trapezohedron?

5.311 A cylinder is inscribed within a sphere. The cylinder has a 6-inch diameter and is 8 inches tall. What is the volume of the sphere?

5.411 A cube has a sphere inscribed within and a sphere circumscribed about it. What is the ratio of the surface area of the inscribed sphere to the surface area of the circumscribed sphere?

5.511 A wooden cube with 18cm edges has each of the eight corners sliced off so that the resulting faces are equilateral triangles whose edges are 6cm long. What volume has been removed from the cube? Express your answer in simplest radical form.

5.611 How many cubic inches of water are in the rectangular prism, which is tilted at a 30-degree angle?

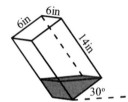

5.6: Similarity

Two polygons are described as similar if all corresponding
angles are congruent, and all corresponding sides are
proportional. In simplest terms, similar polygons are
the same shape but not necessarily the same size.
Polygons may be enlarged, rotated, or even reflected
and remain similar to the original. For example, the
five pentagons below are all similar to one another.

Similarity is indicated by the symbol ~, as in *ABC~DEF*.
Most similarity problems involve triangles. Any two triangles
which share the same angle measures are similar.

Example: The trapezoid below was created by joining two
similar triangles. What is the perimeter of the
quadrilateral?

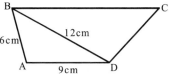

Reasoning:
Corresponding
sides are proportional:

$$\frac{AB}{CD} = \frac{AD}{BD} = \frac{BD}{BC}$$

so $\frac{6}{CD} = \frac{9}{12} = \frac{12}{BC}$

Solving the proportions
gives us $CD = 8$ and $BC =$
16, so the perimeter of the
trapezoid is 39cm.

The ratio of the length of the sides of similar figures is called
scale factor. In the problem above, the ratio of the
sides of triangle ABD to the sides of triangle CDB is
3/4. The lengths of the sides of triangle CDB could
be multiplied by the scale factor of 3/4 to get the
lengths of triangle ABD (and the sides of triangle
ABD could be multiplied by 4/3 to get the lengths of
the sides of triangle CDB).

Similarity and Right Triangles:
The altitude to the hypotenuse of a right triangle divides it into
two smaller right triangles which are similar to the
original. Given any two of the five segment lengths
in the right triangles below, all of the remaining
lengths can be found using a combination of similarity
and the Pythagorean theorem.

Example: The altitude to the hypotenuse of a right triangle
divides the hypotenuse into segments of length 6cm
and 10cm. Find the area of the right triangle.

Reasoning: Triangles ADB and BDC
are similar, which means:

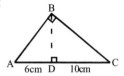

$$\frac{6}{BD} = \frac{BD}{10} \text{ so } BD = \sqrt{60}.$$

The area of the triangle is $\dfrac{16\sqrt{60}}{2} = 16\sqrt{15}$.

Example: Solve for x in the diagram below.

Reasoning: Begin by solving for a:

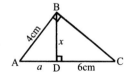

$$\frac{4}{a+6} = \frac{a}{4}, \text{ so } a^2 + 6a = 16.$$

Moving the 16 gives us $a^2 + 6a - 16 = 0$, and factoring yields $(a+8)(a-2) = 0$, so a = 2 or $a = -8$.
Of course, $a = -8$ does not make sense, so $a = 2$.
Applying the Pythagorean theorem, we get
$2^2 + x^2 = 4^2$ which gives us $x = \sqrt{12} = 2\sqrt{3}$.

This is a very useful tool for solving problems which involve
right triangles. Make sure you can see how to find
all five lengths (AB, AD, BC, BD, and CD in the
diagrams above) given any two. The most difficult
scenarios have been covered in the examples.

Similarity and Circles:

The intersection of two chords in a circle creates a pair of similar triangles.

In the diagram below, triangles ABX and DCX are similar.

Proof: Angles ABD and DCA intercept the same arc and are therefore congruent. BAC and CDB are congruent for the same reason. Angles AXB and DXC are vertical angles.

This property is key to solving many problems involving chords and circles.

Example: Chord BD bisects chord AC at X. If BX = 2cm and DX = 6cm, what is the length of chord AC?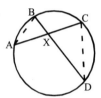

Reasoning: Using similarity, $\dfrac{2}{x} = \dfrac{x}{6}$.

$x = \sqrt{12} = 2\sqrt{3}$ and the length of chord AC is $4\sqrt{3}$.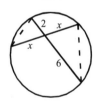

This suggests a generalization which can sometimes shorten the process. Again, do not memorize this property until you fully understand the concept above:

When chords intersect inside a circle: $ab = cd$.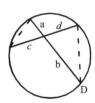

Secants which intersect outside of a circle create similar triangles as well which we will explore next.

Similarity and Circles:
See if you can find a pair of similar triangles in the diagram
    which both include angle X:

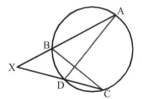

Triangles AXD and CXB are
    similar. Angles A and C
    intercept the same arc,
    and X is the same angle.

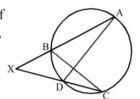

Example: AB is twice the length of
    CD. If XB = 4 and XD = 5,
    what is the length of XA?

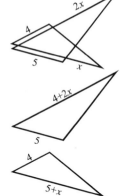

Reasoning: Sometimes it helps to
    pull the similar triangles
    from the diagram.

$$\frac{5}{4} = \frac{4 + 2x}{5 + x}, \text{ so } 5(5 + x) = 4(4 + 2x).$$

Solving for x we get $x = 3$, which
    makes XA=10.

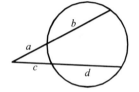

This suggests another generalization.
When secants intersect as shown:
$$a(a + b) = c(c + d).$$

For more, including relationships involving a tangent intersect-
    ing a secant, research *power of a point theorem*.

Similarity and Parallel Lines:

The intersection of transversals creates a pair of similar triangles. These triangles are easy to confuse with those formed by the intersection of chords on a circle, so be careful!

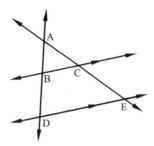 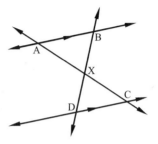

Triangles ABC and ADE are similar (angles ABC and ADE are corresponding, and the triangles share angle A).

$$\frac{AB}{AD} = \frac{AC}{AE} = \frac{BC}{DE}$$

Triangles AXB and CXD are similar (angles ABX and CDX are alternate interior angles, as are BAX and CDX).

$$\frac{AX}{CX} = \frac{BX}{DX} = \frac{AB}{CD}$$

Check for Understanding:

Find the missing length x in each diagram below. Express your answers as common fractions in simplest form.

5.021

5.121

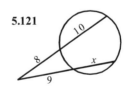

5.221

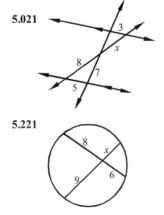

5.321

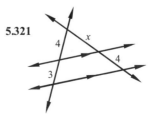

Practice: Similarity.

5.031 You are estimating the height of a
semicircular arch. Exactly 1 foot
from the base of the arch, the arch
is 5 feet tall. What is the height of
the arch at the center?

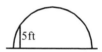

5.131 A square with 4cm sides is drawn so that
its right edge is tangent to a circle, and
the circle passes through two of its
vertices. What is the diameter of the
circle?

5.231 Chord AB on circle C of radius 3
intersects a diameter at X. If
AX = 3 and BX = 2, find the length
of CX. Express your answer in
simplest radical form.

5.331 Trapezoid ABCD has base lengths
AB = 30 and CD = 54cm, with
congruent 56cm diagonals. Find
the area of triangle ABX.
Express your answer in simplest
radical form.

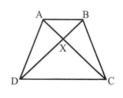

5.431 Circle A has a radius of 28 inches, and
circle B has a 44-inch radius. The
distance between their centers is 90
inches. What is the length of segment
CD, which is tangent to both circles?

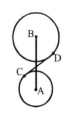

5.531 Express the length of chord
AB in circle C as a common
fraction in simplest form.

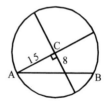

More Proportional Relationships in Similar Triangles:

We have only mentioned the basic proportional relationships of corresponding sides in similar triangles. Several other proportional relationships can be used. (See also **p.126**).

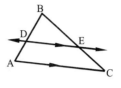

$$\frac{BD}{BE} = \frac{BA}{BC}$$ (Corresponding sides on the same triangle.)

$$\frac{BD}{BE} = \frac{DA}{EC}$$ (Differences of side lengths proportional to the sides.)

Angle Bisector Theorem:

A triangles angle bisectors do not bisect the opposite sides, but there is a very useful relationship between each angle bisector in a triangle and the side it intersects.

The angle bisector of an angle in a triangle divides the opposite side into two segments whose lengths are in the same ratio as the sides adjacent to the angle:

$$\frac{AB}{AC} = \frac{BD}{CD}$$

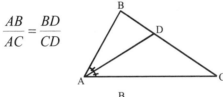

Proof:

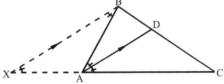

Add line XB parallel to the angle bisector. Angle ABX and BAD are alternate interior angles, while DAC and BXA are corresponding. Triangle ABX is therefore isosceles with AB=AX. Triangles DAC and BXC are similar triangles in which:

$$\frac{AC}{CD} = \frac{XA}{BD}.$$ By substitution, $\frac{AC}{CD} = \frac{AB}{BD}$, or $\frac{AB}{AC} = \frac{BD}{CD}.$

Example: Find the length of AX in rectangle ABCD below.

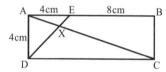

Reasoning: Using the Pythagorean theorem we find that $AC = 4\sqrt{10}$. Recognizing that ADE is an isosceles right triangle, we can see that angle ADE = 45°, so angle EDC is also 45°. DX therefore bisects angle ADC. By the angle bisector theorem:

$$\frac{AD}{DC} = \frac{AX}{XC}, \text{ so } \frac{AX}{XC} = \frac{1}{3}.$$

This is easy enough to solve in our heads since $AC = 4\sqrt{10}$:

$$\frac{AX}{XC} = \frac{\sqrt{10}}{3\sqrt{10}} \text{ gives us } AX = \sqrt{10}.$$

Practice: Angle Bisector Theorem.

5.141 What is the length of the angle bisector to the short leg of a 9-12-15 right triangle? Express your answer in simplest radical form.

5.241 Find the length of AB in the figure. Express your answer in simplest radical form.

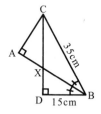

5.341 The legs of a right triangle are in the ratio 1:2. The angle bisector to the short leg divides it into two segments, one of which is 1cm longer than the other. Express the perimeter of the triangle in simplest radical form.

Similarity: Scale Factor and Area.

All squares are similar to one another. Consider what
happens to the area of a square when the side
lengths are doubled. The perimeter is doubled as
well, but what happens to the area? It is obviously
not just doubled, but quadrupled.

Consider what happens when the sides of a square are
tripled, or increased by 50%. By what factor is the
square's area increased? Working with just a few
examples suggests that when the side lengths are
increased by a scale factor s, the area is increased
by a factor s^2.

Would the same relationship hold true for any shape?

Example: A triangle has an area of 30cm^2. What would be
the area of a similar triangle whose sides are three
times the length of the original?

Reasoning: First, take any triangle whose area is 30cm^2.
We will use a 5-12-13 right triangle, but any triangle
will work. Triple the lengths of the sides to make a
15-36-39 right triangle. Its area is $(15 \cdot 36)/2 =$
270cm^2, nine times the area of the original. Applying
the rule: increasing the side lengths by a scale factor
of 3 increases the area by a scale factor of $3^2 = 9$,
making it 9 times bigger. $9(30) = 270$cm^2.

This property is true for any two similar polygons:

When the side lengths of any polygon are increased by a
scale factor s, the area is increased by a factor s^2.

Example: The area of a regular pentagon with 5cm sides is
about 43cm^2. What would be the approximate area
of a pentagon whose sides are 7cm long? Round
your answer to the tenth.

Reasoning:
A pentagon with 7cm sides will be $(7/5)^2$ times the area of a
pentagon with 5cm sides, so we multiply:

$$43\left(\frac{7}{5}\right)^2 = \frac{43 \cdot 49}{25} \approx 84.3 \, \text{cm}^2.$$

Similarity: Volume.
Consider a unit cube. What happens to its volume when we
double its height? What if we double its height and
width? What if we double all three dimensions of the
cube? Try tripling the dimensions.

You should see that doubling one dimension only doubles the
volume, doubling two dimensions increases the
volume by a factor of $2 \cdot 2 = 2^2 = 4$, and doubling all
three dimensions increases the volume by a factor
of $2 \cdot 2 \cdot 2 = 2^3 = 8$.

When all of the edge lengths/dimensions of a three-dimensional solid are increased by a scale factor s, the
surface area is increased by a scale factor of s^2, and
the volume is increased by a scale factor of s^3.

Example: Three similar cones stand outside the local art
museum. The cones are 36, 40, and 44 inches tall
and made from solid marble. What is the difference
in weight between the medium cone and the largest
cone if the smallest cone weighs 1,458 pounds?

Reasoning: The weight of each cone is porportional to its
volume (each is solid marble). Because three
dimensions of each cone are increased, to find the
weight of the larger cones, we multiply by the cubes
of the scale factors:

Medium: $1,\!458\left(\frac{10}{9}\right)^3 = 2,\!000$ Large: $1,\!458\left(\frac{11}{9}\right)^3 = 2,\!662$

The difference in these weights is 662 pounds.

Practice: Similarity, Area and Volume.

5.051 What is the ratio of the area of the small inscribed circle to that of the large inscribed circle?

5.151 The area of a triangle with side lengths 13, 20, and 21 is 126 units^2. What would be the area of a triangle with side lengths of 130, 200, and 210?

5.251 A small statue is an exact replica of the statues at Easter Island and is just 2 feet tall. The real statues are 14 feet tall and weigh 27,440 pounds. If the stone replica is made of the same stone as the real statues, how many pounds does it weigh?

5.351 The surface area of a solid clay hemisphere is 10cm^2. A larger solid clay hemisphere has a surface area of 40cm^2. If the larger hemisphere weighs 2 pounds, how many pounds does the smaller one weigh?

5.451 Similar pyramids have altitudes of 3cm and 4cm. The volume of the smaller pyramid is 30cm^3. What is the volume of the larger pyramid?

5.551 A cube has a volume of 3cm^3. The cube is enlarged until its surface area is 100 times the surface area of the original cube. What is the volume of the enlarged cube?

5.651 Kaitlyn is making a snowman with three large balls of snow. She rolls three snowballs so that top has a 2-foot diameter, the middle has a 3-foot diameter, and the bottom has a 4-foot diameter. If the weight of the top ball is 80 pounds, what is the weight of the entire snowman?

Chapter Review

5.161 Angle B is obtuse in triangle ABD. How many integral lengths x satisfy the length of AC?

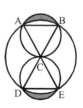

5.261 Diameters AE and BD of length 6cm form the sides of congruent equilateral triangles ABC and CDE which are circumscribed by circles. Find the combined area of the shaded lunes, which include the area inside the smaller circles but outside the larger circle.

5.361 A cone has a radius of 6cm and a height of 20cm is half-full of water (by volume). What is the depth of the water in the cone to the nearest tenth of a centimeter?

5.461 An icosahedron has 20 faces, all of which are equilateral triangles. How many vertices are there on a regular icosahedron?

5.561 The areas of the faces of a right rectangular prism are 6, 9, and 12cm². To the nearest tenth of a centimeter, what is the length of the diagonal of the prism?

5.661 What is the volume of the prism in problem **5.561**? Express your answer in simplest radical form.

5.761 Two altitudes are drawn in an isosceles triangle as shown. Find the length of segment AD.

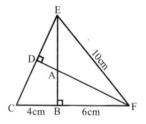

5.071 What is the difference in area between the inscribed circle and the circumscribed circle in a 12-gon of edge length 2cm? *Submitted by student Calvin Deng.

5.171 On square ABCD, E is the midpoint of side AB. Diagonal AC intersects segment ED at X. Find the length of segment EX if AB = 6cm.

5.271 The diagonals of right trapezoid are perpendicular. What is the area of the trapezoid if the parallel bases measure 8cm and 18cm?

5.371 Right triangle ABC has points A and B on the circumference of a circle, and intersects the circle at points X and Y. Find the area of the triangle if BX = 16, AY = 32, and YC = 3.

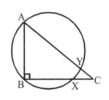

5.471 Tangent semicircles have their diameters on the sides of a square of side length 1. Express the combined area of the four semicircles in simplest radical form.

5.571 Triangle FEC is equilateral with a side length of 20cm and FE tangent to the circle at F. Find the length of chord FA if ED = 8cm.
*Submitted by student Jason Liang.

5.671 What is the area of the largest semicircle which can be inscribed within rhombus ABCD of edge length 3cm if the measure of angle A is 60 degrees?

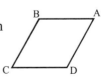

Keys and Solutions
Chapter VI

Algebra
Key and Solutions

Problems within the text are ordered with the last three digits reversed. This way, if you are looking for a solution you will not accidently see the answer to the next problem. Problems marked with a ▆▆ do not include a written solution, only the answer.

1.001 $(x-5)(x-4)$	**1.131** 46/3cm	**1.280** $4x^2-9$
1.010 6hrs	**1.140** 65	**1.281** 600 miles.
1.011 $(x^2+9)(x+3)$	**1.141** 1/4	**1.290** 7
$\cdot(x-3)$	**1.150** 18	**1.291** 143 minutes.
1.020 -1	**1.151** 97	**1.300** $x=5$
1.021 $(8x+1)(2x-5)$	**1.161** 159	**1.301** $(7x-9)^2$
1.030 7.5	**1.170** $3x-3$	**1.310** 9
1.031 $6\sqrt{3}$	**1.171** $\sqrt{14}-3$	**1.311** $5(c-3)(c-2)$
1.040 45	**1.180** $y^2-22y+121$	**1.320** $-1/2$
1.041 $4n^{-8}$ or $4/n^8$	**1.181** 140	**1.321** (see solutions)
1.050 6	**1.190** 21	**1.330** 340lbs
1.051 10	**1.191** 677	**1.331** 24ft
1.061 1,000,000	**1.200** $x=-5/3$	**1.340** 37.5%
1.070 $7a-8$	**1.201** $(3x+1)^2$	**1.341** $4\sqrt[3]{9}$ cm
1.071 1	**1.210** 15 minutes	**1.350** 56π cm^2
1.080 $a^2-4a-21$	**1.211** $(a-3b)^2$	**1.351** 11
1.081 $2\sqrt{34}$	**1.220** $2x-3y=5$	**1.361** 33
1.090 34cm^2	**1.221** 5	**1.370** $6a^2-17a+12$
1.091 1/18	**1.230** 401 years	**1.371** $(3+\sqrt{13})/2$
1.100 $x=5$	**1.231** 36ft	**1.380** $6x^2-13x-5$
1.101 $(x-28)(x+3)$	**1.240** 10	**1.381** 9
1.110 15 problems	**1.241** $x=625$	**1.390** 12cm
1.111 $(x+2)(x-2)$	**1.250** 17/21	**1.391** 168 feet
$\cdot(x+1)(x-1)$	**1.251** 16	**1.400** $x=4$
1.120 16/15	**1.261** 55/9	**1.401** $(11x+1)$
1.121 $4\sqrt{3}$	**1.270** $7a-4b$	$(11x-1)$
1.130 4	**1.271** 25	**1.410** -36

1.420 $b = -1$

1.421 $x = 13$

1.430 10sec

1.431 1.5in

1.440 \$1.00

1.441 $5\sqrt{2} - 1$

1.450 30

1.451 62

1.461 4

1.470 $8x^2 + 23x - 3$

1.471 $(a^{n+1} - 1)/(a - 1)$

1.480 $4a^2 + 4ab + b^2$

1.481 7/3

1.490 2,000

1.491 22.5

1.500 $x = 15$

1.501 $(5x + 3)(5x - 3)$

1.510 48cm²

1.520 108 units²

1.521 4.5cm

1.530 8,160

1.531 27min

1.540 162°

1.541 $x = 11$

1.550 25.2 mph

1.551 119

1.561 35

1.570 $8a^2 - 3a + 14ab - 6b - 4b^2$

1.571 $(1 + \sqrt{7})/2$

1.580 $a^3 + 9a^2 - 4a - 36$

1.581 5

1.600 $x = 7$

1.601 $8xy(x - 3)$

1.610 30 miles

1.620 $b = 4$

1.621 16

1.630 \$6.00

1.631 7/9

1.640 74.5

1.641 64

1.650 $y = -2x + 9$

1.651 8

1.661 19

1.671 144

1.681 12

1.701 $2(x - 3)(x - 4)$

1.710 2cm

1.720 $9x - 4y = -72$

1.721 6/7

1.730 \$4,500

1.731 1

1.741 72cm³

1.750 6

1.751 92

1.761 1,023/1,024

1.771 $\sqrt{2}$

1.781 3:40pm

1.801 $4(x + 3)(x - 3)$

1.810 15min

1.820 10

1.821 $3 \cdot 5^2 \cdot 11 \cdot 31 \cdot 41$

1.841 $9 + 5\sqrt{3}$

1.851 3

1.861 2/3

1.881 72 min

1.900 6hrs 45min

1.901 $7(a - 2)^2$

1.910 1hr 15min

1.920 10

1.921 $38 + 17\sqrt{5}$

1.941 400

1.981 $5\sqrt{3}$

1.010 Intuitively, there are $\dfrac{15}{9} = \dfrac{5}{3}$ as many beavers doing

twice the work. It will take $\dfrac{3}{5} \cdot 2 = \dfrac{6}{5}$ the time, or 6

hours. Alternatively, using $w = rt(b)$ to solve for the

rate we have $1 = 5(9)r$ so $r = \dfrac{1}{45}$. Plug this in and

solve for t in the equation $2 = \dfrac{1}{45}(15)t$ and we get

$t = \mathbf{6}$ hours.

1.011 $x^4 - 81 = (x^2 + 9)(x^2 - 9) = (x^2 + 9)(x + 3)(x - 3)$.

1.020 Using the slope formula: $m = \dfrac{y_2 - y_1}{x_2 - x_1} = \dfrac{0 - 9}{0 - (-9)} = -1$

1.021 For $16x^2 - 38x - 5$, we multiply ac to get $-80x^2$ and
look for factors which have a sum of $-38x$. Use
$-40x$ and $2x$ to rewrite the expression then factor
by grouping:

$16x^2 - 40x + 2x - 5$
$= 8x(2x - 5) + 1(2x - 5)$
$= (8x + 1)(2x - 5)$

1.030 Solve the system of equations by elimination:

$$a + b = 20$$
$$\underline{+\ a - b = 5}$$
$$2a \quad\ = 25$$, which makes $a = 12.5$. Substituting
this back into either equation we get $b = \mathbf{7.5}$ (which
is the smaller of the two numbers).

1.031 We have the equations: $a + b = 12$ and $ab = 9$. Solve the first equation for a: $a = 12 - b$ and substitute this into our second equation to get $(12 - b)b = 9$ which gives us the quadratic: $b^2 - 12b + 9 = 0$. It is not factorable, so we substitute values into the quadratic formula and solve:

$$x = \frac{12 \pm \sqrt{144 - 4(9)}}{2} = \frac{12 \pm \sqrt{108}}{2} = \frac{12 \pm 6\sqrt{3}}{2} = 6 \pm 3\sqrt{3},$$

giving us two roots whose difference is

$$(6 + 3\sqrt{3}) - (6 - 3\sqrt{3}) = 6\sqrt{3}.$$

1.040 The ratio of sugar to cookies must remain the same, so we write a proportion:

$$\frac{2\frac{2}{3}}{24} = \frac{5}{c} \text{ gives us } \frac{8}{3}c = 5(24), \text{ so } c = \mathbf{45} \text{ cookies.}$$

1.041 $\left[2(n^2)^{-2}\right]^2 = \left[2(n^{-4})\right]^2 = 4n^{-8}$ or $\dfrac{4}{n^8}$.

1.050 Intuitively, it takes 6 lumberjacks 7 minutes, or 42 "lumberjack minutes" to saw through 8 trees. If there are 7 lumberjacks, it will take them $42/7 = \mathbf{6}$ minutes to saw through 8 trees.

1.051 $\dfrac{1 + 3 + 5 + 7 + 9 + 11 + 13 + 15 + 17 + 19}{10} = \mathbf{10}.$

The mean of the first n positive odd integers is n.

1.061 The average of the first 1,000 odd integers is 1,000, the same as the median (see **p.53**). The first term is 1 and the last term is $1 + 999(2) = 1,999$, so the median is $(1 + 1,999)/2 = 1,000$. There are 1,000 integers, so their sum is $1,000^2 = \mathbf{1,000,000}$. The sum of the first n odd integers for any value n is n^2.

1.070 $3a - 4(2 - a) = 3a - 8 + 4a = 7a - 8$

1.071 Let $x = 0.\overline{9}$, then $10x = 9.\overline{9}$ and $10x - x = 9.\overline{9} - 0.\overline{9}$,
making $9x = 9$ and $x = \mathbf{1}$.

1.081 We have the equations: $a + b = 16$ and $ab = 30$.
Solve the first equation for a: $a = 16 - b$ and substitute this into our second equation to get
$(16 - b)b = 30$ which gives us the quadratic:
$b^2 - 16b + 30 = 0$. It is not factorable, so we substitute values into the quadratic formula and solve:

$$x = \frac{16 \pm \sqrt{256 - 4(30)}}{2} = \frac{16 \pm \sqrt{136}}{2} = \frac{16 \pm 2\sqrt{34}}{2} = 8 \pm \sqrt{34},$$

giving us two roots whose difference is
$(8 + \sqrt{34}) - (8 - \sqrt{34}) = 2\sqrt{34}$.

1.090 We have $s^2 = 50$ and we are looking for $(s + 4)(s - 4)$,
which is a difference of squares equal to $s^2 - 16$.
We know the value of $s^2 = 50$, so $s^2 - 16 = 50 - 16 = \mathbf{34cm^2}$.

1.091 We use s to represent the amount of sugar and j to
represent the amount of juice used in the original
recipe. When the sugar is doubled, we have:

$$\frac{2s}{2s + l} = \frac{10}{100} \text{ (the ratio of the sugar to the total drink}$$

is 10%). Solving, we get $20s = 2s + l$, which makes
$18s = l$, or $18 = \dfrac{l}{s}$ and $\dfrac{s}{l} = \dfrac{1}{18}$.

1.110 We use $w = rt(s)$ to find the rate: $9 = 30(4)r$ gives us
$r = \dfrac{3}{40}$. Plug this in with the new values to solve for
the work (problems) done by 5 students in 40
minutes: $w = \dfrac{3}{40} \cdot 40 \cdot 5 = \mathbf{15}$ problems.

1.111 The equation $x^4 - 5x^2 + 4$ factors into $(x^2 - 4)(x^2 - 1)$. Each factor is a difference of squares and can be factored further:

$$(x^2 - 4)(x^2 - 1) = (x+2)(x-2)(x+1)(x-1).$$

1.120 The intercepts of $3x - 5y = 8$ occur when $x = 0$ and when $y = 0$. When $x = 0$ we have $-5y = 8$, so the y-intercept occurs at $y = -\dfrac{8}{5}$. When $y = 0$ we have $3x = 8$, so the x-intercept occurs at $x = \dfrac{8}{3}$. The sum of the intercepts is: $-\dfrac{8}{5} + \dfrac{8}{3} = \dfrac{16}{15}$.

1.121 If we label the sides of the rectangle a and b, we have perimeter $2(a + b) = 16$ so $a + b = 8$, and the area of the rectangle is $ab = 8$. By the Pythagorean theorem, the diagonal length we are looking for will be $\sqrt{a^2 + b^2}$. We do not have to solve for a and b separately once we recognize that: $a^2 + b^2 = (a + b)^2 - 2ab = (8)^2 - 2(8) = 48$, which makes the diagonal length $\sqrt{48} = 4\sqrt{3}$.

1.130 This one we can do without writing a system in our heads using the 'cheat' method: If she had 18 dimes, this would be \$1.80, which is \$0.60 short of the correct amount. Each time we replace a dime with a quarter, we add \$0.15, so we need to replace 4 dimes with **4** quarters.

1.131 If we call the width w, the length is $3w + 1$ and the area equation becomes $w(3w + 1) = 10$, or $3w^2 + w - 10 = 0$. This can be factored into $(3w - 5)(w + 2) = 0$ which gives us $w = \dfrac{5}{3}$ (-2 does not make sense as the side length of a rectangle). The perimeter is therefore:
$$2w + 2(3w + 1) = 8w + 2 = 8 \cdot \frac{5}{3} + 2 = \frac{46}{3} \text{ cm.}$$

1.140 We can write the following equations based on the information given, where c and g represent the number of cherry and grape candies after your friend eats some of them:

$$\frac{c+1}{2g} = \frac{3}{5} \text{ and } \frac{c}{g} = \frac{7}{6}.$$ These equations become:

$5c + 5 = 6g$ and $6c = 7g$. Solve this system of equations to get $c = 35$ and $g = 30$, so there are **65** candies left in the bag (there were 96 to begin with).

1.141 $\sqrt{\frac{13}{56}} \cdot \sqrt{\frac{7}{26}} = \sqrt{\frac{13 \cdot 7}{56 \cdot 26}} = \sqrt{\frac{1 \cdot 1}{8 \cdot 2}} = \sqrt{\frac{1}{16}} = \frac{1}{4}$

1.150 We are given that $\frac{p}{a} = \frac{120}{100} = \frac{6}{5}$ and $\frac{b}{a} = \frac{4}{3}$. We want whole numbers for p, a, and b in $p{:}a{:}b$, so we set a to 15 (the LCM of 3 and 15), which gives us $\frac{p}{a} = \frac{18}{15}$ and $\frac{b}{a} = \frac{20}{15}$. Therefore $p{:}a{:}b = 18{:}15{:}20$, and the smallest possible number of pears is **18**.

1.151 The sum of his first 7 test scores is $7(88) = 616$, and to have an average of 90 for 9 tests requires a sum of $9(90) = 810$. This requires $810 - 616 = 194$ more points in 2 tests, or an average of $194/2 = \mathbf{97}$. Alternatively, we need to add 2 points to an average which is spread over 9 tests. This requires a score $9(2)/2 = 9$ points higher than his current average: $88 + 9 = 97$.

1.161 The common difference is found by $\frac{24 - 18}{9 - 5} = \frac{6}{4} = \frac{3}{2}$. We must add this common difference 90 times to get from the 9th to the 99th term: $24 + 90 \cdot \frac{3}{2} = \mathbf{159}$.

1.170 $8x-(3+5x)=8x-3-5x=3x-3$.

1.171 For $x=\dfrac{5}{6+\dfrac{5}{6+\dfrac{5}{6+...}}}$ we have $x=\dfrac{5}{6+x}$ or

$x(6+x)=5$. Solve the quadratic $x^2+6x-5=0$ to get $x=-3\pm\sqrt{14}$. Only the positive solution makes sense: $x=\sqrt{14}-3$.

1.181 We will express joogs and zoogs in terms of 15 moogs. 15 moogs = 9 zoogs and 15 moogs = 35 joogs, so 9 zoogs = 35 joogs. 36 zoogs would therefore be worth **140** joogs.

1.190 For a and b we have $a + b = 5$ and $ab = 2$, and we are looking for $a^2 + b^2$.

$a^2+b^2=(a+b)^2-2ab$, so $(5)^2-2(2)=$**21**.

1.191 First we note that a sum of squares a^2+b^2 can be written as $(a+b)^2-2ab$. In this case, we get a difference of squares:

$3^{12}+2^2=(3^6+2)^2-2(2)(3^6)=(3^6+2)^2-2^2 3^6$.

Consider $a=3^6+2$ and $b=2\cdot3^3$,

$(3^6+2)^2-2^2 3^6=a^2-b^2=(a+b)(a-b)$.

$a=731$ and $b=54$, so we have

$(731+54)(731-54)=785\cdot677=5\cdot157\cdot677$.

677 is the largest prime factor. This is a hard problem, don't worry too much if you missed it.

1.210 Working together for 12 minutes, Jeremy and Michael can solve 8 cubes (3 by Jeremy who take 4 minutes per cube and 5 by Michael). This is 1:30 per cube while working together. It would therefore take them **15** minutes to solve 10 cubes.

1.211 This is a perfect square. $a^2-6ab+9b^2=(a-3b)^2$.

1.220 First, find the slope: $\dfrac{-5-(-1)}{-5-1} = \dfrac{-4}{-6} = \dfrac{2}{3}$.

We will use point-slope form (there are many other ways which work well). I used the first point.

$y + 1 = \dfrac{2}{3}(x - 1)$ Multiply the equation by 3 to get

$3y + 3 = 2x - 2$, so $2x - 3y = 5$.

1.221 We are given $a^2 - b^2 = 80$, and $a + b = 16$ and asked for $a - b$: $a^2 - b^2 = (a+b)(a-b) = (16)(a-b) = 80$, so

$a - b = \dfrac{80}{16} = \mathbf{5}$.

1.230 Label the age (in 2005) of the first painting a and the age of the second painting b. The statements can be written algebraically: $2005 - a = 2(2005 - b)$ and $b = 3a$. Substituting $3a$ for b in the first equation, we get $2005 - a = 2(2005 - 3a)$. Solving, we get $a =$ **401** years. (The ages are 401 and 1,203, the dates are 1604 and 802).

1.231 Labeled as shown, we can write the equations: $4x + 2y = 48$ and $xy = 72$. Solve the first equation for y to get $y = 24 - 2x$, which we substitute into the second equation to get $x(24 - 2x) = 72$:

$24x - 2x^2 = 72$

$12x - x^2 = 36$

$0 = x^2 - 12x + 36$

$0 = (x - 6)^2$

$x = 6$

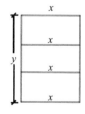

This make $y = 12$ and the perimeter of the enclosure is **36** feet.

1.240 Starting with 100 pounds of plums, there are 92 pounds of water (92%) and 8 pounds of pulp. After drying, the prunes still contain 8 pounds of pulp. If a prune is 20% water, then 8 pounds of pulp represents 80% of the mass, so the prunes weigh **10** pounds.

1.241 $\sqrt[6]{x} = \sqrt[3]{5^2}$ means the same thing as $x^{\frac{1}{6}} = 5^{\frac{2}{3}}$, so

$$\left(x^{\frac{1}{6}}\right)^6 = \left(5^{\frac{2}{3}}\right)^6 \text{ gives us } x = 5^4 = \textbf{625}.$$

1.250 5% more than a is b means $1.05a = b$, and b is 15% less than c can be written $b = 0.85c$. This leads us to $1.05a = 0.85c$, or $21a = 17c$, so $\dfrac{a}{c} = \dfrac{17}{21}$.

1.251 Start with 7 integers labeled in order a, b, c, d, e, f, and g. We are given the median: $d = 8$. The distinct mode of 9 means that e and f must be 9 (or e, f, and g could all be 9). The mean gives us the sum: 49. To maximize the range we want a, b, and c to be as small as possible, allowing f to be as large as possible while keeping the sum equal to 49. Make a, b, and c equal to 1, 2, and 3. This makes the set (whose sum is 49) 1, 2, 3, 8, 9, 9, and f.
$1+2+3+8+9+9+f = 49$, so $f = 17$ and the range is $17 - 1 = \textbf{16}$.

1.261 Call the first three terms a, b, and c, and the next three terms d, e, and f. We note that b is the average of the first three terms: 20/3, and e is the average of the next three terms: 25/3. The common difference can be found using b and e (the 2nd and 5th terms):

$\dfrac{25/3 - 20/3}{5 - 2} = \dfrac{5/3}{3} = \dfrac{5}{9}$. Subtract this from b to find

the first term a: $\dfrac{20}{3} - \dfrac{5}{9} = \dfrac{55}{9}$.

1.270 $(3a - b) - (3b - 4a) = 3a - b - 3b + 4a = 7a - 4b$.

1.271 Forget the first 20 momentarily and just let

$x = \sqrt{20 + \sqrt{20 + \sqrt{20...}}}$, then $x^2 = 20 + x$, so

$x^2 - x - 20 = 0$. This factors into $(x - 5)(x + 4) = 0$,

so $x = 5$ (it is assumed that we are looking for the positive square root). Add the 20 from the beginning of the expression and we get **25**.

1.281 Use $d = rt$ to write two equations: $d = 3(r + 25)$ and

$d = 4(r - 25)$ which gives us $3(r + 25) = 4(r - 25)$.

Solving for r we get $r = 175$ (mph). Plug this into either of the first two equations to get $d = $ **600** miles.

1.290 Note that $ab + bc = b(a + c)$, so $7 + 5 = b(4)$. There-

fore, $b = 3$ and $a + b + c = (a + c) + b = 4 + 3 = $ **7**.

1.291 We can use the harmonic mean of 11 and 13 minutes to find the time it takes for Rohan and Lewis to both chop 6 pounds of carrots (12 pounds total, working together). We then multiply that value by 12 (because they are chopping 144 pounds):

$$\frac{2(11)(13)}{11 + 13} \cdot 12 = \frac{2(11)(13)}{24} \cdot 12 = \textbf{143} \text{ minutes.}$$

1.310 Start with the equation $j = 3m - 3$. Plug-in 33 for j and we solve to get $m = 12$. A nice thing to know is that when James is twice Molly's age, she will be the age he was when she was born. The difference in their ages gives us the age James was when Molly was born: 21. When James is twice Molly's age he will be 42, which is **9** years from now.

1.311 I generally re-arrange these first: $30 - 25c + 5c^2 = $

$5c^2 - 25c + 30 = 5(c^2 - 5c + 6) = 5(c - 3)(c - 2)$.

1.320 The graph of $4x - 2y = 3$ has a slope of $\frac{-4}{-2} = 2$, and

the perpendicular slope is $-\frac{1}{2}$.

1.321 $256x^8 - 1 = (16x^4 + 1)(16x^4 - 1)$
$$= (16x^4 + 1)(4x^2 + 1)(4x^2 - 1)$$
$$= (16x^4 + 1)(4x^2 + 1)(2x + 1)(2x - 1)$$

1.330 Take the four equations and add them together:

$$a + b + c = 240$$
$$b + c + d = 250$$
$$a + c + d = 260$$
$$+ \ a + b + d = 270$$
$$\overline{3a + 3b + 3c + 3d = 1{,}020}$$

Divide both sides of the equation by 3 to get
$a + b + c + d =$ **340** pounds.

1.331 Labeled as shown, we can write the equations:
$4x + y = 48$ and $xy = 144$.
Solve the first equation for y to
get $y = 48 - 4x$, which we
substitute into the second equation to get $x(48 - 4x) = 144$,
which gives us $48x - 4x^2 = 144$,
or $4x^2 - 48x + 144 = 0$. Simplify
this and factor: $x^2 - 12x + 36 = 0$, so $(x - 6)^2 = 0$.
The solution $x = 6$ makes $y =$ **24 feet**.

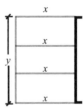

1.340 The prices are currently 80% of their original value, so
we look for a value x where $0.8x = 0.5$. This gives
us $x = 5/8 = 0.625$ or 62.5% of the already marked-
down prices, which is an additional **37.5%** off.

1.341 If we can triple the volume by multiplying the edge
length by $\sqrt[3]{3}$, then to get one-third the volume, we
will need to divide the edge length by $\sqrt[3]{3}$: $\dfrac{12}{\sqrt[3]{3}}$. To
rationalize the denominator, we multiply by a cube
root that will make $\sqrt[3]{3}$ a perfect cube:

$$\frac{12}{\sqrt[3]{3}} \cdot \frac{\sqrt[3]{9}}{\sqrt[3]{9}} = \frac{12\sqrt[3]{9}}{\sqrt[3]{27}} = \frac{12\sqrt[3]{9}}{3} = 4\sqrt[3]{9} \text{ cm (about 8.3cm)}.$$

1.350 Call the three radii a, b, and c. The short leg of the triangle is therefore $a + b$, the other leg $a + c$ and the hypotenuse $b + c$. This gives us the system of three equations:

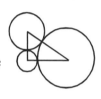

$a + b = 6$, $a + c = 8$, and $b + c = 10$.

Subtract the second from the first to get $b - c = -2$. Add this to the third equation to get $2b = 8$, so $b = 4$. Substitute this value into the other equations to find $a = 2$ and $c = 6$. The combined area of the three circles is therefore $4\pi + 16\pi + 36\pi = 56\pi$ units^2.

1.351 The current set $\{3, 4, 5, 5, 8\}$ has a mean, median, and mode of 5. Of the four integers added to the set, at least three must be 6's to make the mode 6. The mean of the new set must be 6 as well, which means the sum of the integers in the set must be 54. The 7 integers we know already have a sum of $3 + 4 + 5 + 5 + 6 + 6 + 6 + 8 = 43$. This means that the fourth (and largest) number added to the set must be $54 - 43 = $ **11**. The new set: $\{3, 4, 5, 5, 6, 6, 6, 8, 11\}$.

1.361 The arithmetic sequence is easy enough to just count up to... 16, 24, 32, 40, $\underline{48}$ is the 5th term. The common ratio in the geometric sequence is 3/2, so the 5th term will be $16\left(\dfrac{3}{2}\right)^4 = \underline{81}$. (Perhaps we could have also counted to this one). $81 - 48 = $ **33**.

1.371 For $x = 3 + \cfrac{1}{3 + \cfrac{1}{3 + \cfrac{1}{3 + \dots}}}$ we have $x = 3 + \dfrac{1}{x}$ or

$x - 3 = \dfrac{1}{x}$, so $x^2 - 3x = 1$ or $x^2 - 3x - 1 = 0$. The positive solution to this quadratic is $x = \dfrac{3 + \sqrt{13}}{2}$.

1.381 We want to add n such that the mean of $\{6, 11, 13, 7, 14, n\}$ is $n + 1$:

$$\frac{6 + 11 + 13 + 7 + 14 + n}{6} = n + 1, \text{ so } 51 + n = 6n + 6.$$

Solving we get $n = \textbf{9}$.

1.390 Given the area, we have $(x - 3)(x + 3) = 216$ or $x^2 - 9 = 216$, so $x = \sqrt{225} = 15$ and the short side is $15 - 3 = \textbf{12cm}$ long.

1.391 We are looking for the sum of the terms: $24 + 18 + 18 + 13.5 + 13.5 + \ldots$ which resembles an infinite geometric series (except that all but the first term is repeated). Remove that first term (for now) and solve for $36 + 27 + 20.25 \ldots$ which is an infinite geometric series with common ratio 3/4 and first term 36. Use the formula (**p. 56**) to get the total

distance (less the initial drop): $d = \dfrac{36}{1 - 0.75} = 144\,\text{ft}$,

then add back the 24-foot initial drop to get **168** feet.

1.410 Even integers have a positive difference of 2, so four consecutive even integers can be labeled n, $(n + 2)$, $(n + 4)$, and $(n + 6)$. This allows us to write the equation: $n + (n + 2) + (n + 4) + (n + 6) = 3n$. Solving, we get $4n + 12 = 3n$, so $n = -12$, and the sum of the integers is $3(-12) = \textbf{-36}$.

1.420 Given the point $(b, -3)$, we can substitute these two values into the equation $y = 2x + b$, giving us $-3 = 2(b) + b$. Solve for b to get $b = \textbf{-1}$.

1.421 In the equation $\dfrac{2x^2 - 5x - 12}{2x + 3} = 9$ we can factor the

numerator to get $\dfrac{(2x + 3)(x - 4)}{2x + 3} = 9$ which simplifies

to $x - 4 = 9$, so $x = \textbf{13}$.

1.430 We will call Kenny's running speed in flights per minute k and the speed of the escalator (also in flights per minute) e. When Kenny runs up the down escalator, we have $k - e = 2$ (the two here represents 2 flights of stairs per minute because it takes 30 seconds). When Kenny runs up the up escalator we have $k + e = 10$. Adding these two equations we get $2k = 12$, so Kenny's speed alone is $12/2 = 6$ flights per minute, or **10 seconds** per flight of stairs.

1.431 If the width of the photograph is 4.25, then the width of the frame is $4.25 + 2x$ and the height is $7.75 + 2x$. We are given the area of the border: 45. This gives us the equation solved below:

$$(4.25 + 2x)(7.75 + 2x) - (4.25)(7.75) = 45$$
$$32.9375 + 8.5x + 15.5x + 4x^2 - 32.9375 = 45$$
$$4x^2 + 24x = 45$$
$$4x^2 + 24x - 45 = 0$$
$$(2x - 3)(2x + 15) = 0$$

We use the positive solution: $x = $ **1.5 inches**.

1.440 Between them they have 100 ounces, so each gets $100/3$ ounces. Harold has $120/3$ ounces, so he gives Greg $20/3$ ounces, while Jake has $180/3$ ounces and must give Greg $80/3$ ounces. Harold contributed $1/5$ of the water that Greg drank, so he should get **$1** (which is $1/5$ of the money Greg gave them).

1.441 Rationalizing each denominator is key here:

$$\frac{1}{\sqrt{1} + \sqrt{2}} \cdot \frac{\sqrt{1} - \sqrt{2}}{\sqrt{1} - \sqrt{2}} = \frac{\sqrt{1} - \sqrt{2}}{-1} = \frac{\sqrt{2} - \sqrt{1}}{1}$$

and we are left with the sum of:

$$\frac{\sqrt{2} - \sqrt{1}}{1} + \frac{\sqrt{3} - \sqrt{2}}{1} + \frac{\sqrt{4} - \sqrt{3}}{1} + ... + \frac{\sqrt{50} - \sqrt{49}}{1}$$
$$= -\sqrt{1} + \left(\sqrt{2} - \sqrt{2}\right) + \left(\sqrt{3} - \sqrt{3}\right) + ... + \left(\sqrt{49} - \sqrt{49}\right) + \sqrt{50}$$
$$= \sqrt{50} - \sqrt{1} = 5\sqrt{2} - 1.$$

1.450 Using m to represent my current age and f to represent my father's current age, the first equation is:

$$m = \frac{1}{2}f - 6, \text{ or } 2m + 12 = f.$$

In six years, m becomes $(m + 6)$ and f becomes $(f + 6)$ and the second equation is:

$$m + 6 = \frac{1}{3}(f + 6) + 6, \text{ or } 3m - 6 = f.$$

Both equations were solved for f to allow us to substitute and solve $2m + 12 = 3m - 6$ to get $m = 18$, which makes $f = 48$. If my father is 30 years older than I am, he was **30** when I was born.

1.451 Intuitively, if a tenth score of 80 increases a quiz average by 2 points, we can consider taking 20 of these points and distributing 2 each to every score. This means the old average must have been 60 and the new average is therefore 62. For a more algebraic approach, call the old average a. This gives us the equation:

$\dfrac{9a + 80}{10} = a + 2$, so $9a + 80 = 10a + 20$, making his

old average $a = 60$ and his new average is $60 + 2 = \mathbf{62}$.

1.461 First note that $2^0 = 1$ and $2^{10} = 1{,}024$. We can use a common ratio of 2^{10}, 2^5, 2^2, or 2^1 for a total of **4** geometric sequences:

1, 1,024.
1, 32, 1,024.
1, 4, 16, 64, 256, 1,024.
1, 2, 4, 8, 16, 32, 64, 128, 256, 512, 1,024.

1.471 Consider the sum $a^0 + a^1 + a^2 + a^3 ... + a^n$:

if $x = a^0 + a^1 + a^2 + a^3 ... + a^n$,

then $ax = a^1 + a^2 + a^3 + a^4 ... + a^{n+1}$, and

$ax - x = a^{n+1} - a^0$. Factor out the x on the left:

$x(a-1) = a^{n+1} - 1$ and divide by $(a-1)$ to get:

$$x = \frac{a^{n+1} - 1}{a - 1}.$$

1.481 If $3x + \dfrac{3}{x} = 5$, then $\left(3x + \dfrac{3}{x}\right)^2 = 25$, which gives us:

$9x^2 + 18 + \dfrac{9}{x^2} = 25$, so $9x^2 + \dfrac{9}{x^2} = 7$. Divide both

sides of this equation by 3 to get $3x^2 + \dfrac{3}{x^2} = \dfrac{7}{3}$.

1.490 For the sum to be as small as possible, we want the numbers to be as close together as possible. Note that $999,996 = 1,000,000 - 4 = (1,000 + 2)(1,000 - 2)$, so $1,002 \cdot 998 = 999,996$ and the smallest possible sum is $1,002 + 998 = \mathbf{2,000}$.

1.491 We can find a^2, b^2, and c^2 separately using the following:

$a^2 = \dfrac{ab \cdot ac}{bc} = \dfrac{40}{5} = 8$

$b^2 = \dfrac{ab \cdot bc}{ac} = \dfrac{20}{10} = 2$

$c^2 = \dfrac{bc \cdot ac}{ab} = \dfrac{50}{4} = 12.5$ so $a^2 + b^2 + c^2 = \mathbf{22.5}$

1.510 If we label the sides of the rectangle x and $3x$, the perimeter is $x + 3x + x + 3x = 8x = 32$, so $x = 4$. The sides are therefore 4 and 12, which gives an area of **48cm²**.

1.520 If we find the x and y-intercepts of the graph, we can use these as the height and base of the triangle bounded by both axis. The y-intercept is 12 or (0, 12) if you prefer. We find the x-intercept by setting y to zero and solving for x, which gives us 18 for the x-intercept. The area of the triangle is

therefore: $A = \dfrac{1}{2} \cdot 12 \cdot 18 = \textbf{108 units}^2$.

1.521 Call the small radius r and the large radius R. $\pi(R^2 - r^2) = 9\pi$, so $R^2 - r^2 = 9$ which makes $(R + r)(R - r) = 9$. We notice that $(R - r) = 2$ (half the difference in the diameters), so $2(R + r) = 9$. This gives us the sum of the radii: $R + r = \textbf{4.5}$.

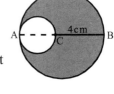

1.530 We are given enough information to write three equations: $a + b = 37$, $b + c = 41$, and $a + c = 44$. Subtract the first from the second to get $c - a = 4$. Add this to $a + c = 44$ and we get $2c = 48$, so $c = 24$. Plug-in to get $a = 20$ and $b = 17$. $abc = \textbf{8,160}$.

1.531 Using $d = rt$, we have distance 5.4 miles, rate x mph, and time (in minutes) $x + 15$. Convert the time in minutes to hours by dividing by 60 and we have:

$$5.4 = x\left(\dfrac{x+15}{60}\right).$$

This leads us the quadratic $x^2 + 15x - 324 = 0$ and factors into $(x - 12)(x + 27) = 0$. The positive solution $x = 12$ means that he rode 12mph and took $12 + 15 = \textbf{27}$ minutes to get to school.

Algebra: Solutions

1.540 The sum of the interior angles in a pentagon is 540°
(**p.180**). Labeling the angles $2x$, $3x$, $4x$, $5x$, and $6x$ we
have $2x + 3x + 4x + 5x + 6x = 540$, so $20x = 540$ and
$x = 27$. This makes the largest angle $6(27) = $ **162°**.

1.541
$$2^x = \left(4^{\frac{1}{3}} \cdot 16^{\frac{3}{4}} \right)^3$$
$$2^x = \left((2^2)^{\frac{1}{3}} \cdot (2^4)^{\frac{3}{4}} \right)^3$$
$$2^x = \left(2^{\frac{2}{3}} \cdot 2^3 \right)^3$$
$$2^x = \left(2^{\frac{11}{3}} \right)^3 = 2^{11} \text{ so } x = \textbf{11}.$$

1.550 Let's put the formula for harmonic mean to work here,
using r to represent the rate in mph that Franklin
must ride on the return trip:

$$\frac{2 \cdot 18 \cdot r}{18 + r} = 21, \text{ so } 36r = 378 + 21r.$$

Solving for r we get **25.2 mph**.

1.551 This is a case where guess-and-check can save some
time if we recognize that the integers can be 101,
103, 105, 107... until the 10th integer is 119. A more
rigorous approach probably looks something like this:
Call the integers a, b, c, d, ...i, j.
$a + b = 2(102) = 204$
$a + b + c = 3(103) = 309$, so $c = 105$.
$a + b + c + d = 4(104) = 416$, so $d = 107$.
... until
$a + b + c + d + ... + i = 9(109) = 981$, and
$a + b + c + d + ... + j = 10(110) = 1,100$, so $j = $ **119**.

1.561 Her 12th birthday was exactly halfway between her 7th
and 17th birthdays, so we only need to find the
geometric mean of 5 and 245: $\sqrt{5 \cdot 245} = $ **35**.

1.571 Let $x = 1 + \cfrac{3}{2 + \cfrac{3}{1 + \cfrac{3}{2 + \cfrac{3}{1 + \ldots}}}}$ Then: $x = 1 + \cfrac{3}{2 + \cfrac{3}{x}}$

$$= 1 + \cfrac{3}{\cfrac{2x+3}{x}} = 1 + \frac{3x}{2x+3}, \text{ so } x - 1 = \frac{3x}{2x+3}, \text{ and}$$

$2x^2 + x - 3 = 3x$. Subtract $3x$ to get the quadratic

$2x^2 - 2x - 3 = 0$, which has solutions: $x = \dfrac{1 \pm \sqrt{7}}{2}$.

Only the positive solution makes sense, so:

$$x = \frac{1 + \sqrt{7}}{2}.$$

1.581 To begin, write an equation to model the question:

$$\frac{a-b}{\dfrac{1}{b} - \dfrac{1}{a}} = 5 \text{ means that } \frac{a-b}{\left(\dfrac{a-b}{ab}\right)} = 5, \text{ so}$$

$$a - b \cdot \frac{ab}{a-b} = 5 \text{ giving us } ab = \mathbf{5}.$$

1.610 We use $d = rt$ to write two equations, but we must be careful with the units. Anil's speed is given in miles per hour, so 5 minutes is converted to 1/12 hour.

On the highways: $d = 45t$

On the back roads: $d - 3 = 36\left(t + \dfrac{1}{12}\right)$

Convert the second equation into $d = 36t + 6$, which means that $45t = 36t + 6$ (because $d = d$). Solving

for the time in hours gives us $t = \dfrac{2}{3}$ hr, which is equal to 40 minutes. Averaging 45mph on the highway route for 40 minutes, Anil will travel **30 miles**. This is really a system of equations as discussed in chapter 1.3.

1.620 Remember that the slope of a standard form linear equation is $-A/B$. The slope of $2x - 5y = 7$ is 2/5. We are looking for a value b for which $10x + by = 7$ has a slope of $-5/2$:

$$\frac{-10}{b} = \frac{-5}{2}, \text{ so } b = \mathbf{4}.$$

1.621 If the sides of the rectangle are a and b, we are given that $ab = 9$ and $\sqrt{a^2 + b^2} = \sqrt{46}$. This gives us $a^2 + b^2 = 46$. We are looking for $2(a+b)$. Notice that $(a+b)^2 = a^2 + b^2 + 2ab$, so $(a+b)^2 = 46 + 2(9) = 64$. If $(a+b)^2 = 64$ then $a + b = 8$ ($a + b$ cannot be negative for the side lengths of a rectangle). The perimeter is $2(a + b) = \mathbf{16cm}$.

1.630 This is more a puzzle than an algebra problem, but it does involve the concept of substitution. Consider the following method of purchasing the letters used to spell TWELVE: Buy the words TWO and ELEVEN, then sell back the letters you don't need: O, N, and E (which happen to spell ONE!). $3 + $5 minus $2 = **$6** to buy TWELVE.

1.631 The sum of the roots can be found by $\dfrac{-b}{a} = \dfrac{7}{9}$.

1.640 If her time decreases by 2% six times, her new time will be $(0.98)^6$ times what her original time was. This means that if x is her original time, then

$$x(0.98)^6 = 66, \text{ so } x = \frac{66}{(0.98)^6} \approx \mathbf{74.5} \text{ seconds.}$$

1.641 We need the smallest integer for which $n^{\frac{1}{3}}$ and $n^{\frac{1}{4}}$ are both integers, so we look for the smallest possible value of a^{12}, in which case $\left(a^{12}\right)^{\frac{1}{3}} = a^4$ and $\left(a^{12}\right)^{\frac{1}{4}} = a^3$. If we use $a = 2$ we have $\left(2^{12}\right)^{\frac{1}{3}} = 16$, $\left(2^{12}\right)^{\frac{1}{4}} = 8$, and $\sqrt{2^{12}} = 2^6 = \mathbf{64}$.

1.650 The line which passes through the two points of intersection is the perpendicular bisector of the segment which connects the centers of the circles (this is easiest to see by connecting all four points to make a rhombus, in which the diagonals are perpendicular bisectors, see **p.183**). The slope between the centers of the circles is 1/2, so the perpendicular slope is -2. The midpoint is (3,3). (Average the x and y coordinates to get the midpoint.) The equation of the line which passes through (3,3) with a slope of -2 is $y = -2x + 9$.

1.651 Intuitively, the difference between 19 and 35 points is 16 points. If these points are evenly distributed among the games she has played there will be a 2-point difference in her average score, meaning the 16 points would be evenly distributed between **8** games. Algebraically, call t the total number of points she has scored so far this season and g the total number of games in a season. If we add 19 to her total we get an average of 18 points per game means: $t + 19 = 18g$, while adding 35 to her total makes her average 20 points per game: $t + 35 = 20g$. Solving this system of equations also gives us $g = \mathbf{8\ games}$.

1.661 After some quick guessing-and-checking, we see that the common ratio must certainly be less than 2 (otherwise, the long side is always greater than the sum of the two shorter sides, as in 1-2-4). Using a common ratio of 3/2 allows us to use 4-6-9 as the lengths of the sides, in which case the perimeter of the triangle is $4 + 6 + 9 = \mathbf{19}$ units.

1.671 Let $x = 2\sqrt{3\sqrt{2\sqrt{3\sqrt{2...}}}}$, then $x^2 = 4 \cdot 3\sqrt{x} = 12\sqrt{x}$ and $x^4 = 144x$, making $x^3 = 144$, so $x = \sqrt[3]{144}$. **144** is our answer.

1.681 Look at this in reverse, we are trying to find $a + \sqrt{b}$ for which $(a + \sqrt{b})^2$ is equal to $32 + 10\sqrt{7}$. When we square $a + \sqrt{b}$ we get $a^2 + 2a\sqrt{b} + b$, so $a^2 + b$ must equal 32 and $2a\sqrt{b}$ must equal $10\sqrt{7}$, making $a = 5$ and $b = 7$. $a + b = $ **12**.

1.701 $2x^2 - 14x + 24 = 2(x^2 - 7x + 12) = 2(x - 3)(x - 4)$

1.710 For the hexagon we have the sum of the sides:
$n + (n+1) + (n+2) + (n+3) + (n+4) + (n+5) = 45$,
or $6n + 15 = 45$ which gives us $n = 5$.
For the pentagon we have
$n + (n+1) + (n+2) + (n+3) + (n+4) = 45$, or
$5n + 10 = 45$ which gives us $n = 7$. The difference in the lengths of the shortest sides is **2cm**.

1.720 The easiest way to do this is to convert the equation into standard form and then switch the coefficients of x and y.

$y = \dfrac{4}{9}x - 8$ Multiply the equation by 9.

$9y = 4x - 72$ Subtract $9y$ and add 72.

$4x - 9y = 72$ The y-intercept is $\dfrac{72}{-9} = -8 \ (0,-8)$.

The x-intercept is $\dfrac{72}{4} = 18 \ (18,0)$.

To switch intercepts, we can just switch the a and b values of the equation (the coefficients of x and y): $-9x + 4y = 72$. Multiply by -1 to get $9x - 4y = -72$.

1.721 We are given $a + b = 6$ and $a^2 + b^2 = 22$. We are asked to find $\dfrac{1}{a} + \dfrac{1}{b}$, which is equal to $\dfrac{a+b}{ab}$, so all we need is ab. Because $a+b=6$, $(a+b)^2=36$, and $(a+b)^2=a^2+b^2+2ab$, if we subtract $a^2+b^2=22$ from $(a+b)^2=36$ we are left with $2ab=14$, so $ab=7$ and $\dfrac{1}{a}+\dfrac{1}{b}=\dfrac{a+b}{ab}=\dfrac{6}{7}$.

1.730 We can do the math in our heads: \$8,000 loses 50% to become \$4,000. \$4,000 gains 50% back to get to \$6,000. Down 50% again gives us \$3,000, and finally back up again by 50% gets us to **\$4,500**. We can do this with any starting value by multiplying by 0.5 and 1.5 repeatedly. The investment loses 25% every 2 days at this rate.

1.731 First, complete the distribution on $(j-1)(1-k)$ to get $j+k-1-jk=(j+k)-jk-1$, so we only need the sum and product of the roots (not the actual roots themselves). The sum of the roots of $2x^2-5x+1=0$ is $\dfrac{-b}{a}=\dfrac{5}{2}$ and the product is $\dfrac{c}{a}=\dfrac{1}{2}$, so $(j-1)(1-k)=(j+k)-jk-1=\dfrac{5}{2}-\dfrac{1}{2}-1=\mathbf{1}$.

1.741 Call the edge lengths of the prism a, b, and c. We are given $ab=12$, $ac=16$, and $bc=27$ and asked to find abc. If we multiply all three of our equations together we get $a^2b^2c^2=12\cdot16\cdot27$. To get abc, we take the square root of both sides of the equation. $abc=\sqrt{12\cdot16\cdot27}=\sqrt{4\cdot16\cdot81}=2\cdot4\cdot9=\mathbf{72cm^3}$.

1.750 Every spider (s) has 7 more "legs than bugs" (for every spider, there are 8 legs but only one bug, hence, 7 more legs than bugs), while every beetle (b) has 5 more "legs than bugs". This gives us the equation $7s+5b=162$. We are also told that $b=s+18$. Substitute and solve $7s+5(s+18)=162$, so $12s+90=162$. This gives us $s=\mathbf{6\ spiders}$.

1.751 A 95 on his next three tests will increase his average to 93, which will be out of 9 tests. $93(9) = 837$ points on 9 tests. Subtract $95(3) = 285$, leaving 552 points on his first 6 tests, for an average of $552/6 = \textbf{92}$.

1.761 Let $x = \dfrac{1}{2} + \dfrac{1}{4} + \dfrac{1}{8} + \ldots + \dfrac{1}{1{,}024}$, then

$$2x = 1 + \dfrac{1}{2} + \dfrac{1}{4} + \ldots + \dfrac{1}{512} \text{ and subtracting the two:}$$

$$2x - x = 1 - \dfrac{1}{1{,}024} = \dfrac{1{,}023}{1{,}024}.$$

1.771 Let $x = 1 + \dfrac{1}{1 + \dfrac{2}{1 + \dfrac{1}{1 + \ldots}}}$, then $x = 1 + \dfrac{1}{1 + \dfrac{2}{x}}$, so

$$x = 1 + \dfrac{1}{\dfrac{x+2}{x}} = 1 + \dfrac{x}{x+2} = \dfrac{x+2}{x+2} + \dfrac{x}{x+2} = \dfrac{2x+2}{x+2}$$

Multiplying both sides by x, we get $x(x+2) = 2x+2$, or $x^2 + 2x = 2x + 2$. This makes $x^2 = 2$, so $x = \sqrt{2}$. (only the positive solution makes sense here).

1.781 Take this one step at a time. Tejas paints 1/3 of the fence in 2 hours, so he paints at a rate of 1/6 fence per hour. Working together, Tejas and Jason finish $\dfrac{4}{5} - \dfrac{1}{3} = \dfrac{7}{15}$ of the fence, of which $\dfrac{1}{6}$ was completed by Tejas, meaning that on his own, Jason can complete $\dfrac{7}{15} - \dfrac{1}{6} = \dfrac{3}{10}$ on his own in one hour. Only $\dfrac{1}{5}$ of the fence is left to be painted, which will take Jason $\dfrac{1/5}{3/10} = \dfrac{2}{3}$ of an hour or 40 minutes. He will finish painting at **3:40pm**.

1.801 $4x^2 - 36 = 4(x^2 - 9) = 4(x+3)(x-3)$

1.810 We will use the harmonic mean to find his average

speed on the way there: $\dfrac{2 \cdot 4 \cdot 6}{4+6} = \dfrac{24}{5}$ miles per hour

for 25 minutes (5/12 hour) means that the distance is

$\dfrac{24}{5} \cdot \dfrac{5}{12} = 2$ miles. Running 2 miles at 8mph will take

2/8 hour = **15 minutes**.

1.820 Find the intercepts of the graph:
The y-intercept is at $(0,-8)$,
and the x-intercept is at
$(-6,0)$. We can use the
distance formula (**p.201**) or
simply recognize that we have
a right triangle with legs 6 and
8 and hypotenuse $\sqrt{6^2 + 8^2} =$
10 units.

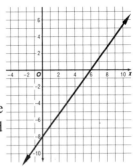

1.821 $2^{20} - 1 = (2^{10}+1)(2^{10}-1) = (2^{10}+1)(2^5+1)(2^5-1)$
$= (1{,}025)(33)(31) = (5 \cdot 5 \cdot 41)(3 \cdot 11)(31)$
$= \mathbf{3 \cdot 5^2 \cdot 11 \cdot 31 \cdot 41}$

1.841 By the Pythagorean theorem, we have:
$x^2 + (x+1)^2 = (x+3)^2$, or $2x^2 + 2x + 1 = x^2 + 6x + 9$,
which simplifies to $x^2 - 4x - 8 = 0$. Using the
quadratic formula to solve, we get positive solution
$x = 2 + 2\sqrt{3}$, which is the short leg of the triangle.
This makes $3 + 2\sqrt{3}$ the length of the longer leg, and
the area of the triangle is:

$$\frac{1}{2}(2+2\sqrt{3})(3+2\sqrt{3}) = \frac{1}{2}(18+10\sqrt{3}) = 9+5\sqrt{3}.$$

1.851 The middle number must be 7, and the sum of the three
integers must be 18 (meaning the sum of the first and
last integers must be 11). We cannot use 5 and 6 (6

would be the median) or 4 and 7 (7 would be the mode), so we only have {3, 7, 8}, {2, 7, 9}, and {1, 7, 10}. There are **3** distinct sets.

1.861 The sum of a geometric series is given by the formula $\dfrac{a}{1-r}$. The common ratio is $\dfrac{2}{5}$, as is the first term of the series. This gives us $\dfrac{2/5}{1-2/5} = \dfrac{2/5}{3/5} = \dfrac{2}{3}$.

1.881 We can see that if we wanted to record for 6 hours and then play the 6-hour tape back, we would need 3 battery packs to record and 2 to play back for a total of 5 battery packs. If 5 battery packs will allow 6 hours of filming, then 1 battery pack will allow 6/5 = 1.2 hours or **72 minutes**. Alternatively, using the harmonic mean of 2 and 3, we see that a battery will last $\dfrac{2 \cdot 2 \cdot 3}{2+3} = \dfrac{12}{5}$ hours if half is used for taping and half is used for playback, so we can record for half that length of time (6/5 hour = 72 minutes).

1.900 If 3 men take 9 hours to paint 4 rooms, it would take 1 man 3 times as long to paint 4 rooms: 27 hours. This means it will take 27/4 = 6.75 hours or **6 hours and 45 minutes** for one man to paint one room.

1.901 $7a^2 - 28a + 28 = 7(a^2 - 4a + 4) = 7(a-2)^2$

1.910 If Tobey mows 1 lawn in 5/6 hour, then he mows at a rate of 6/5 lawns per hour. This means that in 30 minutes, Tobey will mow 6/10 or 3/5 of the lawn, meaning Nick must mow 2/5 lawn in a half-hour or 4/5 lawn per hour. At this rate, it will take him 5/4 hours or **1 hour 15 minutes** to mow a whole lawn.

1.920 Begin by mapping the possible coordinate pairs where $0 \le x \le y \le 5$. The equation passes through the origin and one of the 21 points shown. We are looking for all distinct slopes $\dfrac{y}{x}$.

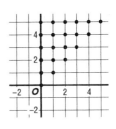

This now becomes simply a matter of careful counting and avoiding duplicates. Starting with $y = 5$ we have $\dfrac{5}{5}, \dfrac{5}{4}, \dfrac{5}{3}, \dfrac{5}{2}$, and $\dfrac{5}{1}$. $\dfrac{5}{0}$ cannot be used as a slope m in the equation given. When $y = 4$ we have three new slopes: $\dfrac{4}{3}, \dfrac{4}{2}$, and $\dfrac{4}{1}$. For $y = 3$ we have $\dfrac{3}{2}$ and $\dfrac{3}{1}$, and for $y = 2$ and $y = 1$ we have no new slopes. This gives us a total of **10** distinct slopes.

1.921 $(a + \sqrt{b})^2 = a^2 + 2a\sqrt{b} + b = 9 + 4\sqrt{5}$, so b must be 5 (the value under the radical) and a must be 2 (because $2a\sqrt{5} = 4\sqrt{5}$. To find $(a + \sqrt{b})^3$ we just multiply $(2 + \sqrt{5})$ by $(9 + 4\sqrt{5})$:
$$(2 + \sqrt{5})(9 + 4\sqrt{5}) = 18 + 8\sqrt{5} + 9\sqrt{5} + 20$$
$$= 38 + 17\sqrt{5}.$$

1.941 We look for a way to get 5^n in the expression 25^{2n+1}:
$$25^{2n+1} = \left(5^2\right)^{2n+1} = \left(5^2\right)^{2n} \cdot 5^2 = 5^{4n} \cdot 5^2 = \left(5^n\right)^4 \cdot 5^2.$$
Now we can substitute 2 for 5^n to get $(2)^4 \cdot 5^2 = $ **400**.

1.981 If $a + b = 15$, then $(a + b)^2 = 225$, which is also equal to $a^2 + 2ab + b^2$. Subtract $a^2 + b^2 = 150$ from $a^2 + 2ab + b^2 = 225$ to get $2ab = 75$. Now we have $a+b=15$, so $a=15-b$, and we plug-this into $2ab=75$ to get $2(15-b)b=75$ which leads to the quadratic $2b^2-30b+75=0$. The solutions are $\dfrac{15\pm5\sqrt{3}}{2}$, and their positive difference is:

$$\frac{15+5\sqrt{3}}{2}-\frac{15-5\sqrt{3}}{2}=5\sqrt{3}.$$

Counting
Key and Solutions

Problems within the text are ordered with the last three digits
reversed. This way, if you are looking for a solution you
will not accidently see the answer to the next problem.
Problems marked with a ▓ do not include a written
solution, only the answer.

2.001	6	**2.141**	455	**2.301**	48
2.010	46	**2.150**	465	**2.310**	27
2.011	15	**2.151**	55	**2.311**	1,140
2.020	12	**2.161**	66	**2.320**	27
2.021	81	**2.170**	12	**2.321**	27
2.030	435	**2.171**	32	**2.330**	408
2.031	336	**2.180**	20,160	**2.331**	35
2.040	480	**2.181**	1,270	**2.340**	1,024
2.041	60	**2.191**	34	**2.341**	80,640
2.051	126	**2.200**	49	**2.350**	56
2.060	18,432	**2.201**	24	**2.361**	56
2.061	1,820	**2.210**	200	**2.371**	6
2.070	25	**2.211**	0	**2.380**	120
2.071	1,024	**2.220**	33	**2.381**	20
2.080	720	**2.221**	480	**2.400**	3,075
2.081	2,940	**2.230**	210	**2.401**	5,040
2.090	151,200	**2.231**	325	**2.410**	21
2.091	96	**2.240**	256	**2.411**	56
2.100	99	**2.241**	28ft	**2.420**	428
2.101	120	**2.250**	99	**2.421**	386
2.110	10	**2.261**	2,700	**2.430**	90
2.111	15	**2.270**	1	**2.431**	34,650
2.120	3	**2.271**	16	**2.440**	512
2.121	816	**2.280**	120	**2.441**	10
2.130	120	**2.281**	278,208	**2.450**	17
2.131	20,160	**2.291**	360	**2.461**	60
2.140	128	**2.300**	190	**2.471**	382

2.480	336	**2.611**	380	**2.771**	16
2.481	5,400	**2.620**	3	**2.780**	360
2.500	16	**2.621**	100	**2.781**	40
2.501	360	**2.630**	61	**2.800**	900
2.511	100	**2.631**	54	**2.801**	90
2.520	31	**2.640**	5	**2.811**	243
2.521	55	**2.650**	17,576	**2.840**	200
2.530	8	**2.671**	340	**2.850**	18
2.531	2,520	**2.680**	24	**2.880**	180
2.540	1,536	**2.681**	148	**2.881**	252
2.541	256	**2.700**	19	**2.900**	25
2.550	666	**2.701**	117	**2.901**	60,480
2.561	5,376	**2.711**	196	**2.911**	1,020
2.571	386	**2.720**	$n(n-1)/2$	**2.920**	10
2.580	2,520	**2.721**	120	**2.930**	216
2.581	10	**2.731**	1,072	**2.950**	120
2.600	18	**2.740**	10	**2.980**	840
2.601	1,440	**2.750**	768	**2.981**	10,079

2.001 Consider three tiles: $\boxed{F}\boxed{OO}\boxed{T}$. There are 3! = **6** ways to arrange them, and each arrangement will include a double-O.

2.010 $100 = 10^2$ and $10{,}000 = 100^2$, so we are really just looking for the number of even integers between 10 and 100 inclusive. There are $100 - 10 + 1 = 91$ integers. The first and last are even, so there are 46 even (and 45 odd). This gives us **46** even perfect squares.

2.020 22 spotted dogs plus 30 short-haired dogs makes 52 dogs (but there are only 40). This means that 12 dogs must have been counted twice, so at least **12** have short hair and spots.

2.021 There are $99 - 10 + 1 = 90$ two-digit integers. 11, 22, 33, 44, ... 88, and 99 (9 integers) use the same digit twice, so there are $90 - 9 = $ **81** two-digit integers that use two different digits.

2.030 Each point must be connected to 29 other points, so it would appear to take $29 \cdot 30 = 870$ lines, however, connecting point B to A is the same as connecting A to B, so we divide by 2 to eliminate the duplicates and are left with **435** lines.

2.031 The gold can be awarded to 8 different dogs, after which 7 dogs can win silver and 6 can win bronze: $8 \cdot 7 \cdot 6 = \mathbf{336}$ ways.

2.040 3 styles times 8 waist sizes times 10 inseam lengths times 2 colors = **480** different pairs.

2.041 There are 5 choices for the hundreds digit (1, 3, 5, 7, or 9) then 4 for the tens digit and 3 for the ones digit for a total of $5 \cdot 4 \cdot 3 = \mathbf{60}$ whole numbers.

2.051 Consider placing 5 dividers to separate 4 items (each can either be fries, apple pie, onion rings, chicken nuggets, hamburger, or cheeseburger). Using | to represent dividers and o to represent items, one such arrangement of dividers and items would be:

$$|oo||o||o$$

The diagram above represents 0 fries, 2 pies, 0 onion rings, 1 chicken nuggets, 0 hamburgers, and 1 cheeseburger. There are $9C4 = \mathbf{126}$ ways to arrange the four o's between the five dividers (which separate the items into six categories).

2.060 There are $3 \cdot 6 = 18$ ways to choose a lettuce and a dressing. Each of the toppings can either be on the salad or not on the salad, so each topping represents two choices. This gives $2^{10} = 1,024$ ways to add toppings. Multiply by the 18 salad/dressing combinations to get **18,432** possible salads.

2.061 Consider 12 bills and 4 dividers (which separate the bills into five numbered briefcases). There are $16C4$ = **1,820** ways to arrange 4 dividers among 12 bills. (There are 16 objects to arrange, so we can place the 4 dividers in $16C4$ ways).

2.070 $\dfrac{25!}{24!} = \dfrac{25 \cdot \cancel{24} \cdot \cancel{23} \cdot ... \cancel{3} \cdot \cancel{2} \cdot \cancel{1}}{\cancel{24} \cdot \cancel{23} \cdot ... \cancel{3} \cdot \cancel{2} \cdot \cancel{1}} = \mathbf{25}.$

2.071 $\dbinom{10}{0} + \dbinom{10}{1} + \dbinom{10}{2} + ... + \dbinom{10}{0}$ is the sum of the entries in the tenth row of Pascal's triangle: $2^{10} = \mathbf{1,024}$.

2.080 $P(10,3) = 10 \cdot 9 \cdot 8 = \mathbf{720}.$

2.081 The 6 slices can be divided among the 4 students who are not vegetarians. Use 3 dividers and 6 slices which gives us $9C3 = 84$ ways to divide the pepperoni slices. The 3 slices of cheese pizza can be divided among all 5 students. Using 4 dividers and 3 slices we get $7C3 = 35$ ways to distribute the cheese slices. This gives us a total of $35 \cdot 84 = \mathbf{2,940}$ ways to distribute all 9 slices.

2.090 BOOKKEEPER has two O's, two K's, and three E's. There are 10! ways to arrange all ten letters, but many of these arrangements create the same word. The O's can be arranged 2 ways without changing the word, the K's can be arranged 2 ways, and the E's can be arranged $3! = 6$ ways. We divide the 10! arrangements by $(2 \cdot 2 \cdot 6)$ to eliminate duplicates and get **151,200**.

2.091 The three couples can be arranged $3! = 6$ ways on the sofa from left to right, after which each couple can be arranged 2 different ways for a total of $2^3 = 8$ ways. After the couples are seated, there are two places for grandma to be seated (between the first two couples or between the 2nd and 3rd couple). $6 \cdot 8 \cdot 2 = \mathbf{96}$ seating arrangements.

2.100 From 500 to 600 exclusive there are $600 - 500 - 1 = \mathbf{99}$ integers.

2.101 Consider arrangements of the tiles: R EE C I P .
There are 5! = **120** ways to arrange the tiles, each
creating an arrangement which includes a double-E.

2.110 Around a 30-foot circle, you can set **10** place-settings if
they are placed every 3 feet (exactly as you would
expect, this one is not "tricky".)

2.111 This problem (paired with the one before it) was
intended to help you make the discovery that
$C(6,2) = C(6,4)$. Choosing 2 of 6 items can be done
the same number of ways as choosing 4 of 6 (there
will always be 2 left over). $C(6,4) = C(6,2) = $ **15**.

2.120 We can solve this problem with or without a Venn
diagram. The number in the overlapping region will
be counted three times (two extra times). When we
add the number of appetizers, soups, and salads, we
get 16. This is 6
more than the num-
ber of people.
Because no person
ordered just two
items, **3** items must
have been counted
two extra times.

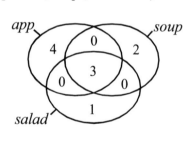

2.121 There are $_7C_4 = 35$ ways to choose four spaces, and
only one of these arrangements does not have any
spaces next to each other (leaving 34 combinations).
Each of these arrangements has 4! ways to assign
coworkers to the spaces, so we have 34(4!) = **816**
ways to assign the four spaces.

2.130 Each of the 16 teams plays 15 games. To avoid
counting games twice (the Cavaliers playing the
Hokies is the same as the Hokies playing the Cavaliers) we divide by 2. $(16 \cdot 15)/2 = $ **120** games.

2.131 PRACTICE has 8 letters with two C's. 8!/2 = **20,160**.

2.140 There are two possible outcomes for each of 7 flips for a total of 2^7 = **128** possible outcomes. Note that HHHTTTT is considered different from TTTTHHH.

2.141 Choosing 3 from a group of 15, there are 15 choices for the first selection, 14 next, and then 13 for the final selection on the team. Picking Al, Bill, and Carly is the same as choosing these three players in any of 3! = 6 arrangements.

$$15C3 = \frac{15 \cdot 14 \cdot 13}{3 \cdot 2 \cdot 1} = \mathbf{455} \text{ possible teams.}$$

2.150 The sum of $1 + 2 + ... + 30 = \dfrac{30(31)}{2} = \mathbf{465}$.

2.151 Three of the roses have already been selected because we know that there must be at least one of each color. This leaves 9 roses to choose from three colors. Place 2 dividers among 9 roses to divide them into red, white, and pink groups. There are $11C2$ = **55** ways to place 2 dividers among 9 roses. (There are 11 objects to arrange, 2 are dividers).

2.161 We place two dividers among 10 points to divide them into groups representing speed, handling, and acceleration. There are $12C2$ = **66** ways to arrange 2 dividers among 10 points (12 items, 2 are dividers).

2.170 $\dfrac{5!}{10} = \dfrac{5 \cdot 4 \cdot 3 \cdot 2}{5 \cdot 2} = \mathbf{12}$

2.171 We look to the odd entries in the 6th row of Pascal's triangle: 1 <u>6</u> 15 <u>20</u> 15 <u>6</u> 1 which represent $6C1$, $6C3$, and $6C5$. The sum of these entries is **32**. Note for future reference that the sum of the odd entries in row n is equal to the sum of the even entries, or half the total: 2^{n-1}.

2.180 $8P6 = 8 \cdot 7 \cdot 6 \cdot 5 \cdot 4 \cdot 3 = \mathbf{20,160}$.

2.181 After the 1 in 1,000,000 there are 6 digits. At first it seems that we can simply place 4 fives $6C4 = 15$ ways and then choose any one of 10 digits for each of the remaining two places $10^2 = 100$ ways for a total of 1,500 ways. However, we over-count when there are more than 4 fives. We must count three cases. When there are exactly four 5's there are $6C4 = 15$ times $9^2 = 81$ ways to fill the remaining two places (with something other than a 5) = 1,215 numbers. With exactly five 5's there are $6C5 = 6$ ways to place the fives and 9 ways to fill the remaining place = 54 numbers. There is only one way to have six 5's. This gives us a total of $1,215 + 54 + 1 = \textbf{1,270}$ numbers.

2.191 There is 1 way that we can arrange all 8 dominoes vertically. If we place dominoes horizontally, they must be placed in pairs (treat the pair as one unit). With one horizontal pair there are 6 vertical dominoes and we have $7C1 = 7$ ways to arrange them. With 2 horizontal pairs, there are 4 remaining vertical dominoes which makes $6C2 = 15$ ways to arrange them. With 3 horizontal pairs, there are 2 remaining vertical dominoes which makes $5C3 = 10$ ways to arrange them. Finally, four horizontal pairs leaves zero vertical dominoes and only 1 way to arrange them. $1 + 7 + 15 + 10 + 1 = \textbf{34}$ ways to arrange the 8 dominoes. Alternatively, we can tie this to the Fibonacci sequence. There

is clearly only one way to tile a 1 by 2 board. On a 2 by 2 board, the dominoes can be placed either vertically or horizontally for a total of 2 ways. If we go to a 3 by 2 board, we can place the first domino vertically leaving a 2 by 2 board (giving us two ways to tile it), or we can place two dominoes horizontally leaving a 1 by 2 board with one way to tile it.

This gives us $1 + 2 = 3$ ways to tile a 2 by 3 board. Moving up to a 4 by 2 board, the first tile can be vertical (leaving a 3 by 2 board with 3 ways to tile it) or horizontal (leaving a 2 by 2 board with 2 possible tilings). This gives $2 + 3 = 5$ possible arrangements. Continue the pattern and you can see that the number of ways to tile an 8 by 2 board is equal to the number of ways to tile a 7 by 2 plus the number of ways to tile a 6 by 2. The pattern is the Fibonacci sequence and we are looking for the 8th term if we start: 1, 2, 3, 5, 8, 13, 21, **34** ...

2.200 Of the 99 integers between 500 and 600, the first and last are odd, meaning there is one more odd than even. There are therefore 50 odds and **49** evens.

2.201 If we place a T at the beginning of the word, we are left with 4, 3, 2, and 1 letter to place 2nd through 5th. There are $4 \cdot 3 \cdot 2 \cdot 1 = $ **24** letter arrangements.

2.210 The problem asks for integers, and consecutive negative integers have a positive product so we cannot forget to count them. We can start with $-100(-99)$ and get all the way up to $99 \cdot 100$. The first integer in each pair can be anywhere from -100 to 99 (inclusive). $99 - (-100) + 1 = $ **200** pairs of consecutive integers whose product is less than 10,000.

2.211 $C(85, 25)$ is equal to $C(85, 60)$, which makes their difference **0**. When you choose 25 items from a set of 85, the leftover items form a set of 60. (See **2.111**)

2.220 There are 27 perfect squares from 1^2 to 27^2. There are 9 perfect cubes from 1^3 to 9^3, however, some of these are also perfect squares and will be counted twice. Any integer raised to the 6th power is both a perfect square and a perfect cube. 1^6, 2^6, and 3^6 are each counted twice. This gives us $27 + 9 - 3 = $ **33** squares and cubes from 1 to 729.

cubes n^6 squares

2.221 It is easier to count the ways in which six friends can line up with Alice and David standing together, and subtract them from the total number of ways the students can stand in line without restrictions. There are 6! = 720 ways that 6 students can line up. If we pair Alice and David together (Alice immediately to the left of David), there are 5! = 120 ways to arrange them. David and Alice can switch places (Alice immediately to the right of David), doubling this number to 240. 720 − 240 = **480** ways.

2.230 $20 + 19 + 18 + \ldots + 1 = \dfrac{20(21)}{2} = $ **210** cans.

2.231 26 students each complete a project with each of 25 other students, however, Dhruv working with Calvin is the same as Calvin working with Dhruv. We must divide by 2 to avoid over-counting:

$$\dfrac{26(25)}{2} = \textbf{325} \text{ projects.}$$

2.240 Because digits may be repeated, there are 4 choices for each digit which gives us $4^4 = $ **256** four-digit numbers.

2.241 Each side includes three sides of 4-inch posts (1 foot) and two 3-foot spaces between them (6 feet). The length of each side is 7 feet, so the perimeter is 4 · 7 = **28** feet.

2.250 Watch-out for overcounting! 99 people each shake the hand of 2 other people, but if we count each of these 198 handshakes, we have counted the handshakes twice. Divide by 2 to get **99**. Consider each person shaking the hand of the person on his/her right in turn. The person whose hand they are shaking is shaking the hand of the person to his/her left.

2.261 Consider each set of bills separately. For the $1 bills, use 2 dividers to separate 4 bills. There are $6C2 = 15$ ways to do this. Use 2 dividers to separate the three $5 bills in $5C2 = 10$ ways. The two $20 bills can be distributed $4C2 = 6$ ways and the $100 bill can be given to any one of the three (3 ways). This gives us $15 \cdot 10 \cdot 6 \cdot 3 = \textbf{2,700}$ ways to distribute the money.

2.270 $\dfrac{20 \cdot 19!}{20!} = \dfrac{20 \cdot 19 \cdot 18 \cdot \ldots \cdot 2 \cdot 1}{20 \cdot 19 \cdot 18 \cdot \ldots \cdot 2 \cdot 1} = \mathbf{1}$

2.271 $\dbinom{9}{5}$ and $\dbinom{9}{6}$ are entries on the 9th row of Pascal's triangle. The sum of these two entries is the entry on row 10 which falls between the two: $\dbinom{10}{6}$.

$10 + 6 = \mathbf{16}$. The rule: $\dbinom{n}{r} + \dbinom{n}{r+1} = \dbinom{n+1}{r+1}$.

2.280 The first digit can be any one of the 6 numbered balls, after which there are 5 left and then 4 remaining for the last draw, for a total of $6 \cdot 5 \cdot 4 = \mathbf{120}$ different 3-digit numbers.

2.281 We are filling the blanks in A _ _ - _ _ _ where the first blank must be filled with one of 24 remaining letters (not A or O), the second blank will be filled with one of 23 letters which remain. The first number can be chosen from among 9 (no 0), the second will be one of the remaining 8, and one of the 7 digits that have not been used will fill the fifth blank. $24 \cdot 23 \cdot 9 \cdot 8 \cdot 7 = \textbf{278,208}$ standard license plates.

2.291 Call the charms A, B, C, D, E, F, and G. Placed in a row, there are 7! ways to order the charms. On a bracelet, however, ABCDEFG is the same as BCDEFGA because the charms can be rotated around the bracelet. We can rotate each arrangement so that charm A is always first. There are then 6! ways to arrange the charms after A, however, the bracelet can also be flipped over, so that the arrangement ABCDEFG is the same as AGFEDCB (see below). We divide 6!
by 2 to get **360** distinct
arrangements of charms
on the bracelet.

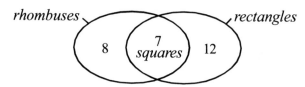

2.300 If the first number is 130, you will add five once to get the 2nd number, twice to get the 3rd number, and so on until you add five 12 times to get the 13th number. $130 + 12(5) = \textbf{190}$.

2.301 There are 2 choices for the first letter (either E or I), after which there are 4 letters available to be the 2nd letter, then 3, 2, and 1 left to finish the word. This gives a total of $2(4!) = 2 \cdot 4 \cdot 3 \cdot 2 \cdot 1 = 48$ possible arrangements.

2.310 There are 33 multiples of 3 ($3 \cdot 1$ through $3 \cdot 33$). Multiples of 3 that are multiples of 5 are multiples of 15. Six multiples of 15 ($15 \cdot 1$ through $15 \cdot 6$) must be excluded to give us **27** whole numbers.

2.311 $20C3 = \textbf{1,140}$.

2.320 A Venn diagram helps us organize. The area in the diagram where rectangles and rhombuses overlap represents squares. Fill this region in first then complete the diagram. All of these shapes are parallelograms. There are **27** parallelograms.

2.321 It is much easier to count the integers less than 50 which are divisible by 3 or 5. There are 16 numbers less than 50 divisible by 3 (3 · 1 through 3 · 16) and 9 which are divisible by 5 (5 · 1 through 5 · 9), however, we have counted multiples of 15 twice: 15, 30, and 45, so we subtract these from the total. This makes $16 + 9 - 3 = 22$ numbers less than 50 that are divisible by 3 or 5. There are 49 integers less than 50, so there are $49 - 22 = \mathbf{27}$ positive integers less than 50 which are not divisible by 3 or 5.

2.330 If we place a "bowling pin" at the center of the triangles as shown, we can see that this is just a bowling pin counting problem. There are 3 toothpicks for each "bowling pin" for a total of:

$$\frac{16(17)}{2} \cdot 3 = \mathbf{408} \text{ toothpicks.}$$

2.331 The mouse must move up 3 times and right 4 times. There are $7C3 = \mathbf{35}$ ways to arrange three "up" moves among 7 total moves.

2.340 There are 2 choices for each of 10 digits, so we have $2^{10} = \mathbf{1,024}$ numbers.

2.341 Whether we start with 27 or 28, there are 7 digits left. There are $8 \cdot 7 \cdot 6 \cdot 5 \cdot 4 \cdot 3 \cdot 2 = 40,320$ ways to fill these digits without replacement. 2 choices for the first pair of digits followed by 40,320 possibilities for the remaining digits gives a total of **80,640** NC zip codes that do not repeat digits.

2.350 For the sum of two numbers to be odd, one must be odd and the other must be even. Each of the 8 odd integers must be connected to each of 7 even integers. $8 \cdot 7 = \mathbf{56}$ lines. Note that there is no need to correct for over-counting in this problem as each case was only counted once.

2.361 There are too many cases to count quickly with casework. Consider placing three dividers among 9 dots, for example, the diagram below would represent rolling a 2, then a 4, then a 2, then a 1 (2 + 4 + 2 + 1 = 9).

●●|●●●●|●●|●

We cannot place a divider at the front or back, and dividers cannot be adjacent. This gives us 8 slots to fill with 3 dividers or 8C3 = **56** ways. None of these includes a number greater than 6, so we do not need to discount any impossible scenarios (below we see a representation of rolling 1, 1, 1, 6).

●|●|●|●●●●●●

2.371 We look for a row in Pascal's triangle in which the sum of the first three entries (0, 1, and 2 heads) is 22. This occurs on row 6, so $n = $ **6**.

$$\binom{6}{0} + \binom{6}{1} + \binom{6}{2} = 1 + 6 + 15 = 22.$$

2.380 5 books can be placed 1st, then 4, 3, 2, and 1. 5! = **120**.

2.381 No two of the numbers rolled can be the same. There are 6C3 = 20 ways to select three numbers (from the six possible) and there is one way to order each of these from least to greatest for white/green/red. This leaves us with just **20** ways.

2.400 The check numbering can be considered an inclusive counting problem. We look for n where $3,474 - n + 1 = 400$. Solving, we get $n = $ **3,075**.

2.401 This is the same as asking for the number of arrangements of the letters in the word BEGINNIG (removing one N to be placed at the front). This leaves 8 letters with two N's, I's, and G's so we have:

$$\frac{8!}{2 \cdot 2 \cdot 2} = \textbf{5,040} \text{ arrangements.}$$

2.410 There are several ways to look at this problem, but drawing each post seems unreasonable. If we place a post at each vertex we are left with 114 posts. 114/6 = 19 additional posts to be placed on each side for a total of **21** on each side when you include the post at each vertex. If we divide 120 by 6 to get 20, we miss the fact that 6 posts are each counted on two sides. Include the missed post to get 21.

2.411 $8C3 = $ **56** leadership teams.

2.420 The trick is to avoid over-counting. The floor value of a number, indicated by $\lfloor x \rfloor$ represents the greatest integer value of x and basically means round down, for example: $\lfloor 9.8 \rfloor = 9$ and $\lfloor 73/11 \rfloor = 6$. There are $\left\lfloor \dfrac{1,000}{5} \right\rfloor = 200$ multiples of 5, $\left\lfloor \dfrac{1,000}{6} \right\rfloor = 166$ multiples of 6, and $\left\lfloor \dfrac{1,000}{7} \right\rfloor = 142$ multiples of 7. If we add these three values to get 508, we will double-count multiples of two of these integers and triple-count multiples of all three. We must subtract multiples of both 5 and 6 (which are multiples of 30): $\left\lfloor \dfrac{1,000}{30} \right\rfloor = 33$, multiples of 5 and 7: $\left\lfloor \dfrac{1,000}{35} \right\rfloor = 28$, and multiples of 6 and 7: $\left\lfloor \dfrac{1,000}{42} \right\rfloor = 23$. By subtracting these we eliminate duplicates, but we have actually removed too many numbers. The numbers which are multiples of 5, 6, *and* 7 have been removed 3 times (we wanted to remove them twice because they were originally triple-counted). We must add back $\left\lfloor \dfrac{1,000}{5 \cdot 6 \cdot 7} \right\rfloor = 4$ integers. (continued)

Summarizing, we have:

$$\left[\frac{1,000}{5}\right]+\left[\frac{1,000}{6}\right]+\left[\frac{1,000}{7}\right]-\left[\frac{1,000}{30}\right]-\left[\frac{1,000}{35}\right]-\left[\frac{1,000}{42}\right]$$

$$+\left[\frac{1,000}{210}\right]=200+166+142-33-28-23+4=\mathbf{428}$$

integer multiples of 5, 6, and/or 7 from 1 to 1,000.

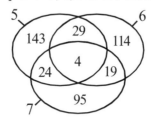

2.421 There are $10C5 = 252$ ways to flip the same number of
heads as tails (choose any 5 of the 10 to be heads),
and $2^{10} = 1,024$ ways to flip a coin 10 times. Half of
the rest of the times there will be more heads than
tails. $(1,024-252)/2 = \mathbf{386}$ ways. Pascal's triangle
can be used for an alternate method (see **p.97**).

2.430 Each vertex can be connected to every other vertex by
a diagonal except that it cannot be connected to itself
or the two adjacent vertices. This means that each
of *n* vertices on a polygon can be connected by a
diagonal to $n-3$ vertices. For a 15-gon, each vertex
will be connected to 12 others by a diagonal. This
gives $15 \cdot 12 = 180$ diagonals, but each has been
counted twice because diagonals AB and BA are the
same. Divide by 2 to get **90** diagonals in a 15-gon.

2.431 MISSISSIPPI has 11 letters with four I's, four S's, and
two P's: $\dfrac{11\,!}{4!\cdot 4!\cdot 2!} = \mathbf{34,650}$ arrangements.

2.440 This is different from the previous problem in that the
first digit must be a 1 (for example: 0,010,101,011 is
not a 10-digit number). There are $2^9 = \mathbf{512}$ ways to
select the other 9 digits.

2.441 Every 6-unit path from the top left corner to the bottom right corner can be covered with three dominoes. Starting from the top we must find a path which goes right twice and down three times. There are $5C2 =$ **10** ways to arrange 2 moves right among 3 down.

2.450 22 isosceles + 25 right triangles = 47 triangles, but there are only 30. We must have counted **17** triangles twice. These triangles are isosceles *and* right.

2.461 The first man must have at least CA on his chest, and the last man must have at least RS. This leaves VALIE for the middle man. You can find all 10 ways to assign VALIE with careful casework or consider placing 2 dividers, each in one of these 6 places: _ V _ A _ L _ I _ E _ . There are $6C2 = 15$ ways, but we cannot have |V|ALIE or V|A|LIE or any of the 5 arrangements which leave just one letter for the middle man. This gives us 10 ways to divide the letters and there are $3! = 6$ ways to choose who stands 1st, 2nd, and 3rd for a total of $10 \cdot 6 = $ **60** ways.

2.471 We look to row 9 of Pascal's triangle to find values for $9C0 + 9C1 + 9C2 + 9C3 + 9C4 + 9C5 = 1 + 9 + 36 + 84 + 126 + 126 = $ **382** combinations of toppings.

2.480 8 students can be chosen as president leaving 7 for vice president and 6 to be chosen as secretary for a total of $8P3 = 8 \cdot 7 \cdot 6 = $ **336** leadership teams.

2.481 $10C2 \cdot 10C3 = 45 \cdot 120 = $ **5,400** choices.

2.500 Besides just counting them on your fingers, this can be solved by counting the number of problems from 10 to 40 inclusive: $40 - 10 + 1 = 31$. You start and end on an even problem so there are more evens than odds: **16** evens and 15 odds.

2.501 There are $6! = 720$ arrangements of the 6 digits. In these 720 arrangements, each can be paired with its palindrome (the same number written in reverse order, like 235,146 and 641,532). Only one of the two will have the 1 to the left of the 2, so we need to divide 720 by 2 to get **360** arrangements.

2.511 Every triangle has either point A or point B as one vertex. Using B as one vertex, we need two more vertices to make a triangle. There are 5 points on segment AK that can be used as vertices of a triangle with vertex B. We can choose 2 of these in $_5C_2 = 10$ ways. The same can be done on AJ, AI, AH, and AG for a total of 50 triangles. Using A we have a symmetrical situation in which 50 triangles have one vertex at A for a total of **100** triangles.

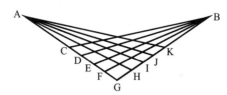

2.520 Using a common denominator, we have 45/60 students who like sweet tea, 36/60 like unsweet tea, and 10/60 like neither. This gives us a total of 91/60, which means that 31/60 of students must like both sweet and unsweet tea. The fewest number of students who could have been surveyed is 60, so at least **31** students must like both.

2.521 There are $8^2 = 64$ possible rolls. It is easier to count rolls which produce a prime number than a composite. A prime product will occur only when one of the dice shows a 1 and the other shows a prime: (1, 2) (1, 3) (1, 5) and (1, 7). These four can all be reversed for a total of 8 rolls which have a product that is prime. Finally (and easy to forget), rolling two ones produces a product that is neither prime nor composite, so we have $64 - 8 - 1 = $**55** rolls.

2.530 If n people shake $n - 2$ hands (they do not shake their spouses hand or their own hand) for a total of 112 handshakes, then $\frac{n(n-2)}{2} = 112$. You can solve the quadratic or guess-check to get $n = 16$, so **8** couples attended.

2.531 There are 7! = 5,040 ways to arrange 1st through 7th place. In exactly half of these arrangements, Raj finishes ahead of Thomas (there are an equal number of arrangements with Thomas ahead as with Raj ahead). 5,040/2 = **2,520** ways.

2.540 It is a common mistake to assume 3 · 9 = 27 pizzas, however, each of the 9 toppings creates two possibilities: it can be included or not included on a pizza. Think of this as filling out a pizza order by putting checks beside the toppings you want. Each of 9 boxes will be checked or not checked for a total of 2^9 = 512 possible topping combinations (including no toppings at all). Now we multiply by the three choices of size. 3 · 512 = **1,536** pizza choices.

2.541 There are 13 lattice points which satisfy $|x| + |y| \le 0$ shown below and then removed from the coordinate plane for clarity:

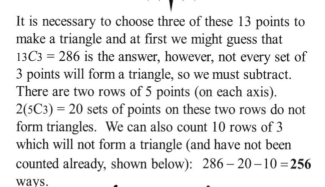

It is necessary to choose three of these 13 points to make a triangle and at first we might guess that $13C3$ = 286 is the answer, however, not every set of 3 points will form a triangle, so we must subtract. There are two rows of 5 points (on each axis). $2(5C3)$ = 20 sets of points on these two rows do not form triangles. We can also count 10 rows of 3 which will not form a triangle (and have not been counted already, shown below): $286 - 20 - 10 = $**256** ways.

(6)   (4)

2.550 There are 499 even integers ($2 \cdot 1$ through $2 \cdot 499$), and 33 multiples of 3 ($3 \cdot 1$ through $3 \cdot 333$). To avoid over-counting, we must subtract from this total any number which is divisible by both 2 and 3 (all multiples of 6). There are 166 multiples of 6 ($6 \cdot 1$ through $6 \cdot 166$) giving us $499 + 333 - 166 = $ **666** positive integers. It seems obvious after the fact that 2 out of 3 positive integers are divisible by 2, 3, or both: 1, $\underline{2}$, $\underline{3}$, $\underline{4}$, 5, $\underline{6}$, 7, $\underline{8}$, $\underline{9}$, $\underline{10}$, 11, $\underline{12}$, 13, $\underline{14}$, $\underline{15}$, ...

2.561 There are $2^8 = 256$ ways to assign 8 arrows either left or right. We must then place gaps between arrows to separate them into words. Consider the set of 8 arrows: >>>>>>>>. There are $7C2 = 21$ ways to choose two spaces in this (or any other) arrangement, giving us $256 \cdot 21 = $ **5,376** code phrases.

2.571 We can have $10C0$, $10C1$, $10C2$, $10C3$ or $10C4$ combinations of teammates depending on how many we want to choose. Look to the 10th row of Pascal's triangle to get these values quickly: $1 + 10 + 45 + 120 + 210 = $ **386** possible combinations of teammates.

2.580 There are 7 choices for your top pick, then 6, 5, 4, and 3 choices: $7 \cdot 6 \cdot 5 \cdot 4 \cdot 3 = $ **2,520** rankings.

2.581 This is tricky casework. The following list has all of the ways that the dots can be placed on 4 faces:

$(6, 0, 0, 0)$ $(5, 1, 0, 0)$
$(4, 2, 0, 0)$ $(4, 1, 1, 0)$
$(3, 3, 0, 0)$ $(3, 2, 1, 0)$ $(3, 1, 1, 1)$
$(2, 2, 2, 0)$ $(2, 2, 1, 1)$

Next, it requires some mental gymnastics to visualize which (if any) of the above can have the dots placed in multiple ways so that the die cannot be rotated to appear the same. For example, it should be clear that only one die can have 6 dots on one face. No matter what face the dots are on, we can place that face down and it will appear like any of the others. The only dot pattern where arrangement matters is the $(3, 2, 1, 0)$ pattern. Consider the face with 0 dots placed on a table. The 3, 2, 1 can be placed in either way shown, and no rotation will make these dice appear the same. This gives us two arrangements for (3, 2, 1, 0) and one of each for the other 8 for a total of **10** distinct dice.

2.600 There are $30 - 10 + 1 = 21$ jerseys. If there are 3 left over, 18 jerseys were handed out to **18** players.

2.601 Consider Molly and Katie as one person and arrange the seven students as if they were 6. There are 6! = 720 ways to do this. Additionally, Katie and Molly can stand in two orders (either KM or MK), doubling the number of arrangements to **1,440**.

2.611 There are $6C3$ = 20 ways to walk 3 blocks north and three blocks west (consider the number of arrangements of NNNWWW). On the way back, he cannot take the same path, so there are 19 paths to choose for the walk back. This gives us $20 \cdot 19 = $ **380** different ways to walk to the deli and back.

2.620 The dealer has 50 cars, but when we add the number of Porches, black cars, and convertibles we get 18 + 25 + 16 = 59 cars. This means that there were 9 over-counts (some twice, some three times). There are 3 black convertibles, 4 black Porches, and 5 convertible Porches. If we subtract these 12 over-counts from 59 we get 47, so we need to add back 3 (because the black convertible Porches would have been subtracted too many times). There are **3** black convertible Porches. The Venn diagram below shows the distribution.

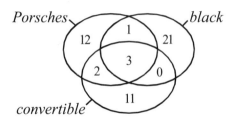

2.621 When we draw five lines with each intersecting the other four, we get $(5 \cdot 4)/2 = 10$ points of intersection (this is a handshake problem). The simplest way to do this is to draw a star. Connecting three of these points to create a triangle requires that we select 3 of the 10 points of intersection $10C3 = 120$ ways, however, there are 5 sets of 4 collinear points (selecting three of these will not make a triangle). We must subtract $5(4C3) = 20$ sets of points which will not form a triangle, leaving us with **100** triangles.

2.630 $1 + 2 + 3 + ... + 59 + 60 = \dfrac{60(61)}{2} = 30(61)$, which gives us a prime factorization of $2 \cdot 3 \cdot 5 \cdot \mathbf{61}$.

2.631 There are $9C3 = 84$ ways to connect the vertices of a nonagon to form a triangle. I find that it is easier to count the isosceles and equilateral triangles: there are 3 types of isosceles triangles (that are not equilateral) for each of the nine vertices of the nonagon. There are also 3 equilateral triangles. This leaves $84 - 3(9) - 3 = \mathbf{54}$ scalene triangles.

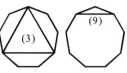

2.640 Somewhat surprisingly, there are only **5**:

2.650 There are 26 letters and repeats are allowed. $26^3 = \mathbf{17,576}$ codes.

2.671 We are looking for $10C3 + 10C6 + 10C9$. These are the 4th, 7th, and 10th entries on the 10th row of Pascal's triangle: $120 + 210 + 10 = \mathbf{340}$ ways.

2.680 4 letters can be 1st, then 3, 2, and 1. 4! = **24** arrangements.

2.681 There are $11C3$ = 165 ways to choose 3 of the 11 points. When three points are collinear they do not form a triangle. Careful counting reveals 9 rows of 3 points and 2 rows of 4.

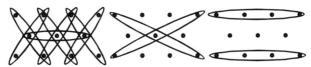

Each row of 4 points has $4C3$ = 4 sets of 3 points which will not form a triangle. This makes a total of 9 + 4 + 4 = 17 sets of 3 points that will not form a triangle. Subtract 17 from 165 to get **148** triangles.

2.700 One slice gives us two pieces, 2 gives us 3, etc. until **19** slices make 20 pieces.

2.701 Put RED on a single tile, then we can arrange the five tiles 5! = 120 ways. RED O R D E , however, we over-count three situations where the word RED appears twice: REDREDO, REDORED, and OREDRED (for example, RED R E D O is the same as R E D RED O). Subtract these three over-counts to get **117** ways.

2.711 There are $12C3$ = 220 ways to choose three of the twelve points. There are 6 rows of 4 points. If three points are chosen which are on the same line, they cannot be connected to form a triangle. For each row of 4 dots there are $4C3$ = 4 sets of points which will not form a triangle. This makes a total of 4 · 6 = 24 sets which will not form a triangle. 220 − 24 = **196** triangles.

2.720 If there are n people, each person will shake $n-1$ hands (every one but his own). We divide by 2 to avoid counting each handshake twice.

The formula is therefore $\dfrac{n(n-1)}{2}$.

2.721 To count the total number of ways to get from A to B, we must go up 4 times and right 6 times. This gives us $10C4 = 210$ ways to get from A to B. There are $4C2 = 6$ ways to get from A to X and $6C2 = 15$ ways to get from X to B. This makes $6 \cdot 15 = 90$ ways to get from A to B through X. Subtract this from 210 to get **120** ways which do not pass through X.

2.731 Of course it is easier to count the rectangles with 1 or fewer red squares. Each of the 64 single squares and the 112 double squares (7 per row, with 8 horizontal and 8 vertical rows) has one or fewer red squares. Finally, there are three triple squares per row which have only one red square (48 total). Subtract these from 1,296 to get **1,072** rectangles with more than one red square.

2.740 Call the faces of the cube: top, bottom, left, right, front, and back. There is 1 cube whose faces are all white. There is 1 cube with 1 black face. There are 2 cubes with 2 black faces: one with the top and bottom black (or any two opposite faces), and one with the top and left black (or any two faces which share an edge). There are 2 cubes with 3 black and 3 white faces: one with top/bottom/front and one with top/left/front. There are 2 cubes with 4 black faces (this is the same as having 2 white faces), 1 with 5 black faces, and 1 with 6 black faces: $1 + 1 + 2 + 2 + 2 + 1 + 1 = \mathbf{10}$ distinct cubes.

2.750 The first digit must be a 1, 2, or 3 (not a 0). Each of the next 4 digits can be a 0, 1, 2, or 3. This gives us $3 \cdot 4 \cdot 4 \cdot 4 \cdot 4 = 3 \cdot 4^4 = \mathbf{768}$ integers.

2.771 The number of ways is given by the entries in Pascal's triangle. Each time you move down a row, there are 2 choices. We go down 4 rows so we have $2^4 = \mathbf{16}$ ways to spell COUNT.

2.780 LADDER has 6 letters with two D's: $\dfrac{6!}{2!} = \textbf{360}$ arrangements.

2.781 This is a massive exercise in casework, and somewhat difficult to show clearly. Below are all the parallelograms with the number of each within (**40 total**).

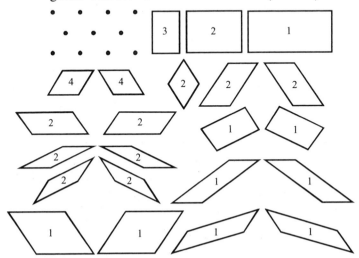

If you find another, please write me on my web site.

2.800 From 100 to 999 there are $999 - 100 + 1 = \textbf{900}$ 3-digit whole numbers.

2.801 Fortunately, there are two D's, two E's and two R's. For a word beginning with D and ending with D, we have to arrange 5 more letters, two of which are E's and two of which are R's: $\dfrac{5!}{2! \cdot 2!} = 30$ words which begin and end with D. There are an equal number which begin and end with E and with R for a total of $3 \cdot 30 = \textbf{90}$ arrangements.

2.811 Every possible pentagon uses one of the three parallel lines on each side. This gives us three choices for each of 5 sides. $3^5 = \textbf{243}$ pentagons.

2.840 First, note that for any four points which form a rectangle, there 4 right triangles:

Now we just need to count rectangles. We have already counted the squares (there are 20 in the example on the same page). Now we look for rectangles that are not squares:

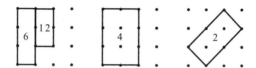

This gives us 44 rectangles (including squares) with four right triangles each, for a total of 176.

Unfortunately, we missed some triangles that are not part of any of these rectangles (in fact, I missed all of the triangles below in the first printing of this book, there are 8 of each type).

This brings our total to **200**.

2.850 My strategy on these problems is to count singles, doubles, triples, etc. (as shown below).

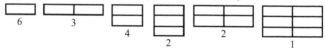

There are a total of **18** rectangles.

2.880 ICICLE has 6 letters with two I's and two C's:

$$\frac{6!}{2!\,2!} = \mathbf{180} \text{ letter arrangements.}$$

2.881 This is a sticks-and-stones problem in disguise. Think of this as distributing "points" to each place value. A number less than 1,000,000 can have a maximum of 6 digits: ones, tens, hundreds, thousands, ten-thousands and hundred-thousands. Use 5 dividers to separate 5 "points" to be distributed among six place values. For example, in the diagram below, points are distributed: 0, 1, 1, 2, 0, 1. This represents the number 11,201. **|•|•|••||•**

There are $_{10}C_5$ ways to arrange 5 dividers and 5 "points". $_{10}C_5 = 252$ numbers.

2.900 There are 7 whole numbers from 0 through 6. Between each of the 6 pairs of consecutive whole numbers there are 3 marks, making 18 additional marks. This gives us a total of **25** marks.

2.901 First, place the principal in one of the three shady spots. This leaves 8 spaces for 6 teachers. There are $_8P_6 = 8 \cdot 7 \cdot 6 \cdot 5 \cdot 4 \cdot 3 = 20,160$ ways for the remaining teachers to park. Multiply this by the three places the principal can park and we get **60,480** ways.

2.911 With 20 vertices, there are $_{20}C_3 = 1,140$ ways to choose three points as vertices of a triangle. There are $_5C_3 = 10$ of these triangles on each of the 12 pentagonal faces, for a total of 120 triangles on the faces of the dodecahedron. Then, from any vertex, you can go in three different directions along the edges to another vertex. We can connect these three vertices to form an equilateral triangle where each side is a face diagonal. There are 20 of these (one per vertex). So, there are a total of $1,140-120-20=$**1,000** triangles.

2.920 Each of the 5 points must be connected by a line to 4 others. We divide by 2 to avoid counting each line twice. $(5 \cdot 4)/2 = $ **10** lines.

2.930 Each roll has 6 possible outcomes for a total of $6^3 =$ **216** possible outcomes.

2.950 Each of the 16 points must be connected by a line to 15 others. We divide by 2 to avoid counting each line twice. $(16 \cdot 15)/2 = $ **120** lines.

2.980 COOKBOOK has 8 letters with four O's and two K's:

$\dfrac{8!}{4! \cdot 2!} = $ **840** arrangements.

2.981 MISSPELL has 8 letters with two S's and two L's.

$\dfrac{8!}{2! \cdot 2!} = 10{,}080$ arrangements, but one of these is the

correct spelling, so there are **10,079** misspellings.

Probability
Key and Solutions

Problems within the text are ordered with the last three digits
reversed. This way, if you are looking for a solution you
will not accidently see the answer to the next problem.

3.010 1/2	**3.260** 19/27	**3.510** 5/36
3.020 144/625	**3.270** 2/5	**3.520** 14/33
3.030 1/12	**3.280** 15	**3.530** 5/32
3.040 5/143	**3.290** 12/47	**3.550** 27/28
3.050 5/6	**3.300** 3/4	**3.560** 234/425
3.060 30/91	**3.310** 1/100	**3.570** $0.133...
3.070 1/4	**3.320** 80/243	**3.580** $1
3.080 6/5 points	**3.330** 5/84	**3.590** 60.7%
3.090 7.75	**3.340** 5/14	**3.600** 1/102
3.100 1/4	**3.350** 3/4	**3.610** 1/2
3.110 1/12	**3.360** 3/7	**3.620** 5/1,296
3.120 35/66	**3.370** 49/81	**3.650** 3/4
3.130 3/35	**3.380** 20	**3.660** 12/35
3.140 9/44	**3.390** 25/648	**3.680** 84
3.150 3/4	**3.400** 11/221	**3.690** 2π units^2
3.160 6/35	**3.410** 5/324	**3.700** 1/52
3.170 1/2	**3.420** 29%	**3.710** 1/720
3.180 $ 239	**3.430** 3/5	**3.750** 11/12
3.190 6/11	**3.440** 34/95	**3.760** 1/2
3.200 1/8	**3.450** 19/49	**3.790** 2/35
3.210 125/729	**3.460** 65.7%	**3.800** 1/26
3.220 20/27	**3.470** 5/8	**3.810** 3/8
3.230 2/27	**3.480** 11.25	**3.890** 24.2%
3.240 2/11	**3.490** 6	**3.900** 2/51
3.250 3/4	**3.500** 44/4,165	**3.990** 3/8

3.010 The toss of a fair coin is independent of prior events. A *fair* coin will always land on heads with a probability of **1/2** regardless of previous outcomes.

3.020 Let O represent a made free-throw and X represent a miss. The probability of making a free throw is 2/5, so the probability of a miss is 3/5. The probability $P(\text{OOOXX})$ of making the first three and missing the last two is:

$$\frac{2}{5}\cdot\frac{2}{5}\cdot\frac{2}{5}\cdot\frac{3}{5}\cdot\frac{3}{5} \text{ and there are } \binom{5}{2}=\frac{5\cdot4}{2} \text{ ways to}$$

arrange the missed shots (for example, OOXOX and XOOOX). Multiplying gives us:

$$\frac{2}{5}\cdot\frac{2}{5}\cdot\frac{2}{5}\cdot\frac{3}{5}\cdot\frac{3}{5}\cdot\frac{5\cdot4}{2}=\frac{144}{625}.$$

3.030 There are $_9C_3 = 84$ ways to choose 3 digits from a set of 9. Of these 84 ways, there are 7 sets of consecutive integers (starting with 1-2-3 and ending with 7-8-9). $7/84 = $ **1/12**.

3.040 There are $_{13}C_5 = 1{,}287$ ways to choose 5 cards from a set of 13. If we have KQJ in the set, we must choose 2 of the remaining 10 cards to complete the set. There are $_{10}C_2 = 45$ ways to complete the set, making the probability $45/1{,}287 = $ **5/143**.

3.050 It is easier to count the number of ways to roll a 4 or less. There is one way (1,1) to roll a 2, there are 2 ways to roll a 3 (1,2) and (2,1), and 3 ways to roll a 4 (1,3), (2,2), and (3,1) for a total of 6 out of the $6^2 = 36$ possible rolls, leaving 30 ways to roll greater than a 4. $30/36 = $ **5/6**.

3.060 Selecting blocks without replacement gives us:

$$\frac{10}{14}\cdot\frac{9}{13}\cdot\frac{8}{12}=\frac{30}{91}.$$

3.070 If point X is selected within the shaded area, the height of triangle ABX will be greater than 4 times the height of triangle BCX, making its area greater than twice that of triangle BCX (its base is half that of triangle BCX). The shaded area is **1/4** the total area.

3.080 Guessing randomly on 5 questions, you could expect to be correct once, earning 6 points. This gives each guess an expected value of **6/5** or **1.2** points.

3.090 We will do digit sums and expected value for the months and years separately to simplify things. The expected value for the digit sum of a month is $(1 + 2 + 3 + ... + 9) + (1 + 0) + (1 + 1) + (1 + 2) = 51$. Because each month occurs the same number of times we just divide this by 12 to get 4.25. The expected value for the digit sum of a year between 10 and 15 is $[(1 + 0) + (1 + 1) + (1 + 2) + (1 + 3) + (1 + 4) + (1 + 5)]/6 = 21/6 = 3.5$. The expected sum of the digits is therefore $4.25 + 3.5 = \textbf{7.75}$.

3.100 There are 13 hearts in a standard deck of 52 cards, so the probability of drawing a heart is $13/52 = \textbf{1/4}$.

3.110 The probability of rolling a 5 on the red die is 1/6 and the probability of an even number on the green die is 1/2, making the probability of a 5 on red and even on green: $\dfrac{1}{6} \cdot \dfrac{1}{2} = \dfrac{1}{12}$.

3.120 There are $12C2 = 66$ ways to select 2 representatives. With 7 boys and 5 girls there are 7 choices for the boy and 5 for the girl, or $7 \cdot 5 = 35$ different pairs, making the probability 35/66. Alternatively, we find the probability of selecting boy then a girl and add it to the probability of selecting a girl then a boy:
P(Boy, Girl) = (7/12)(5/11) = 35/132 and
P(Girl, Boy) = (5/12)(7/11) = 35/132, so P(Boy, Girl *or* Girl, Boy) = 35/132 + 35/132 = **35/66**.

3.130 There are $8C4 = 70$ ways to select 4 of the 8 vertices. Only 6 of these combinations form rectangles (shown), making the probability 6/70 or **3/35**.

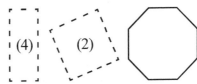

3.140 There are $12C3 = 220$ ways to select three students from a group of 12. If Adam is selected, there are 10 students left (excluding Billy) and we need to choose two to pair with Adam. $10C2 = 45$ pairs can be selected, meaning there are 45 groups of 3 students which include Adam but not Billy out of the 220 possible groups. $45/220 = \textbf{9/44}$.

3.150 There are $4! = 24$ ways to arrange the digits. To be divisible by 4, the integer formed must end in either 12, 24, or 32. Two of each of these makes 6 numbers divisible by 4: 3,412; 4,312; 1,324; 3,124; 1,432; and 4,132. This means there are 18 out of the 24 that are not divisible by 4 or **3/4**.

3.160 There are $8C4 = 70$ ways to select 4 of the 8 vertices of a cube. For all four points to be on the same plane, they can all be on the same face (6 ways), or on one of 6 diagonal planes slicing through the cube (one is shown). $12/70 = \textbf{6/35}$.

3.170 The larger shaded ring has an area of $(6^2 - 5^2)\pi = 11\pi$ and the smaller ring has an area of $(4^2 - 3^2)\pi = 7\pi$, for a combined area of 18π. The entire circle has an area of 36π, making the probability of landing in a shaded area **1/2**.

3.180 $\$0 + \$2 + \$10 + \$50 + \$100 + \$250 + \$1,000 = \$1,912$. $\$1912/8 = \textbf{\$239}$.

3.190 Think of the game playing out in rounds. Each round consists of each player taking a roll (of course, Ben may lose before his roll in any given round). Alice has a 1/6 chance of rolling a 6 to win the game on the first roll of each round. The probability that Ben will win a round requires that Alice not roll a 6 (and Ben must roll a 6). This will occur with probability (5/6)(1/6) = 5/36. If no one wins a round, a new round begins and this continues until someone wins. Alice will win 1 of 6 (or 6 of 36) rounds, while Ben will win 5 of 36 rounds. The ratio of Alice's wins to losses (odds) is therefore 6:5, making the probability of Alice winning: **6/11** (with Ben winning 5 of 11 games).

3.200 With replacement, the probability that each selected card will be red is 1/2. $(1/2)^3 =$ **1/8**.

3.210 The probability of drawing an odd digit from the digits 1 through 9 is 5/9. We multiply this three times:

$$\left(\frac{5}{9}\right)^3 = \frac{125}{729}.$$

3.220 The probability of flipping tails on a single toss is 2/3. The probability of flipping three tails in a row is $(2/3)^3$ = 8/27. There are three ways to flip two tails and a heads (TTH, THT, and HTT). The probability of each is $(1/3)(2/3)^2 =$ 4/27. Multiply this by three to get 12/27. The probability of flipping more tails than heads is the combined probability of flipping two or three tails on three tosses. 8/27 + 12/27 = **20/27**.

3.230 The total number of ways colors can be chosen for the flag is $3^4 = 81$ (four stripes can each be one of three colors). Now look at the ways that we can choose colors where no two same-colored stripes share an edge. Begin by choosing any of the 3 colors for the vertical stripe. Once we choose a color for this stripe, none of the other stripes can be the same color. We can pick 1 of the 2 remaining colors for the middle horizontal stripe. The remaining stripes must both be the remaining color. This gives us only $3! = 6$ ways that no two same-colored stripes can share an edge. $6/81 = \mathbf{2/27}$.

3.240 There are many ways to approach this problem: First, the probability of two girls being in any one group is:

$3\left(\dfrac{2}{12} \cdot \dfrac{1}{11} \cdot \dfrac{10}{10}\right) = \dfrac{1}{22}$ (the three is there because the

group may be selected GGB, GBG, or BGG). There are four groups, making the probability 2/11. Alternatively, there are $12C3 = 220$ ways to form a group and 10 ways to form a group with the two girls (2 girls plus 1 of the 10 remaining boys) for a probability of 1/22 that any one of the groups has both girls. Once again, 4 groups quadruples this probability to give us 2/11. Finally (and perhaps easiest), consider the probability that one of the girls has already been assigned to a group. 2 of the 11 available spaces are in her group, making the probability **2/11** that the second girl is placed with the first.

3.250 There are $2^3 = 8$ ways to flip 2 coins. Only HHH and TTT do not show at least one tails or one heads, so there are 6 of 8 possibilities which show at least one of each, making the probability **3/4**.

3.260 The toast will land buttered-side down 2/3 of the time. At least one piece will land buttered-side up as long as all three pieces do not land buttered-side down. The probability that all three will land buttered-side down is $(2/3)^3 = 8/27$. Subtract this from 1 to get **19/27**.

3.270 Consider the triangle in the orientation shown. Triangles CXB and AXB have the same height (the perpendicular from B to the hypotenuse of triangle ABC). The ratio of their bases CX:AX = 2:3, so the ratio of their areas is $2h$:$3h$ or 2:3, making the shaded area 2/5 of the total area and the probability of a random point inside the triangle being selected within the shaded region is **2/5**.

3.280 The sum of the first nine digits is $\dfrac{9(10)}{2} = 45$, making the average of any row or column 45/3 = 15. The sum of each diagonal is 15 as well, so the expected value is **15**.

3.290 The surface area of the prism is $2(3 \cdot 4) + 2(3 \cdot 5) + 2(4 \cdot 5) = 94\,\text{cm}^2$, and the small faces have a combined area of $2(3 \cdot 4) = 24\,\text{cm}^2$. The probability of a randomly selected point being on one of the two smaller faces is therefore 24/94 = **12/47**.

3.300 Your first selection can be any card from the deck. The probability that the second card will be from a different suit is 39/52 = **3/4**.

3.310 There are $10^3 = 1{,}000$ possible combinations of three digits for the last 3 digits of a phone number (000 through 999), and only 10 have the same three digits, so the probability is 10/1,000 or 1/100. Alternatively, the first digit doesn't matter. The probability of each of the next digits being the same as the first is 1/10, which gives us $(1/10)^2 = \mathbf{1/100}$.

3.320 A student will select a chocolate chip cookie with a probability of 2/3. Using C for chocolate chip and O for oatmeal, the probability that the first three students will choose chocolate chip followed by two students selecting oatmeal is:

$$P(\text{CCCOO}) = \left(\frac{2}{3}\right)^3\left(\frac{1}{3}\right)^2 = \frac{8}{243},$$ but there are

$_5C_2 = 10$ ways to arrange CCCOO, making the probability **80/243**.

3.330 There are $_9C_3 = 84$ combinations of 3 numbers. Only two common factors greater than 1 are possible: 2 and 3. There are 4 even numbers, and $_4C_3 = 4$ possible sets of 3 even numbers. There is one set of three numbers which have 3 as a common factor {3,6,9}. This means that there are 5 out of 84 combinations of 3 numbers which share a common factor greater than 1: **5/84** is the probability of selecting one of these sets.

3.340 For a set of three numbers to have a product that is odd, all of the numbers must be odd. The question is therefore: What is the probability that one of the sets contains only odd numbers? There are $_9C_3 = 84$ combinations of 3 numbers and $_5C_3 = 10$ combinations of 3 odd numbers. The probability of any one set containing only odd numbers is 10/84 or 5/42, and there are three sets, which makes the probability $3(5/42) = 15/42 = $ **5/14**.

3.350 It is easiest to calculate the probability that the product is odd, which requires that both rolls be odd. The probability of rolling an odd number is 1/2, so the probability of rolling two odds in a row is $(1/2)^2 = 1/4$. Subtract this from 1 to get the probability that the product of the two rolls is even: **3/4**.

3.360   There are 8 vertices of a cube, which means there are $8C3 = 56$ ways to connect three of the vertices to form a triangle. There are $4C3 = 4$ possible triangles on each of 6 faces for a total of 24 out of 56 triangles: $24/56 = \mathbf{3/7}$.

3.370   Consider the area of quadrilateral ABXD as the sum of the areas of triangles ADX and ABX. Each has a base length 3, so the sum of the heights of the triangles must be 8/3 for the combined area to be greater than 4 (X must be anywhere within the shaded area). The area of the unshaded triangle is $(1/2)(8/3)^2 = 32/9$ and the area of the entire figure is 81/9, making the shaded area 49/9. The probability that point X is within the shaded area is therefore

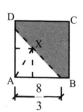

$$\frac{49/9}{81/9} = \mathbf{49/81}.$$

3.380   The expected value is the average value of the bills in the bag. Let x represent \$1 bills and y represent \$5 bills: $x + 5y$ is the total value and $x + y$ is the number of bills:
$\frac{x+5y}{x+y} = 1.2$, so $x + 5y = 1.2x + 1.2y$. We will solve for the ratio x/y: $3.8y = 0.2x$ gives us $\frac{3.8}{0.2} = \frac{x}{y} = \frac{19}{1}$, so there must be a minimum of **20** bills in the bag (one \$5 bill and nineteen \$1 bills).

3.390   There are $6^5 = 7{,}776$ ways to roll a set of 5 dice. We will use **XXXOO** to represent the full house, where **X** represents one number rolled and **O** represents a different number. There are $5C2 = 10$ arrangements of **XXXOO**, and we can choose from 6 numbers to use for **X** and 5 are left for **O**. This gives us $10 \cdot 6 \cdot 5 = 300$ of the 7,776 ways, or a probability of **25/648**.

3.400 There are 3 face cards in each suit for a total of 12 face cards in a deck of 52 cards. The probability that the top card is a face card is 12/52, and if the top card is a face card, the probability that the second card is a face card is 11/51. The probability that both are face cards is:

$$\frac{12}{52} \cdot \frac{11}{51} = \frac{11}{221}.$$

3.410 There are $6^6 = 46{,}656$ possible rolls. The first roll can be any of the first 6 digits, after which there are only 5 available rolls, then 4, 3, 2, and 1, meaning there are 6! ways to roll a 1-6 in any order:

$$\frac{6!}{6^6} = \frac{\cancel{6} \cdot 5 \cdot 4 \cdot \cancel{3} \cdot \cancel{2}}{\cancel{6} \cdot 6 \cdot 6 \cdot \underset{3}{\cancel{6}} \cdot \underset{3}{\cancel{6}} \cdot \cancel{6}} = \frac{5}{324}$$

3.420 The probability of rain expressed as a fraction is 2/5 (and the probability that it will not rain is 3/5), so the probability of three rainy days in a week is

$$\left(\frac{2}{5}\right)^3 \cdot \left(\frac{3}{5}\right)^4 = \frac{647}{78{,}125}.$$ We must multiply this by the number of ways to arrange these three rainy days in a 7-day week: $7C3 = 35$, so $35 \cdot \dfrac{647}{78{,}125} \approx \mathbf{29\%}$.

3.430 There are $7C3 = 35$ ways to connect three of the vertices to form a triangle. We can use any vertex of the heptagon as the apex angle for three different isosceles triangles for a total of 21 possible isosceles triangles (out of 35). This makes the probability **3/5**.

3.440 There are $20C3 = 1,140$ sets of 3 students who can be chosen from a group of 20. We are looking to form a group with 1 vegetarian and 2 non-vegetarians. There are $3C1 = 3$ ways to choose the vegetarian and $17C2 = 136$ ways to choose the non-vegetarians, for a total of $3 \cdot 136 = 408$ ways to form a group with one vegetarian and two non-vegetarians, which gives us a probability of $408/1,140 = 34/95$.
Alternatively, The probability of selecting vegetarian, non-vegetarian, non-vegetarian in that order is:

$\dfrac{3}{20} \cdot \dfrac{17}{19} \cdot \dfrac{16}{18} = \dfrac{34}{285}$, and we can arrange these picks

three different ways (the veg. can be 1st, 2nd, or 3rd),

which gives us: $3 \cdot \dfrac{34}{285} = \dfrac{34}{95}$.

3.450 We will find the probability that no two dates fall on the same day of the week and subtract this from 1. The first date selected can be on any one of the seven days. The second date must fall on one of the six remaining days, and the third date must fall on one of the remaining 5 days for a probability of:

$\dfrac{7}{7} \cdot \dfrac{6}{7} \cdot \dfrac{5}{7} = \dfrac{30}{49}$, making the probability that at least two

of the dates fall on the same day of the week

$1 - \dfrac{30}{49} = \dfrac{19}{49}$.

3.460 There is a 70% chance that it will not snow on each of the next three days. The probability that it will not snow at all is $(0.7)^3 = 0.343$ or 34.3%. This leaves a probability that it will snow at least once:
$1 - 0.343 = 0.657 = \mathbf{65.7\%}$.

3.470 The remaining sides of the triangle must have a sum that is greater than 5 and a difference that is less than 5 as represented by the shaded area in the graph below. The shaded area is **5/8** the total area.

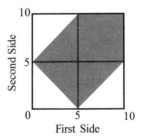

3.480 To solve this problem, we will solve for each of the four digits on a digital clock separately (2:34 will be considered 02:34). The digit farthest to the left will be a 1 for 3 out of 12 hours, for an expected digit value of 0.25. The next (hours) digit will be 1, 2, 3, 4, 5, 6, 7, 8, 9, 0, 1, 2 for equal amounts of time for an expected value of 48/12 = 4. The next digit will be 0, 1, 2, 3, 4, and 5 with equal frequency for an expected value of 2.5. Finally, the minutes digit will be 0 through 9 with equal frequency for an expected value of 4.5. The expected value for the sum of the digits is the sum of the expected values for each digit: 0.25 + 4 + 2.5 + 4.5 = **11.25**.

3.490 For the product of two integers to be odd, both integers must be odd. If there are three odd integers, then there are $_3C_2 = 3$ combinations of two odd integers, and this is 1/5 the total number of combinations. There must be 15 total combinations. $_6C_2 = 15$ so there are **6** integers in the set altogether (3 odd and 3 even).

3.500 The first card can be of any suit. The next three cards must be of the same suit as the first, so we have:

$$\frac{52}{52} \cdot \frac{12}{51} \cdot \frac{11}{50} \cdot \frac{10}{49} = \frac{44}{4,165}$$

3.510 The modified die will have faces with 2, 3, 4, 5, 6, and 7 dots. There will still be 36 possible rolls with a pair of the modified dice. Of those 36 rolls, 5 will show an 8: (2,6), (3,5), (4,4), (5,3), (6,2), making the probability of rolling an 8: **5/36**.

3.520 The probability of selecting two blue socks then two black socks is found by:

$$\frac{7}{12} \cdot \frac{6}{11} \cdot \frac{5}{10} \cdot \frac{4}{9} = \frac{7}{99},$$ and there are $_4C_2 = 6$ ways to

arrange the order of two black and two blue socks. Multiplying, we get a probability of:

$$6 \cdot \frac{7}{99} = \frac{14}{33}.$$

Alternatively, there are $_{12}C_4 = 495$ ways to choose 4 socks from a set of 12. There are $_7C_2 = 21$ ways to choose two of the blue socks and $_5C_2 = 10$ ways to choose two black socks, which makes $21 \cdot 10 = 210$ ways to choose 2 blue and two black socks from the drawer. $210/495 = $ **14/33**.

3.530 Call the six faces of the cube: top, bottom, left, right, front, and back. With six faces and two choices of color for each face, there are $2^6 = 64$ ways to paint the faces of the cube. Of these 64 ways, there is one way to paint every face white, there are six ways to paint one face black, and three ways to paint two faces black so that no two black faces share an edge (front/back, left/right, or top/bottom). This makes 10 out of 64 ways, or a probability of **5/32**.

3.550 It is much simpler to calculate the probability that all three are the same color. There are three blocks of each color, so the probability is the same for each:

$$\frac{3}{9} \cdot \frac{2}{8} \cdot \frac{1}{7} = \frac{1}{84}.$$ Multiply this by 3 because there are

three colors to get 1/28. The probability that no two

blocks will be different colors is 1/28, so the probability that at least two will be different colored is **27/28**.

3.560 In any suit, there are 13C2 = 78 ways to select two cards, and there are 39 cards that can complete the set, making 78 · 39 = 3,042 ways to create a set with two cards from a given suit and one card from outside that suit. There are four suits, giving us 3,042 · 4 = 12,168 ways. There are 52C3 = 22,100 ways to choose three cards from a set of 52. Simplifying 12,168/22,100 give us **234/425**. Alternatively, consider the probability of choosing two cards of a given suit followed by one from a different suit:

$\frac{13}{52} \cdot \frac{12}{51} \cdot \frac{39}{50} = \frac{39}{850}$. There are three ways to order the selection of the suits (two hearts and a "not heart" can be selected HHX, HXH, or XHH). We must also multiply by the 4 choices for the suit that has two cards. This gives us:

$3 \cdot 4 \cdot \frac{39}{850} = \frac{468}{850} = \frac{234}{425}$. With either method, this is an easy problem to mess up.

3.570 Let's start with a scenario using 64 pennies to see if we can find a pattern. If you insert 64 pennies, you can expect to get back 16 each of pennies, nickels, dimes, and quarters, for a total of 16($0.40) + 16 pennies to reinsert. When you reinsert the 16 pennies, you can expect to get back 4 of each coin for a total of 4($0.40) + 4. Finally, inserting the four pennies you can expect to get back $0.40 + a penny. We see that the expected value of 64 pennies is 16($0.40) + 4($0.40) + 1($0.40) + 1 penny.

Now, let's use this pattern to solve for *n* pennies: For every *n* pennies inserted, we can expect to get:

$$\frac{n}{4}(0.40) + \frac{n}{16}(0.40) + \frac{n}{64}(0.40) + \ldots$$

$$= n(0.10) + \frac{n}{4}(0.10) + \frac{n}{16}(0.10) + \ldots$$

$$= 0.10n\left(1 + \frac{1}{4} + \frac{1}{16} + \frac{1}{64}\ldots\right).$$ The infinite series in

parenthesis is equal to $\dfrac{4}{3}$ (see **p.56**), so we have

$0.10n\left(\dfrac{4}{3}\right) = 0.1\bar{3}n$. The expected value of each

penny is $0.40/3 = **\$0.1\bar{3}**$.

3.580 There are 12 blocks, so there are $12C2 = 66$ ways to
draw two blocks. Assume you draw all 66 possible
pairs. There are $4C2 = 6$ ways to draw two red and
$5C2 = 10$ ways to draw two blue blocks (earning $48
total) and there are $3C2 = 3$ ways to draw two white
blocks (earning $18). In 66 draws, you could expect
to win $66 for an expected value of **\$1**.

3.590 If point X is selected on the semicircle,
angle AXB will be a right angle
(see inscribed angles **p.185-186**). If X is
chosen utside of the semicircle the
angle will be acute. Inside the circle, the angle will
be obtuse. Use 4cm for the side of the square. The
area of the semicircle is 2π cm^2 and the area of the
square is 16cm^2. The shaded area is therefore
$(16 - 2\pi)$ cm^2 and the probability that point X will be
within the shaded area is:

$$\frac{16 - 2\pi}{16} \approx **60.7\%**.$$

3.600 There are 2 red aces in a 52-card deck. If the top card is a red ace, 13 of the remaining 51 cards are spades: $\dfrac{2}{52} \cdot \dfrac{13}{51} = \dfrac{1}{102}$.

3.610 The units digit of each integer can be odd or even, with equal probability. For the sum of the three units digits to be even, we can have either 2 odd digits and 1 even digit: {O,O,E}, {O,E,O}, or {E,O,O}, or we can have 3 even digits: {E,E,E}. There are $2^3 = 8$ possibilities (think of this as counting coin flips, where each flip determines whether the units digit is odd or even), which makes the probability that the sum is even 4/8 = **1/2**.

3.620 There are 6^6 possible outcomes for six rolls of a standard die. Consider **OOOOOX** as a representation of five of the same digit and one different digit. There are 6 ways to arrange **OOOOOX**, six numbers to select for the **O**, and five numbers to select for the **X**. This gives us: $\dfrac{6 \cdot 6 \cdot 5}{6^6} = \dfrac{5}{6^4} = \dfrac{5}{1{,}296}$.

3.650 We will look for the probability that A and B end up in the same pile. There are $9C3 = 84$ ways to choose 3 of 9 letters for a pile. There are 7 possible sets that include A, B, and one of the remaining 7 letters. This makes the probability that any pile of 3 letters will include both A and B 7/84 = 1/12. There are 3 piles, so the probability that 1 of 3 piles will include both A and B is 3(1/12) = 3/12 or 1/4. The probability that A and B will be in different piles is therefore $1 - 1/4 =$ 3/4. Alternatively, place the A first:

$$\text{A}\_\ \_ \quad \_\ \_\ \_ \quad \_\ \_\ \_ \quad \_\ \_\ \_$$

This leaves 8 places for the B. 2 of those places are in the same pile as the A, while 6 are in one of the other piles. 6/8 = **3/4**.

3.660 There are 7C3 = 35 possible combinations. We are looking for combinations whose sum is prime. Be methodical. The smallest possible sum is 9 and the largest possible sum is 21. Primes between 9 and 21 are 11, 13, 17, and 19. Look for ways to get each:
11 = 2+4+5 = 2+3+6 (2 ways),
13 = 2+5+6 = 2+4+7 = 2+3+8 = 3+4+6 (4 ways),
17 = 2+7+8 = 3+6+8 = 4+6+7 = 4+5+8 (4 ways),
19 = 4+7+8 = 5+6+8 (2 ways).
This gives us a total of 12 out of 35 sums that are prime, or a probability of **12/35**.

3.680 Call the number of $1 and $2 tokens x. The total value of all the tokens is $x + 2x + 18(5) = 3x + 90$. The total number of tokens is $2x + 18$, therefore:
$\dfrac{3x + 90}{2x + 18} = 2.25$, so $3x + 90 = 4.5x + 40.5$. Solving for x we get $x = 33$. There are $33 + 33 + 18 = $ **84** tokens in the bag.

3.690 Call the smallest radius a, the medium radius b, and the largest radius c. The shaded area must equal half the entire area:

$$\pi(b^2 - a^2) = \frac{\pi c^2}{2}, \text{ or } b^2 - a^2 = \frac{c^2}{2}.$$

This simplifies the guess-and-check process, as we look for a difference of squares that is equal to half a perfect square. When $a = 1$, $b = 3$, and $c = 4$:
$3^2 - 1^2 = 4^2 / 2$. The radii can be 1, 3, and 4. However, the problem states that we only need integral diameters. We can use diameters $a = 1$, $b = 3$, $c = 4$ and maintain the proportions of the figure. The shaded area then becomes half the area of the largest circle: $\dfrac{\pi(2)^2}{2} = 2\pi$ units².

3.700 There are two cases to consider: the first card can be an ace of spades, or an ace from another suit. If the ace is the ace of spades, the probability is:

$$\frac{1}{52}\cdot\frac{12}{51}=\frac{12}{52\cdot51}.$$

If the top card is the ace of another suit we have:

$$\frac{3}{52}\cdot\frac{13}{51}=\frac{39}{52\cdot51}.$$

Added together (now you see why I didn't multiply the $52\cdot51$):

$$\frac{51}{52\cdot51}=\frac{1}{52}.$$

3.710 There are $6! = 720$ ways to arrange 6 students in order, and only one of these ways seats the students from oldest to youngest, so the probability is **1/720**.

3.750 Start by placing the 3. Any arrangement can be rotated so that the three is located on top. When we place the three on top, this leaves 4 blanks to fill with 4 integers for $4! = 24$ possible ways to complete the diagram. To avoid consecutive integers, we can have a 1 and a 5 connected to the three as shown in two ways with the 2 and the 4 forced (depending on the placement of the 1 and the 5). This gives us just 2 ways to avoid consecutive integers (shown), so there are $22/24 =$ **11/12** arrangements with at least one connected pair of consecutive integers.

3.760 Consider the question, "What is the probability that there are more tails showing than heads?". The answer to both questions must be the same, and it is impossible to flip an equal number of heads and tails with 27 flips. The answer must therefore be **1/2**.

3.790 There are $8C2 = 28$ ways to choose the first pair of vertices, and $6C2 = 15$ ways to select the second pair of vertices, and because we can switch the order of the selection (the first pair can be selected second), we find that there are $(28 \cdot 15)/2 = 210$ ways to connect two pairs of two vertices. Alternatively, there are $8C4 = 70$ ways to choose four vertices (call these four A, B, C, and D) after which we can connect A to any of the three other vertices (then connecting the remaining pair) to get $70 \cdot 3 = 210$. Intersecting vertices can either intersect in the center of the cube or at the center of one of the six faces. There are 6 pairs which have their intersection on a face. There are 4 diagonals which pass through the center of the cube. We can choose any two of these for $4C2 = 6$ possible combinations of diagonals which intersect at the center of the cube, bringing the total to 12 out of $210 = \mathbf{2/35}$.

3.800 There are two cases to consider: the ace can be an ace of spades, or an ace from another suit. We multiply by 2 because the ace can be the top card or the second card. If the ace is the ace of spades, the probability is:

$$2 \cdot \frac{1}{52} \cdot \frac{12}{51} = \frac{24}{52 \cdot 51}.$$

If the ace is of another suit:

$$2 \cdot \frac{3}{52} \cdot \frac{13}{51} = \frac{78}{52 \cdot 51}.$$

Added together: $\dfrac{102}{52 \cdot 51} = \dfrac{2}{52} = \dfrac{1}{26}.$

3.810 The product will be positive if the two spins are either both positive or both negative.

$$P(\text{both positive}) = \frac{1}{2} \cdot \frac{1}{4} = \frac{1}{8}.$$

$$P(\text{both negative}) = \frac{1}{2} \cdot \frac{1}{2} = \frac{1}{4}.$$

Add these together to get a probability of **3/8**.

3.890 If there is a 75% chance that it will erupt within the next 5 years, then there is a 25% chance that it will not erupt. This means that if n is the probability (expressed as a decimal) that it will not erupt during each of the five years, then $n^5 = 0.25$. $\sqrt[5]{0.25} \approx 0.758$ gives us a probability of about 75.8% each year that it will not erupt, so the probability of eruption during each of the five years is about **24.2%**.

3.900 There are 13 pairs of consecutive cards in each suit (Ace-2 through King-Ace) for a total of 52 pairs of consecutive cards. There are $52C2 = (52 \cdot 51)/2$ combinations that could be the top two cards of a

shuffled deck: $\dfrac{52}{(52 \cdot 51)/2} = \dfrac{52}{26 \cdot 51} = \dfrac{2}{51}.$

Alternatively, for any top card, 2 of the remaining 51 cards in the deck are consecutive. **2/51**.

3.990 Do not be fooled into solving this by counting the number of paths from A to B which pass through X (36) and dividing by the total number of paths from A to B (70). Coin flips create the probabilities shown, as each intersection offers two equally likely choices.

There are two points from which Jennifer can walk to X, each has a 3/8 probability of being reached with Jennifer's coin flip method. Half of the time from each point she will travel to X:

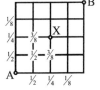

$$\frac{1}{2}\left(\frac{3}{8} + \frac{3}{8}\right) = \frac{3}{8}.$$

Number Theory
Key and Solutions

Problems within the text are ordered with the last three digits
reversed. This way, if you are looking for a solution you
will not accidently see the answer to the next problem.

4.001 abundant		**4.110** 2	
4.002 2		**4.111** GCF: 16, LCM: 560	
4.010 907,654 & 14,256		**4.112** $0.0\overline{2}$	
4.011 GCF: 15, LCM: 180		**4.120** 4	
4.012 $0.4\overline{1}$		**4.121** 4	
4.020 8		**4.122** 1	
4.021 6		**4.130** 7	
4.022 5		**4.131** 60	
4.030 $41 \cdot 7$, $17 \cdot 23$, prime		**4.132** i	
4.031 42		**4.140** 12	
4.032 4		**4.141** 720	
4.040 72: 12 180: 18		**4.142** 3	
210: 16 112: 10		**4.150** 9	
4.041 31		**4.151** 37	
4.042 199		**4.152** 1/2	
4.050 20		**4.160** 315	
4.051 16		**4.170** 9, 196, 14, 14, 9th	
4.052 15		**4.171** 16	
4.060 280		**4.180** a^b	
4.061 1		**4.181** $436,000_8$	
4.070 12, 6, 96, 96, 6th		**4.190** 8	
4.071 $5,000,200_8$		**4.191** 4	
4.080 $3^6 \cdot 5^3$		**4.200** 2, 3, 4, 5, 6, 9, 10	
4.081 250_8		**4.201** deficient	
4.090 50: 93		**4.202** 0	
405: 726		**4.210** 23,232	
210: 576		**4.211** GCF: 7, LCM: 420	
4.091 83,195,146		**4.212** $0.0\overline{71}$	
4.100 2, 3, 4, 6, 8		**4.220** 4	
4.101 deficient		**4.221** Wed.	
4.102 0		**4.222** 7/90	

4.231 19,344

4.232 6

4.240 48

4.241 19

4.242 11,232

4.250 12

4.251 4

4.252 37/150

4.260 720

4.271 a. 83 b. 5
      c. 511

4.280 4

4.281 666_8

4.290 a. 127 b. 255
      c. 511 d. $2^{31} - 1$

4.291 68

4.301 abundant

4.310 99,990

4.311 105

4.312 $0.\overline{06}$

4.320 3,312

4.321 60

4.322 21

4.331 3,600

4.332 26

4.340 9

4.341 409

4.342 6

4.350 9

4.351 1,067

4.352 8,748

4.371 215

4.380 9

4.381 $1,110_6$

4.390 7^3 or 343

4.391 5

4.401 perfect

4.410 8

4.411 36

4.412 $0.0\overline{45}$

4.420 18

4.421 16

4.422 $0.\overline{471}$

4.431 97

4.432 248

4.440 7

4.441 8

4.442 2

4.450 13

4.451 32

4.452 0

4.471 5

4.480 27/32

4.481 $1,332_4$

4.490 12.4

4.491 6

4.500 2,232

4.510 4

4.511 64

4.512 $0.\overline{054}$

4.520 5,744

4.521 19

4.522 3

4.530 440: $2^3 \cdot 5 \cdot 11$
      432: $2^4 \cdot 3^3$
      209: $11 \cdot 19$

4.531 6^8

4.532 < 17 times.

4.540 2^{30}

4.542 1,023

4.550 7

4.551 2209

4.552 23 students

4.571 $2,102_4$

4.581 111_8

4.590 48

4.591 4

4.600 10,008

4.610 90,002

4.620 1,998

4.622 999

4.630 441: $3^2 \cdot 7^2$
      256: 2^8
      576: $2^6 \cdot 3^2$
      (squares)

4.631 10,800

4.632 407

4.640 60, 72, 84, 90, 96.

4.642 2

4.650 10

4.651 27

4.652 94

4.671 $1,000,000,000,000_3$

4.681 25_6

4.690 1

4.720 9,876,513,240

4.722 714,285

4.730 25^2

4.731 416 or 7^{416}

4.742 6

4.750 24

4.751 7^{57}

4.752 44

4.771 0.56

4.781 $2,400_6$

4.790 992

4.820 3

4.830 12^2

4.831 16

4.842 13/90

4.850 10

4.851 11

4.881 101_2

4.920 24,442

4.930 270^2

4.931 33

4.942 1,327,104

4.950 180

4.951 42

4.981 300_9

4.001 $40 = 2^3 \cdot 5$. Its factor sum is $(1+2+4+8)(1+5) = 90$, which is greater than 2(40), making 40 **abundant**.

4.002 The units digit of 1976^{61} is 6 (any number ending in 6 raised to a power ends in 6). The units digit of 2007^{61} is 7 (the digits cycle in sets of four 7-9-3-1, and 60 is divisible by 4, so 2007^{60} ends in a 1 and 2007^{61} ends in a 7). The units digit of $(1976^{61})(2007^{61})$ will be the same as the units digit of $6 \cdot 7$: **2**.

4.010 3,951 is not divisible by 11. **907,654** is divisible by 11. Sum alternating digits and subtract:
$(9+7+5)-(0+6+4) = 21-10 = 11$.
14,256 is also divisible by 11:
$(1+2+6)-(4+5) = 0$

4.011 The GCF is the product of the factors in the overlapping region, while the LCM is the product of all the factors. The **GCF is 15** and the **LCM is 180**.

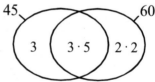

4.020 For 45,2_8 to be divisible by 3, the sum of the digits $4 + 5 + 2 + \_ + 8$ must be divisible by 3. This narrows our choices to 2, 5, and 8. For 45,2_8 to be divisible by eight, 2_8 must be divisible by 8. Of 2, 5, and 8, only the **8** makes 2_8 divisible by 8.

4.021 We find the LCM of 24, 30, and 100 is 600, so you must buy **6** packs of napkins to have the same number of cups, plates, and napkins.

4.022 $\dfrac{1}{256} = \dfrac{1}{2^8} = \left(\dfrac{1}{2}\right)^8 = (0.5)^8$, which must end in a **5** (true for all $1/2^n$ where n is a positive integer).

4.031 $\dfrac{12!}{11!} + \dfrac{10!}{9!} + \dfrac{8!}{7!} + \dfrac{6!}{5!} + \dfrac{4!}{3!} + \dfrac{2!}{1!}$ simplifies to $12 + 10 + 8 + 6$

$+ 4 + 2 = \mathbf{42}$.

4.032 The digits in $0.0\overline{2439}$ repeat in blocks of 5, so the $1,896,250^{\text{th}}$ digit is a 9. The third digit after every 9 will be a 4, so the $1,896,253^{\text{rd}}$ digit is a **4**.

4.041 The number of zeros at the end of a number is determined by the number of times 10 is a factor, so we are looking to pair up as many 2's and 5's in the prime factorization as possible. There are many more 2's than 5's, so we will concentrate on counting 5's. Every number that is divisible by 5 will contribute at least one 5. From $1(5) = 5$ to $25(5) = 125$ there are 25 multiples of 5. Additionally, multiples of 25 contribute two 5's. There are 5 multiples of 25. This gives us an additional five 5's. Finally, 125 contributes three 5's (we have already counted it twice, so we add just one more 5). This gives us a total of $25 + 5 + 1 = 31$ fives. This means that $125!$ has 5^{31} in its prime factorization. Pairing each five with a 2, we see that 10^{31} divides $125!$, and $125!$ therefore ends in **31** zeros.

4.042 199 is prime. The product of its integer factors is **199**.

4.050 $480 = 2^5 \cdot 3^1 \cdot 5^1$, so it has $(5+1)(1+1)(1+1) = 24$ factors. There are $(1+1)(1+1) = 4$ odd factors, so **20** of its factors are even.

4.051 To be divisible by 99, the integer $4\underline{a},\underline{b}13$ must be divisible by both 11 and 9. The sum of its digits must be divisible by 9 and $4 + 1 + 3 = 8$, so $a + b$ must be either 1, 10, or 18. To be divisible by 11, $(4+b+3)-(a+1)$ must be either 0, or 11. This eliminates $a + b = 1$ and $a + b = 18$, so $a + b = 10$. Some quick guess-and-check gives us $a = 8$ and $b = 2$, so $ab = \mathbf{16}$, or solve the system of equations (**p.16**): $a + b = 10$ and $(4+b+3)-(a+1) = 0$ to get $a = 8$ and $b = 2$. The system when $(4+b+3)-(a+1)=11$ gives us 2.5 and 7.5 for a and b.

4.052 For $1/n$ to be represented by a terminating decimal, the prime factorization of n must be of the form $2^a \cdot 5^b$. Be careful counting combinations where $2^a \cdot 5^b \le 100$: Powers of 2: 2^0 through 2^6. Powers of 5: 5^1 and 5^2. 5 times a power of 2: 10, 20, 40, 80. 25 times a power of 2: 50, 100.
We have $n = 1, 2, 4, 8, 16, 32, 64, 5, 25, 10, 20, 40,$ 80, 50, and 100 for a total of **15** values.

4.060 The prime factorization can have a 2 or a 3, but not both. It makes sense to use only the 2. We quickly arrive at $2^3 \cdot 5^1 \cdot 7^1 = \textbf{280}$, which has $4 \cdot 2 \cdot 2 = 16$ factors and is the smallest such integer not divisible by 6. Other candidates: $2^7 \cdot 5^1 = 640$, $2^1 \cdot 5^1 \cdot 7^1 \cdot 11^1 = 770$, and $2^3 \cdot 5^3 = 1{,}000$

4.061 For a fraction $n/496$ in simplest terms to have a numerator of 1, n must be a factor of 496. To find the sum of all such fractions, the numerator will be the factor sum of 496 (**4.790**), not including 496. 496 is a perfect number whose factor sum is 992. If we exclude 496 from the sum, we get 496. Therefore, the sum of all fractions $n/496$ which can be simplified so that the numerator is 1 is $496/496 = \textbf{1}$.

4.071 The place values in base 8 are $\underline{8}^6$, $\underline{8}^5 \, \underline{8}^4 \, \underline{8}^3$, $\underline{8}^2 \, \underline{8}^1 \, \underline{8}^0$, so representing $5(8^6) + 2(8^2)$ is easy: $\textbf{5,000,200}_8$.

4.080 The prime factorization of 45 is $3^2 \cdot 5$, which means 45 has $3 \cdot 2 = 6$ factors (3 pairs) and each pair of factors has a product of 45 ($3^2 \cdot 5$), so the product of these factors is $(3^2 \cdot 5)^3 = \textbf{3}^6 \cdot \textbf{5}^3$.

4.081 In any positive integer base, when we multiply by 10, we add a zero. $25_8 \cdot 10_8 = \textbf{250}_8$.

4.090 $50 = 2 \cdot 5^2$ has a factor sum $(1 + 2)(1 + 5 + 25) = \textbf{93}$. $405 = 3^4 \cdot 5$ has a factor sum $(1 + 3 + 9 + 27 + 81)(1 + 5) = \textbf{726}$. $210 = 2 \cdot 3 \cdot 5 \cdot 7$ has a factor sum $(1 + 2)(1 + 3)(1 + 5)(1 + 7) = \textbf{576}$.

4.091 $9{,}089^2$ ends in a 1 ($9^2 = 81$) and 765^2 ends in a 5, so their sum ends in a $1 + 5 = 6$. Given the choices, **83,195,146** is the only one that makes sense.

4.101 A prime number has only two factors: 1 and itself. The factor sum of a prime number n is therefore $n + 1$. All primes are therefore **deficient**.

4.102 The units digits of the powers of 3 cycle in sets of 4: 3 - 9 - 7 - 1 - 3 - 9 - 7 - 1 ... so to find the units digit for the sum of four consecutive powers of 3, we add $3 + 9 + 7 + 1 = 20$. The units digit is **0**.

4.110 Using the divisibility rule for 11, note that for $89\underline{x}43$ to be divisible by 11, $8 + x + 3$ must equal $9 + 4$ (or the difference of the sums must be divisible by 11, which is not possible in this case). Therefore, $x = $ **2**.

4.111   GCF: **16**
  LCM: **560**

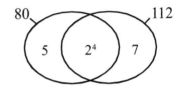

4.120 We will use a casework approach. There are no 1-digit integers that work. There are two 2-digit integers: 24 and 42. 3-digit integers 222 and 444 both work, giving us a total of **4** multiples of 3.

4.121 The LCM of 90 and 78 seconds gives us the amount of time it takes for Janice and Kiera to finish a lap at the same time. The LCM is 1,170 seconds, which is equal to 19.5 minutes. They will need to run for another 19.5 minutes to cross the finish line in a whole number of minutes (39 minutes). In 39 minutes (2,340 seconds), Kiera completes $2,340/90 = 26$ laps, while Janice completes $2,340/78 = 30$ laps, or **4** more laps than Kiera. We could also have found the LCM of 60 (seconds), 78, and 90 to get the number of seconds it would take Janice and Kiera to cross the finish line at the same time in a whole number of minutes.

4.122 $\dfrac{5}{33} = \dfrac{15}{99} = 0.\overline{15}$. The odd digits are 1's and the even digits are 5's, so the 59th digit is a **1**.

4.130 The **7** other primes are 11, 17, 71, 37, 73, 79, and 97.

4.131 $7! = 7 \cdot 6 \cdot 5 \cdot 4 \cdot 3 \cdot 2 \cdot 1 = 7 \cdot 2 \cdot 3 \cdot 5 \cdot 2 \cdot 2 \cdot 3 \cdot 2 = 2^4 \cdot 3^2 \cdot 5 \cdot 7$, which has $5 \cdot 3 \cdot 2 \cdot 2 = \mathbf{60}$ factors.

4.132 P-R-I-Y-A-N-K-A has 8 letters. $955 \equiv 3 \pmod 8$, so she completes her name and writes three more letters. The third letter in her name is **I**.

4.140 An integer with six factors has its prime factorization in the form a^5 or $a^2 b$. $2^2 \cdot 3 = \mathbf{12}$ is the smallest such number.

4.141 The prime factorization of 10! is $2^8 \cdot 3^4 \cdot 5^2 \cdot 7$. Notice that $(2^4 \cdot 3^2 \cdot 5)^2$ is a factor of 10!, so $2^4 \cdot 3^2 \cdot 5 = \mathbf{720}$ is the largest n where n^2 is a factor of $(10!)$.

4.142 The prime factorization of 900 is $2^2 \cdot 3^2 \cdot 5^2$. We can remove a 2, a 3, or a 5 and leave a number that has 18 factors, so there are **3** factors of 900 which have exactly 18 factors (180, 300, and 450).

4.150 The prime factorization of 900 is $2^2 \cdot 3^2 \cdot 5^2$. Odd factors cannot include any 2's, so 900 has $3 \cdot 3 = \mathbf{9}$ odd factors.

4.151 When we look for prime factors of 1,517, we check factors up to $\sqrt{1{,}517}$ (about 39). 37 would typically be the last prime factor we check and we find that $1{,}517 = \mathbf{37} \cdot 41$.

4.152 In base-5, the place values after the decimal point are 5^{-1}, 5^{-2}, 5^{-3}, etc.

Let $0.\overline{2}_5 = x = \dfrac{2}{5} + \dfrac{2}{25} + \dfrac{2}{125}\dots$ (see **p.56**)

Then $5x = 2 + \dfrac{2}{5} + \dfrac{2}{25} + \dfrac{2}{125}\dots$, so $5x - x = 2$, $x = \dfrac{1}{2}$.

4.160 We are looking for an integer with a prime factorization in the form $a^2 \cdot b \cdot c$, or $a^3 \cdot b^2$, or perhaps $a^5 \cdot b$ using prime factors greater than 2. $3^2 \cdot 5 \cdot 7 = 315$, $3^3 \cdot 5^2 = 675$, and $3^5 \cdot 5 = 1{,}215$ so **315** is the smallest odd integer with 12 factors.

4.171 The place values in base 2 are $\underline{2}^4\,\underline{2}^3$, $\underline{2}^2\,\underline{2}^1\,\underline{2}^0$, so the 1 in 10,000 is in the 2^4 place and represents **16**.

4.180 If a has $2b$ factors, it has b pairs of factors, each of which has a product a. The product of the factors of a is therefore $\boldsymbol{a^b}$.

4.190 $6 = 2 \cdot 3$: $(1 + 2)(1 + 3) = 12$
  $\mathbf{8} = 2^3$: $(1 + 2 + 4 + 8) = 15$
  $9 = 3^2$: $(1 + 3 + 9) = 13$

4.191 Looking only at units digits:
  $(346^2 + 364^2)^2 = (...6 + ...6)^2 = (...2)^2 = ...\mathbf{4}$

4.201 Let x be the sum of the factors of 2^n: $(1 + 2 + \ldots\, 2^n)$:

$$x = 1 + 2 + 4 + \ldots + 2^n$$
$$2x = 2 + 4 + \ldots + 2^n + 2^{n+1}$$
$$2x - x = 2^{n+1} - 1$$
$$x = 2(2^n) - 1$$

We see that the factors sum is always one less than twice the power of 2, which makes all powers of 2 **deficient** (just barely).

4.202 Units digits of the powers of 9 cycle 1-9-1-9 ... , so consecutive powers of 9 will end in a 1 and a 9, meaning the sum of consecutive powers of 9 will always end in a zero: $...1 + ...9 = ...\mathbf{0}$.

4.210 The sum of the 2nd and 4th digits must equal the sum of the 1st, 3rd, and 5th digits, so we must use three 2's and two 3's (placed in the tens and thousands place) to make **23,232**.

4.211   GCF: **7**
LCM: **420**

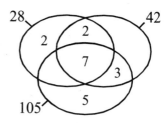

4.220 Integers divisible by both 8 and 9 are divisible by 72. There are **4** multiples of 72 less than 360.

4.221 The number of days it takes for Ken and Larry to get their hair cut again on the same day is the LCM of 20 and 26, which is 260. 7 divides 259 (37 times), so the 259th day is Tuesday again, and day 260 is a **Wednesday**.

4.222 As fractions, $0.\overline{07} = \dfrac{7}{99} = \dfrac{70}{990}$ and $0.0\overline{07} = \dfrac{7}{990}$.

To convert: $x = 0.0\overline{07}$, $10x = 0.\overline{07} = \dfrac{7}{99}$, so

$x = \dfrac{7}{990}$. Added together we get $\dfrac{77}{990} = \dfrac{7}{90}$.

4.231 $7! = 7 \cdot 6 \cdot 5 \cdot 4 \cdot 3 \cdot 2 \cdot 1 = 2^4 \cdot 3^2 \cdot 5 \cdot 7$, so the factor sum is $(1 + 2 + 4 + 8 + 16)(1 + 3 + 9)(1 + 5)(1 + 7)$, or $(31)(13)(6)(8) = \mathbf{19{,}344}$.

4.232 If we call Katy student 1, then Katy $\equiv 1 (\mathrm{mod}\,8)$, and Meera wants to be $\equiv 1 (\mathrm{mod}\,8)$. $350 \equiv 6 (\mathrm{mod}\,8)$, and counting backwards we get $345 \equiv 1 (\mathrm{mod}\,8)$, which is **6 places** to Katy's right (there are 5 students between Meera and Katy).

4.240 An integer with ten factors will have a prime factorization of the form a^9 or $a^4 \cdot b$, so $2^4 \cdot 3 = \mathbf{48}$ is the smallest integer with exactly 10 factors.

4.241 $17! + 18! = 17!(1+18) = 19 \cdot 17!$, making **19** the largest prime factor of $17! + 18!$.

4.242 The sum of the five digits must be 9, and the last digit must be a 2 (a number divisible by 8 must be even). We want to place as many leading ones as possible to keep the integer as small as possible, while keeping the sum of the digits equal to 9 and using at least one 3: this leads us to **11,232**, which is divisible by both 8 and 9.

4.250 $440 = 2^3 \cdot 5 \cdot 11$, so 440 has $4 \cdot 2 \cdot 2 = 16$ factors. Odd factors cannot have any 2's. If we exclude the 2's there are $2 \cdot 2 = 4$ odd factors, meaning **12** of the factors of 440 are even.

4.251 $12,321 = 111^2 = 3^2 \cdot 37^2$. Perfect square factors have only even exponents (including zero): $3^0 \cdot 37^0 = 1$, $3^2 \cdot 37^0 = 9$, $3^0 \cdot 37^2 = 1,369$, and $3^2 \cdot 37^2 = 12,321$ for a total of **4** perfect square factors. (See **p.368**).

4.252 $0.\overline{2} = \dfrac{2}{9} = \dfrac{200}{900}$, $0.0\overline{2} = \dfrac{2}{9} \cdot \dfrac{1}{10} = \dfrac{2}{90} = \dfrac{20}{900}$, and

$0.00\overline{2} = \dfrac{2}{9} \cdot \dfrac{1}{100} = \dfrac{2}{900}$, so

$0.\overline{2} + 0.0\overline{2} + 0.00\overline{2} = \dfrac{200 + 20 + 2}{900} = \dfrac{222}{900} = \dfrac{37}{150}$.

4.260 For a to have 5 factors, its prime factorization must be in the form x^4 for some prime integer x, and for b to have 6 factors its prime factorization must be in the form $y^2 z$ (or y^5) for some prime integers y and z. The product ab must therefore have prime factorization in the form $x^4 \cdot y^5$ or $x^4 \cdot y^2 \cdot z$. To minimize this product we use $2^4 \cdot 3^2 \cdot 5 = $ **720** ($2^5 \cdot 3^4 = 2,592$).

4.271   a. $215_6 = 2(6^2) + 1(6^1) + 5(6^0) = $ **83**
   b. $101_2 = 1(2^2) + 0(2^1) + 1(2^0) = $ **5**
   c. $777_8 = 7(8^2) + 7(8^1) + 7(8^0) = $ **511**

4.280 $30 = 2 \cdot 3 \cdot 5$, so 30 has 8 factors or 4 pairs of factors with each pair having a product of 30, so we have the product $30^4 = (2 \cdot 3 \cdot 5)^4 = 2^4 \cdot 3^4 \cdot 5^4$. $x = 4$

4.290 a. $64 = 2^6$, which has a factor sum:
$(1 + 2 + 4 + 8 + 16 + 32 + 64) = 127 = 2^7 - 1$
b. $128 = 2^7$, which has a factor sum:
$(1 + 2 + 4 + 8 + 16 + 32 + 64 + 128) = 255 = 2^8 - 1$
c. $256 = 2^8$, which has a factor sum:
$(1 + 2 + 4 + 8 + 16 + 32 + 64 + 128 + 256) = 511$.
d. 2^{30} has a factor sum:
$(2^0 + 2^1 + 2^2 + 2^3 + \ldots + 2^{30}) = 2^{31} - 1$.

The sum of the factors of 2^n is $2^{n+1} - 1$. (See **4.201**).

4.291 The units digit of $\sqrt{4,624}$ must be a 2 or an 8. 62 is too small, so we assume $\sqrt{4,624}$ must be **68**.

4.301 A multiple of 6 can be expressed $6n$. $6n$ has divisors 1, n, $2n$, $3n$, and $6n$ (and quite possibly many more, but these are all factors). The sum of these factors is $12n + 1$, so the least possible factor sum of any multiple of 6 is $12n + 1$ (one greater than twice the number). Every integer multiple of 6 is **abundant**. For the same reason, you can tell if any integer is abundant simply by knowing if any one of its factors is abundant (or perfect). For example, $20n$ has divisors 1, n, $2n$, $4n$, $5n$, $10n$, and $20n$ for a factor sum that is at least $42n + 1$.

4.310 The largest 5-digit integer is 99,999. We want the sum of alternating digits to be equal, so we change the units digit to a 0 to get **99,990**. This must be the largest 5-digit multiple of 11 because if we add 11 to 99,990 we get a 6-digit integer.

4.311 The product of two integers is equal to the product of their GCF and LCM, so we divide their product by their GCF to get their LCM: $315/3 = $ **105**.

4.312 $\dfrac{2}{33} = \dfrac{6}{99} = 0.\overline{06}$.

4.320 The digit sum must be at least 9 for the integer to be divisible by 9, so we need at least four digits: 1, 2, 3, and 3. The last digit must be a 2 for divisibility by 8. We try 1,332 and 3,132, but neither is divisible by 8 so **3,312** is the smallest integer divisible by 8 and 9 which uses each of the digits 1, 2, and 3 at least once.

4.321 We solve with a Venn diagram:

LCM(a,b,c) = **60**.

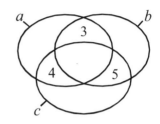

4.322 For the decimal expansion of $n/168$ to terminate, the denominator must have only 2's and 5's in its prime factorization. $168 = 2 \cdot 2 \cdot 2 \cdot 3 \cdot 7$, so we must have a numerator of $3 \cdot 7 =$ **21** to cancel the $3 \cdot 7$ in the denominator. ($21/168 = 1/8 = 0.125$).

4.331 $6! = 6 \cdot 5 \cdot 4 \cdot 3 \cdot 2 = 2^4 \cdot 3^2 \cdot 5$

$600 = 2^3 \cdot 3 \cdot 5^2$

LCM = **3,600**

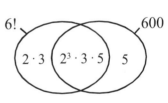

4.332 $(1 + 2 + 3 + ... + 48)$ is equal to $\frac{(48)(49)}{2} = 24(49)$.

$49 \equiv -1 \pmod{50}$, so $24(49) \equiv -24 \pmod{50}$, and $-24 \pmod{50} \equiv 26 \pmod{50}$. We are looking for the value of 26^{49} in modulo 50. $26^1 \equiv 26 \pmod{50}$ and $26^2 = 676 \equiv 26 \pmod{50}$, so $26^{49} \equiv 26 \pmod{50}$ (every power of 26 ends in 76). $(1 + 2 + ... + 48)^{49}$ leaves a remainder of **26** when divided by 50.

4.340 Integers which have an odd number of factors are all perfect squares. There are **9** perfect squares less than 100.

4.341 For $n!$ to end in exactly 100 zeros, it must have exactly one-hundred 5's in its prime factorization (when paired with a 2, these 5's contribute a factor of 10, adding a zero to the end of the number). We first look for multiples of 5: 5! has one 5, 10! has two, etc. 500! has 100 multiples of 5, however, multiples of 25 contributes two 5's and multiples of 125 contribute three 5's. 500! includes 20 multiples of 25 and 4 multiples of 125, so 500! ends in $100 + 40 + 4 = 144$ zeros. Some quick guess-and-check working backwards and we find that 400! ends in $80 + 16 + 3 = 99$ zeros, so 405! ends in $81 + 16 + 3 = 100$ zeros, but we can go as high as 409! without adding another 5, so $n = $ **409** is our answer.

4.342 *Method 1*: Look for a pattern: 2^0 leaves a remainder of 1, $2^0 + 2^1$ leaves a remainder of 3, $2^0 + 2^1 + 2^2$ leaves a remainder of 7, and the pattern of remainders continues: 1 - 3 - 7 - 6 - 4 - 0 - 1 - 3 - 7 - 6 - 4 - 0 ... in a repeating block of 6 digits. 99 leaves a remainder of 3 when divided by 6, so the remainder will be the same as for $2^0 + 2^1 + 2^2 + 2^3$, which is **6**.
Method 2: $(2^0 + 2^1 + 2^2 ... + 2^{99}) = 2^{100} - 1$, so we first look for the value of 2^{100} in modulo 9.

$2^1 \equiv 2 \pmod 9$, $2^2 \equiv 4 \pmod 9$, $2^3 \equiv 8 \pmod 9$,

$2^4 \equiv 7 \pmod 9$, $2^5 \equiv 5 \pmod 9$, $2^6 \equiv 1 \pmod 9$, and the cycle repeats in a block of 6: 2 - 4 - 8 - 7 - 5 - 1 etc. Note that these remainders are easy to find by doubling the previous term and then dividing by 9 where necessary. 100 leaves a remainder of 4 when divided by 6, so 2^{100} leaves the same remainder as 2^4 when divided by 9 (7). Subtract 1 (we were looking for $2^{100} - 1$) and we get a remainder of **6**.

4.350 $1{,}296 = 2^4 \cdot 3^4$. To make a perfect square, we can use any even power of 2 with any even power of 3. There are three of each (2^0, 2^2, and 2^4 along with 3^0, 3^2, and 3^4), giving us $3 \cdot 3 = 9$ ways to create perfect square factors ($1, 4, 9, 16, 36, 81, 144, 324$, and $1{,}296$).

4.351 For a multiple of 11 to have 10 factors, its prime factorization must be in the form 11^9, $11 \cdot a^4$, or $a \cdot 11^4$. We can rule-out 11^9 and $a \cdot 11^4$, as both are larger than 999, so we look for values of a which make $11 \cdot a^4 < 1{,}000$. Only two values work for a: 2 and 3. $11 \cdot 2^4 = 176$ and $11 \cdot 3^4 = 891$, so we have $176 + 891 = \mathbf{1{,}067}$.

4.352 There are an enormous number of sets of positive integers whose sum is 25, so there must be a method. Lets look for a pattern. For 6:
$1 + 5 = 6$ and $1 \cdot 5 = 5$,
$2 + 2 + 2 = 6$ and $2 \cdot 2 \cdot 2 = 8$,
$3 + 3 = 6$ and $3 \cdot 3 = 9$.
It appears that we are better off using 3's (not 2's) if we want to maximize the product for a given sum. Lets compare 3's to 5's:
$3 + 3 + 3 + 3 + 3 = 15$ and $3^5 = 243$,
while $5 + 5 + 5 = 15$ and $5^3 = 125$.
3's are better than 5's when trying to achieve a given sum while maximizing a product for a set of integers. 3's clearly do better than the larger primes like 7 and 11. We therefore look to use as many 3's as possible, with any remainder used in 2's. If the remainder is 1 then we are better off using one less three so that we leave a remainder of $4 = 2 \cdot 2$, which exceeds $1 \cdot 3$. For a sum of 25 we can use seven 3's and two 2's: $3(7) + 2(2) = 25$, $3^7 \cdot 2^2 = \mathbf{8{,}748}$.

4.371 The largest 3-digit number in base 6 is one less than 1000_6, which is $6^3 = 216$ (in base 10), so we have $555_6 = \mathbf{215_{10}}$.

4.380 **9** has 3 factors: 1, 3, and 9, so their product is 3^3.

4.381 When we add we must carry a 1,
because there is no digit 6 in base-6.
$3_6 + 3_6 = 10_6$. and $3_6 + 3_6 + 1_6 = 11_6$.

$$\begin{array}{r} \overset{1\ 1}{333_6} \\ + \ 333_6 \\ \hline 1{,}110_6 \end{array}$$

4.390 Guess-and-check gives us $(1 + 7 + 7^2 + 7^3) = (1 + 7 + 49 + 343) = 400$, so our answer is 7^3 **or 343**.

4.391 $(1 + 2 + ... + 30) = \dfrac{30 \cdot 31}{2} = 15 \cdot 31$, which has a units digit of 5. The units digit remains a **5** when squared.

4.401 Because $8{,}128 = 2^6 \cdot 127$ (which is $64 \cdot 127$), its factor sum is $(1 + 2 + 2^2 + 2^3 + 2^4 + 2^5 + 2^6)(1 + 127) = (2^7 - 1)(128) = (127 \cdot 128)$, which is twice 8,128 (as we can see from the prime factorization of 8,128). 8,128 is therefore **perfect**.

4.410 For a three-digit multiple of 11 to end in a 2, either the tens digit must exceed the hundreds digit by 2 (so that the sum of the units digit and the hundreds digit is equal to the tens digit), or the hundreds digit must exceed the tens digit by 9 (so that the sum of the units digit and the hundreds digit is greater than the tens digit by 11). This gives us the following set of three-digit integers: 132, 242, 352, 462, 572, 682, 792, and 902 for a total of **8** such multiples of 11.

4.411 The product of the GCF and the LCM for a pair of integers is equal to the product of the integers, so $18(180) = 90x$. Solving for x gives us $x = \textbf{36}$.

4.412 $\dfrac{5}{111} = \dfrac{45}{999} = 0.\overline{045}$.

4.420 The sum of the digits must be divisible by 9, so we try 9 2's, but there cannot be an odd number of 2's (the sum of alternating sets of digits must be equal) so we must use a minimum of **18** twos.

4.421 We must divide the chips, pecans, and M&Ms into an equal number of cookies, so we look for the GCF of

80, 112, and 128, which is **16**. (Each giant cookie gets 5 chocolate chips, 7 pecans, and 6 M&Ms).

4.422 $\dfrac{1}{37} = \dfrac{3}{111} = \dfrac{27}{999}$, $\dfrac{1}{9} = \dfrac{111}{999}$, and $\dfrac{1}{3} = \dfrac{333}{999}$, so

$$\dfrac{1}{37} + \dfrac{1}{9} + \dfrac{1}{3} = \dfrac{27}{999} + \dfrac{111}{999} + \dfrac{333}{999} = \dfrac{471}{999} = 0.\overline{471}.$$

4.431 $100! = 100 \cdot 99 \cdot 98 \cdot \mathbf{97} \cdot 96 \cdot 95 \cdot \ldots \cdot 3 \cdot 2 \cdot 1$. There is no way to create a larger prime factor by multiplication, so 97 is the greatest prime factor of 100!.

4.432 We are looking for n such that $31n \equiv 1 \pmod{13}$, but 31 is congruent to 5 in modulo 13. This simplifies our expression to $5n \equiv 1 \pmod{13}$. We see that this works when $n = 8$, which gives us $40 \equiv 1 \pmod{13}$. The eighth multiple of 31 will therefore leave a remainder of 1 when divided by 13: $31 \cdot 8 = \mathbf{248}$.

4.440 Both a and b must be the square of a prime number (only the square of a prime number will have exactly three factors). We organize our work, looking for products $x^2y^2 < 1,000$ where $x < y$, and both x and y are prime. The following **7** pairs (x, y) are the only ones which satisfy the conditions:
(2, 3) (2, 5) (2, 7) (2, 11) (2, 13) (3, 5) and (3, 7).

4.441 The number of minutes in February is $60 \cdot 24 \cdot 28$. We work our way up starting at $2 \cdot 3 \cdot 4 \ldots$ until we have the same factors at $8! = 2 \cdot 3 \cdot 4 \cdot 5 \cdot 6 \cdot 7 \cdot 8$. $n = \mathbf{8}$.

4.442 First, we find the smallest integer that is divisible by 2, 3, 4, 5, 6, 8, 9, 10, and 11: $2^3 \cdot 3^2 \cdot 5 \cdot 11 = 3,960$. Any multiple of 3,960 is divisible by 2, 3, 4, 5, 6, 8, 9, 10, and 11. There are **2** multiples of 3,960 less than 10,000: 3,960 and 7,920.

4.450 A number with 7 factors must have a prime factorization n^6, so $(n^6)^2 = n^{12}$ will have **13** factors.

4.451 $720 = 2^4 \cdot 3^2 \cdot 5$ has $5 \cdot 3 \cdot 2 = 30$ factors. The smallest integer with 32 factors is: $2^3 \cdot 3 \cdot 5 \cdot 7 = 840$. The smallest integer with 36 factors is $2^2 \cdot 3^2 \cdot 5 \cdot 7 = 1{,}260$. This should be enough to convince us that **32** factors is the maximum for any 3-digit integer.

4.452 10! (whether the 10! is in base 9 or base 10) is divisible by 9 and therefore must end in a **0** in base-9.

4.471 242 is one less than 3^5, which is $100{,}000_3$, so it will take **5** digits to represent 242 in base-3: $22{,}222_3$.

4.480 $54 = 2 \cdot 3^3$ and has 8 factors (4 pairs). Each pair can be replaced with a 54 for a product of $54^4 = 2^4 \cdot 3^{12}$. $36 = 2^2 \cdot 3^2$ and has 9 factors, each of which can be replaced with a 6 for a product of $6^9 = 2^9 \cdot 3^9$:

$$\frac{2^4 \cdot 3^{12}}{2^9 \cdot 3^9} = \frac{3^3}{2^5} = \frac{27}{32}.$$

4.481 When we add we must carry a 1, because there is no digit 6 in base-4. $3_4 + 3_4 = 12_4$. and $3_4 + 3_4 + 1_4 = 13_4$.

$$\begin{array}{r} {}^{1\ 1}\ 333_4 \\ +\ 333_4 \\ \hline 1{,}332_4 \end{array}$$

4.490 To find the average of the factors of 48, we find the sum and divide it by the number of factors. $48 = 2^4 \cdot 3$, which has 10 factors and a factor sum of $(1 + 2 + 4 + 8 + 16)(1 + 3) = 124$. The average factor of 48 is $124/10 = \mathbf{12.4}$.

4.491 An integer that is divisible by 2 but not 5 must end in a 2, 4, 6, or 8. $(n^2)^2 = n^4$, and 2^4, 4^4, 6^4, and 8^4 all end in a 6, so the units digit of any integer $(n^2)^2$ where n is divisible by 2 but not 5 will always end in a **6**.

4.500 It must end in a 2 and have a digit sum that is divisible by 3. We must use at least one 3, which means we need three 2's to satisfy the digit sum. Minimize this integer by placing the 3 in the tens place: **2,232**.

4.510 For 1,234,567: $1 + 3 + 5 + 7 = 16$ and $2 + 4 + 6 = 12$. If the units digit of 1,234,567 were a 3, the number would be divisible by 11. 1,234,563 is divisible by 11, so 1,234,567 leaves a remainder of **4** when divided by 11.

4.511 I am a big fan of the Venn diagram with these for organizing my thoughts. If their GCF is 4 and their product is 3,600, then their LCM is 3,600/4 = 900. We are looking for two perfect squares a and b in the diagram which are mutually prime and have a product of 900/4 = 225. $225 = 3^2 \cdot 5^2$, so we can use $a = 9$ and $b = 25$ or $a = 1$ and $b = 225$. To minimize the positive difference we use 9 and 25, so $9 \cdot 4 = 36$ and $25 \cdot 4 = 100$. Their positive difference is **64**.

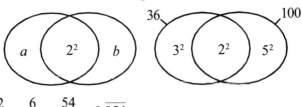

4.512 $\dfrac{2}{37} = \dfrac{6}{111} = \dfrac{54}{999} = 0.\overline{054}$

4.520 We recognize immediately that the units digit must be a 2 or a 4. Look at the last three digits of a number to determine divisibility by 8. Check only those combinations which end in 2 or 4: ~~132~~, ~~142~~, 312, ~~342~~, ~~412~~, 432, ~~124~~, ~~134~~, 214, ~~234~~, ~~314~~, ~~324~~. This gives us two multiples of 8: 4,312 and 1,432. Their sum is **5,744**.

4.521 The slope of the line is 162/126, which simplifies to 9/7. Any x-coordinate which is a multiple of 7 on this line segment will have a corresponding y-coordinate that is an integer multiple of 9: (0,0), (7,9), (14, 18) ... (126, 162). There are 126/7 + 1 = 19 multiples of 7 from 0 to 126 (remember to include 0) and 19 corresponding multiples of 9 for a total of **19** lattice points.

4.522 $\dfrac{110}{111} = \dfrac{990}{999} = 0.\overline{990}$. (**3 digits**)

4.531 We are looking for multiples of 3 (there are 6 in 18!) and multiples of $3^2 = 9$ (there are 2). This gives us 8 threes in the prime factorization of 18! which, when paired with 8 twos, gives us 8 sixes or **6^8**.

4.532 We are trying to advance the clock ahead by one minute. If we push the > button 9 times, we increase the time on the clock by 3 minutes: $9 \cdot 7 = 63 \equiv 3 \pmod{60}$. If we made 5 "laps" using this method (by pushing > 45 times) we would end up 15 minutes ahead of where we started: $5 \cdot 3 = 15 \equiv 1 \pmod 7$. Pushing > 2 less times would put us one minute ahead at 6:04 (in 43 button presses).

However, if we push < 8 times, we end up 4 minutes ahead: $8(-7) = -56 \equiv 4 \pmod{60}$. Taking two "laps" in this manner by pressing < 16 times, we are left 8 minutes ahead: $2 \cdot 4 = 8 \equiv 1 \pmod 7$. One more press of < and we are at 6:04, one minute ahead of where we started in a total of **17** presses of < .

4.540 To have 31 factors, the prime factorization of a positive integer must be in the form a^{30}. To minimize this value we use $a = 2$ to get $\mathbf{2^{30}}$.

4.542 $33,333_4 = 100,000_4 - 1 = 4^5 - 1 = \mathbf{1,023}$.

4.550 The prime factorization of an integer with exactly 3 factors is of the form a^2, so we are asked to find primes which have a square that is 3-digits long. Beginning with $11^2 = 121$ and ending with $31^2 = 961$, we have 11^2, 13^2, 17^2, 19^2, 23^2, 29^2, and 31^2 for a total of **7**.

4.551 $1,849 = 43^2$. We are looking for the square of the next prime, $47^2 = \mathbf{2,209}$.

4.552 We are looking to find a value x where $38x \equiv -1 \pmod{35}$. Because $38 \equiv 3 \pmod{35}$, we simplify our search to $3x \equiv -1 \pmod{35}$. Note that any number which is congruent to $-1 \pmod{70}$ is also congruent to $-1 \pmod{35}$, which helps us see that $x = 23$ is a solution. **23 students** in 38 groups = 874 students (25 rows of 35 = 875 seats).

4.571 $222_8 = 2(8^2) + 2(8) + 2 = 2(64) + 16 + 2$ which can be easily converted to base-4: $= 2(4^3) + 1(4^2) + 2$, which is $\mathbf{2,102_4}$.

4.581 No need for borrowing, this one is easy.

$$\begin{array}{r} 567_8 \\ -\,456_8 \\ \hline 111_8 \end{array}$$

4.590 Look for abundant numbers that are less than half of 100, this is really an educated guess-and-check, choosing numbers which have a lot of factors. Nothing below 36 comes close, so we begin there:
$36 = 2^2 \cdot 3^2$. Factor sum: $(1 + 2 + 4)(1 + 3 + 9) = 91$.
$40 = 2^3 \cdot 3$. Factor sum: $(1 + 2 + 4 + 8)(1 + 5) = 90$.
$42 = 2 \cdot 3 \cdot 7$. Factor sum $(1 + 2)(1 + 3)(1 + 7) = 96$.
$44 = 2^2 \cdot 11$. Factor sum $(1 + 2 + 4)(1 + 11) = 84$.
$45 = 3^2 \cdot 5$. Factor sum $(1 + 3 + 9)(1 + 5) = 78$.
$\mathbf{48} = 2^4 \cdot 3$. Factor sum $(1 + 2 \,... + 16)(1 + 3) = 124$.
Somewhat surprisingly, 48 is the smallest.

4.591 In order for there to be a remainder, the units digits of the consecutive integers can only be 1, 2, 3, and 4 or 6, 7, 8, and 9 (consider what happens when you include a units digit of 0 or 5). In either case, the units digit of the product of the integers will be a 4. This means that when the integer is divided by 10 the remainder is **4**.

4.600 **10,008** has a digit sum of 9 and is divisible by 8.

4.610 If we use a 2 for the units digit, the sums of alternating digits have a difference of $(9 + 0 + 2) - (0 + 0) = 11$, so **90,002** is divisible by 11.

4.620 All three digits must be even for each of ABC, CAB, and BCA to be divisible by 6. The sum of the digits cannot be 9 or 27, so we look for three even digits whose sum is 18. The only three distinct digits which work are 4, 6, and 8. We can use $468 + 684 + 846 =$ **1,998** (note that 486, 648, and 864 yield the same sum).

4.622 Call the larger three-digit integer x and the smaller y. This gives us $1{,}000x + y = 6(1{,}000y + x)$. Simplify this to $1{,}000x + y = 6{,}000y + 6x$ or $994x = 5{,}999y$ which simplifies to $142x = 857y$. The obvious three-digit solutions to this equation are $x = 857$ and $y = 142$. $142 + 857 = \mathbf{999}$.

Alternatively, we recall that $\dfrac{1}{7} = 0.\overline{142857}$, and $\dfrac{6}{7} = 0.\overline{857142}$, giving us $142{,}857$ and $857{,}142$.

4.631 $6! = 2^4 \cdot 3^2 \cdot 5$
$216 = 2^3 \cdot 3^3$
$300 = 2^2 \cdot 3 \cdot 5^2$

LCM $= \mathbf{10{,}800}$

4.632 We begin by finding an integer x where $x \equiv 1 \pmod{14}$ and $x \equiv 2 \pmod{15}$. Looking for the smallest positive integer which leaves a remainder of 1 when divided by 14 and 2 when divided by 15 can be difficult, but notice that the difference between 14 and 15 is equal to the difference in the modular residues 1 and 2. This leads us to look for the first negative solution $x = -13$. Add to this $14 \cdot 15 = 210$ to maintain modular congruence and we get 197 trees. Unfortunately, the problem states that Craig has more than 200 trees so we must add another 210 to get **407** trees.

4.640 $2^2 \cdot 3 \cdot 5 = \mathbf{60}$, $2^3 \cdot 3^2 = \mathbf{72}$, $2^2 \cdot 3 \cdot 7 = \mathbf{84}$, $2 \cdot 3^2 \cdot 5 = \mathbf{90}$, and $2^5 \cdot 3 = \mathbf{96}$.

4.642 We are looking for the remainder when 500 is divided by 6, which is **2** (the 498th person will count off 6, with the last two people numbered 1 and 2).

4.650 The only multiple of 7 having 5 factors is 7^4, so $n = 7^4$ and $3n$ is $3 \cdot 7^4$, which has **10** factors.

4.651 $900/n$ is a positive integer only when n is a factor of 900. $900 = 2^2 \cdot 3^2 \cdot 5^2$ and has 27 factors. There are **27** values of n which make $900/n$ a positive integer.

4.652 The tires have circumference 27π inches and 30π inches. The LCM (270π) inches gives us the distance after which the tires will both reach their original position in the rotation. The stars will be positioned as shown in the drawing 5 times (every 54π inches) during this period. 1/4 mile = 15,840 inches. $15{,}840/(54\pi) = 93.4$. If the wheels begin in the position shown, this makes **94** times.

4.671 $9^6 = (3^2)^6 = 3^{12} = \mathbf{1{,}000{,}000{,}000{,}000{,}000_3}$.

4.681 When we borrow in base 10 we "borrow" 10, but in base 6 we "borrow" 6.

$$\begin{array}{r} {}^{1\;6\;9}\\ \cancel{2}\cancel{1}\cancel{3}_6 \\ -\ 144_6 \\ \hline 25_6 \end{array}$$

4.690 The two values are both equal to $(1 + 2)(1 + 3)(1 + 5)(1 + 7)(1 + 11)$. Their quotient is **1**.

4.720 I like to start these problems with the largest number possible (9,876,543,210) and modify it as necessary. Looking at the number, it is already divisible by 9 and 10, but not by 8 and 11. For 11, the digit sum is 45, so the sum of alternating digits cannot be equal. The difference must be 11 with alternating digit sums of 17 and 28. 9,876,543,210 has alternating digit sums of 25 and 20, so we must increase the digit sum of $9 + 7 + 5 + 3 + 1$ to 28. Trading the 1 for a 4 is the best way to do this ($9 + 7 + 5 + 3 + 4 = 28$). Leave the largest five digits in order on the left and the zero on the right. Look for arrangements of the under-lined digits which make the number divisible by 8 while maintaining the alternating digit sums. 9,876,5<u>24,1</u>30 is not divisible by 8, neither is 9,876,5<u>23,1</u>40, but **9,876,513,240** is.

4.722 We have a single misplaced digit which we will call x and a 5-digit number y. In the correct order, we have $10y + x$, but in the incorrect order written by Michael we have $100{,}000x + y$. The incorrect integer is 5 times the correct integer, giving us $5(10y + x) = 100{,}000x + y$ which simplifies to $49y = 99{,}995x$. Dividing by 7 we get $7y = 14{,}285x$. We can use $x = 7$ and $y = 14{,}285$ which makes Michael's number **714,285**. Alternatively (as in problem **4.622**) the problem suggests a cyclic number found in the repeating block of digits in sevenths:

$$\frac{1}{7} = 0.\overline{142857} \text{ and } \frac{5}{7} = 0.\overline{714285}.$$

4.731 For this problem I will introduce a function called the floor value. The floor value of a number, indicated by $\lfloor x \rfloor$ represents the greatest integer value of x and basically means round down. For example: $\lfloor 9.8 \rfloor = 9$ and $\lfloor 73/11 \rfloor = 6$. To find the power of 7 in 2,500!

we add $\left\lfloor \dfrac{2{,}500}{7} \right\rfloor + \left\lfloor \dfrac{2{,}500}{7^2} \right\rfloor + \left\lfloor \dfrac{2{,}500}{7^3} \right\rfloor + \left\lfloor \dfrac{2{,}500}{7^4} \right\rfloor.$

$\left\lfloor \dfrac{2{,}500}{7} \right\rfloor = 357$, which means there are 357 multiples of 7 in 2,500! Each contributes a 7 to the prime factorization of 2,500! Continuing, there are 51 multiples of 7^2, and each contributes an additional 7. There are 7 multiples of 7^3 and 1 multiple of 7^4. This gives us a total of $357 + 51 + 7 + 1 = 416$ sevens in the prime factorization of 2,500!, making 416 (7^{416}) the power of 7 in 2,500!.

4.742 The units digits in the powers of 2 repeat: 2-4-8-6-2-4-8-6..., and 222/4 leaves a remainder of 2. This means that 222^{222} must end in a 4. Multiplying this result by 9 would give us a units digit **6**.

4.750 For a multiple of 6 to have 9 factors, it must be a perfect square, making our integer $2^2 \cdot 3^2$. Multiplying by 10 we get $2^3 \cdot 3^2 \cdot 5$, which has **24** factors.

4.751 We use the floor function again as explained in **4.731**:

$$\left\lfloor \frac{343}{7} \right\rfloor + \left\lfloor \frac{343}{7^2} \right\rfloor + \left\lfloor \frac{343}{7^3} \right\rfloor = 49 + 7 + 1 = \textbf{57, or } \textbf{7}^{\textbf{57}}.$$

4.752 For any pair of consecutive integers, one must be even and therefore divisible by 2, so we look for the least positive integer whose prime factorization is of the form $2^2 \cdot a$ or $a^2 \cdot 2$ for which an adjacent integer has 6 factors. $2^2 \cdot 11 = \textbf{44}$ and $3^2 \cdot 5 = 45$ are the first pair of consecutive integers which have exactly 6 factors each. Pairs like (75,76) and (98,99) work as well.

4.771 0.24_5 is $2(5^{-1}) + 4(5^{-2}) = \dfrac{2}{5} + \dfrac{4}{25} = \dfrac{14}{25} = \textbf{0.56}$.

4.781 Begin with the subtraction shown on the right. To multiply by 100_6, just add two zeros to get $\textbf{2,400}_6$.

$$\begin{array}{r} {}^{6}\cancel{11}{}^{9}3_6 \\ -\ 45_6 \\ \hline 24_6 \end{array}$$

4.790 $496 = 16 \cdot 31 = 2^4 \cdot 31$ which has a factor sum $(1 + 2 + 4 + 8 + 16)(1 + 31) = (31)(32) = \textbf{992}$. 496 is a perfect number (**p.147**), a number p whose factor sum is $2p$. There are relatively few known perfect numbers, and all known perfect numbers are of the form: $p = 2^{n-1}(2^n - 1)$ where $2^n - 1$ is prime (called a Mersenne prime). In order for $2^n - 1$ to be prime, n must be prime. The largest known primes are all Mersenne primes.

4.820 456,564,465,645 has a digit sum of $4(4+5+6) = 60$, so it is divisible by 3. It is not even, so it is not divisible by 6, but three less than 456,564,465,645 is divisible by 6, so dividing by 6 leaves a remainder of **3**.

4.831 We are looking for a number n for which $n!$ includes fifteen 2's in its prime factorization. This one is small enough that we can get the answer quickly simply by counting up by 2's and adding the powers contributed by each: 2, 4(2^2), 6, 8(2^3), 10, 12($3 \cdot 2^2$), 14, 16(2^4). We are up to fifteen 2's, which means that 2^{15} divides **16**! (but will not divide 15!).

4.842 If $x = 0.1\overline{4}$, then $10x = 1.\overline{4} = 1\frac{4}{9} = \frac{13}{9}$. Dividing by 10 we get $x = \frac{13}{90}$.

4.850 Perfect squares have three factors only when they are the square of a prime. There are 19 perfect squares less than 400. Excluding 1 and all perfect squares of primes: 2^2, 3^2, 5^2, 7^2, 11^2, 13^2, 17^2, and 19^2 leaves us with $19 - 9 = $**10** perfect squares. (We could have just as easily counted composites).

4.851 $1{,}024 = 2^{10}$, so we are looking for $n!$ where there are fewer than 10 twos in the prime factorization. $2 \cdot 4 \cdot 6 \cdot 8 \cdot 10 \cdot 12$ is divisible by 2^{10}, so n must be less than 12. **11**! is not divisible by 1,024 (but 12! is).

4.881 This one is done easily by converting to base 10, but it is good practice with the concept of borrowing for subtraction:

$$\begin{array}{r} \overset{0\,1\,1\,1\,2}{10000}_2 \\ - 1011_2 \\ \hline 101_2 \end{array}$$

4.920 The sum of alternating digits must be equal (we cannot create a difference of 11 with two 5's and two 6's). The four ways this can be done are: 5,665; 5,566; 6,556; 6,655. Their sum is **24,442**.

4.931 We are looking for a number n for which $n!$ includes fifteen 3's in its prime factorization. This one is small enough that we can get the answer quickly simply by counting up by threes and adding the number of 3's

contributed by each until we get to fifteen 3's:
$3, 6, 9 (3^2), 12, 15, 18(2 \cdot 3^2), 21, 24, 27(3^3), 30, 33$.
Counting the 3's above gives us 15. This means that
3^{15} divides **33**! (but will not divide 32!).

4.942 A Venn diagram helps organize:

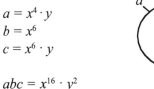
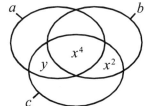

$a = x^4 \cdot y$
$b = x^6$
$c = x^6 \cdot y$

$abc = x^{16} \cdot y^2$

To minimize the product, we use primes $x = 2$
and $y = 3$ to get $x^{16} \cdot y^2 = 2^{16} \cdot 3^2 = $ **589,824**.

4.950 An integer with 18 factors will have a prime factoriza-
tion of the form a^{17}, $a^8 \cdot b$, $a^5 \cdot b^2$, or $a^2 \cdot b^2 \cdot c$. It is
safe to quickly rule out the first two options, and we
try $2^5 \cdot 3^2 = 288$ against $2^2 \cdot 3^2 \cdot 5 = 180$. **180** is the
smallest integer which has 18 factors.

4.951 Another quick Venn diagram gives us $xy = 12$, and we
know that x and y must be mutually prime (otherwise
the GCF would be greater than 6). Neither can be 1
(because a and b are greater than 6). We use $x = 4$
and $y = 3$ to give us
$a = 24$ and $b = 18$, .
whose sum is **42**.

4.981 $444_9 = 4(81) + 4(9) + 4$. $11111_3 = 81 + 27 + 9 + 3 + 1$.
Subtracting, we see that $4(81) - 81 = 3(81)$,
$4(9) - (27 + 9) = 0$, and $4 - (3 + 1) = 0$, so we are left
with just $3(81)$ or $3(9^2) = $ **300₉**.

Geometry
Key and Solutions

Problems within the text are ordered with the last three digits
reversed. This way, if you are looking for a solution you
will not accidently see the answer to the next problem.
Problems marked with a ▇ do not include a written
solution, only the answer.

5.001	$9\pi\sqrt{3}$ cm³	**5.151**	12,600
5.010	21	**5.160**	1/3
5.011	$(576\pi + 216\sqrt{3})$	**5.161**	5
	$\approx 2,183.7$ in³	**5.170**	425π
5.020	22.5°	**5.171**	$\sqrt{5}$ cm.
5.021	$x = 24/5$	**5.180**	29units²
5.030	150°	**5.190**	84cm²
5.031	13ft	**5.200**	33°
5.040	$16\pi + 8$	**5.201**	9/2 cm
5.050	13mi	**5.211**	22
5.051	9/16	**5.220**	80cm
5.060	18in	**5.221**	$x = 48/9$
5.070	7.5cm	**5.230**	35°
5.071	π cm²	**5.231**	$\sqrt{3}$
5.080	2/3 cm	**5.240**	8π
5.090	32cm²	**5.241**	$5\sqrt{35}$ cm
5.100	42°	**5.250**	41cm
5.101	16in	**5.251**	80 lbs
5.110	3	**5.260**	$2\sqrt{3}$
5.111	2% decrease	**5.261**	$3\sqrt{3} - \pi$
5.120	26cm	**5.270**	12cm
5.121	$x = 7$	**5.271**	156cm²
5.130	100°	**5.280**	576cm²
5.131	5cm	**5.290**	$100\pi - 200$
5.140	12π	**5.300**	156°
5.141	$4\sqrt{10}$	**5.301**	14ft 7in
5.150	$2\sqrt{3}$	**5.311**	$500\pi/3$ in³

5.320 18cm

5.321 $x = 16/3$

5.330 95°

5.331 $75\sqrt{7}$

5.340 $3\pi + 18$

5.341 $21\sqrt{5} + 47$

5.350 35.5cm

5.351 1/4 lb

5.360 $(1 + \sqrt{2})$ ft

5.361 15.9

5.371 294

5.380 $(14\pi + 12\sqrt{3})$ cm

5.390 4π

5.400 18°

5.401 $3\sqrt{3}$ cm.

5.411 1/3

5.420 5°

5.430 112.5°

5.431 54in

5.440 13π

5.450 16ft

5.451 $(640/9)$ cm^3

5.460 $4\sqrt{3}$ cm

5.461 12

5.471 $\pi(2 - \sqrt{3})$ units^2

5.480 9in^2

5.490 $4\sqrt{2} + 8$ cm^2

5.500 132°

5.501 18π in^3

5.511 $72\sqrt{2}$ cm^3

5.520 22

5.530 40°

5.531 450/17

5.540 Proof, see solutions.

5.550 $\sqrt{a^2 + b^2 + c^2}$

5.551 3000 cm^3

5.560 $\sqrt{3}/2$

5.561 5.5cm

5.571 38cm

5.580 $27\sqrt{3}$

5.590 1:3

5.600 720cm

5.601 84

5.611 $36\sqrt{3}$ in^3

5.620 180cm

5.630 35°

5.650 7.4cm

5.651 990 lbs

5.660 3π cm^2

5.661 $18\sqrt{2}$

5.671 $3\pi/2$ cm^2

5.690 240cm^2

5.700 60°

5.720 9cm

5.730 81°

5.760 $x^2/4$

5.761 $\sqrt{5}$ cm

5.790 1cm^2

5.800 7

5.820 60cm^2

5.830 70°

5.860 $3\sqrt{10}$

5.890 3.49cm^2

5.900 5cm

5.930 50°

5.960 $9\sqrt{2}$

5.990 24/5 cm

5.001 The radius of the semicircle becomes
the slant height: 6cm. The arc
length of the semicircle becomes the
circumference of the cone: 6π cm.
This makes the diameter of the cone
6cm, and the radius 3cm. Use the Pythagorean
theorem to find the height of the cone: $3\sqrt{3}$ cm. The
volume is:

$$\frac{\pi \cdot 3^2 \cdot 3\sqrt{3}}{3} = 9\pi\sqrt{3}\, \text{cm}^3.$$

5.010 Use the diagram at right. The
same strategy can be used for
any polygon and the maximum
number is $(n-2)(n-3)/2$
(similar to **2.430**), where n is the
number of sides/vertices. For $n = 9$ we get **21**
diagonals. With this method, we essentially create a
polygon with $n-1$ vertices. Count its diagonals and
add one (for the missing "top" of the diagram).

(sides connect below)

5.011 Find the area of the base of the
cylinder. The base can be divided
into a circle sector and two 30-60-90
triangles. The sector is 2/3 of the
circle, which we add to the combined area of the triangles to get the
area of the base:

$$\frac{2}{3}\pi \cdot 36 + 3(3\sqrt{3}) = 24\pi + 9\sqrt{3}$$

Multiply by 24 inches to get the volume of water in
the cylinder: $24(24\pi + 9\sqrt{3}) = 576\pi + 216\sqrt{3}$.

5.020 ABHC is an isosceles trapezoid with angle BCH = 45°,
and triangle ABC is isosceles with base angle BCA
equal to 22.5°, so angle ACH = BCH - BCA =
22.5°. Alternatively, if we circumscribe a circle

about the octagon, we see that ACH is an inscribed angle (**p.185**) whose measure is half of the intercepted arc, which is 1/8 of 360°, making ACH 1/16 of 360° = **22.5°**.

5.030 Triangle ABC is isosceles, so inscribed angle A equals 35°, making minor arc BD = 70°. Angle CBA is 110°, making major arc BDA = 220°. Arc DA is the difference between arcs ADB and BD: 220° - 70° = **150°**.

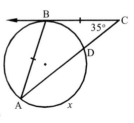

5.031 Adding the lines shown, we see that the 5 foot height is the altitude of a right triangle, creating two smaller similar right triangles in which 1/5 = 5/x, so x = 25 and the diameter of the semicircle is 26. This makes the height at the center (equal to the radius) **13ft.**

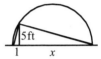

5.040 The small semicircle has a radius of 6 and arc length 6π, the larger semicircle has arc length 10π. The two short segments are equal to the difference of the radii (4cm). Added together, we get $16\pi + 8$.

5.050 The total distance south is 12 miles, and the total distance west is 5 miles. Connect his starting location to his finish to form the hypotenuse of a 5-12-13 right triangle. Parker is **13 miles** from where he started.

5.051 The circles are inscribed within similar triangles. The ratio of their radii will be 15:20 or 3:4, so the ratio of their areas will be 3^2 to 4^2 or 9/16.

5.060 The 120 degree rotation carries the gum
to a height of **18** inches as shown,
using the 30-60-90 right triangle
drawn.

5.070 With the diagram labeled as shown:
$6^2 + (12 - x)^2 = x^2$. Solving for x
gives us $180 = 24x$, or $x = $ **7.5cm.**

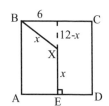

5.071 This solution actually works for any
polygon of any edge length. Label
the radius of the inscribed circle r,
and the radius of the Circumscribed circle R. By the
Pythagorean theorem:
$R^2 - r^2 = 1^2$, so
$\pi R^2 - \pi r^2 = \pi (R^2 - r^2) = \pi$ **cm².**

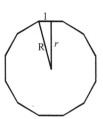

For any polygon of side length s, the difference in
area of the inscribed and circumscribed circles is:

$$\pi \left(\frac{s}{2} \right)^2 = \frac{\pi s^2}{4}$$

5.080 Using the Pythagorean theorem to
solve for r in the diagram as labeled
gives us: $1^2 + (2 - r)^2 = (r + 1)^2$.
Solving for r gives us $r = $ **2/3cm.**

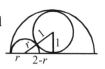

5.090 Rotate the inner square inside the circle until the
vertices are at the midpoints of the sides of the larger
square. Drawing the diagonals of the inner square
should make it clear that the inner square is half the
area of the outer square, or **32cm².**

5.100 At 96°, angle A cannot be a base angle of an isosceles
triangle. Angles B and C are base angles, each
measuring **42°.**

5.101 The volume of the spherical cannonball is equal to the volume of the cylinder of displaced water.

$$\frac{4}{3}\pi(4)^3 = \pi r^2 \cdot \frac{1}{3}.$$

Solving, we get $4^4 = r^2$ which gives us $r =$ **16in**.

5.110 Only triangles of side length 2-3-4, 2-4-5, and 3-4-5 are scalene with a perimeter less than or equal to 12. Do you see why 1-2-3 or 2-4-6 are impossible? Try to draw one with a ruler. This gives us **3**.

5.111 Increasing the radius by 40% increases the area of the base by $(1.4)^2$ or 1.96 times the original. Multiply by half the height and we get 0.98 times the original volume, or a **2% decrease** in volume.

5.120 Triangles ABC and BCD share two side lengths (AB = CD and BC = BC), so the difference in their perimeters (4) is the difference between the lengths of BD and AC, making BD + 4 = AC. We know that AC is twice BD, so BD = 4 and AC = 8, making AB + BC = BC + CD = 13. The perimeter of the parallelogram is twice that: **26cm**.

5.130 Angle A is
$180° - 95° - 35° = 50°$, mak -ing arc DC = 100°. Arc AC is $360° - 160° - 100° =$ **100°**.

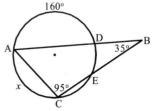

5.131 Adding AB and BC to the diagram, we get right triangle ABC with altitude BX and similar right triangles AXB and BXC, with AX/BX = BX/XC, so AX = 1 and the diameter of the circle is **5cm**.

5.140 There are 3/4 each of 4 circles of diameter 4cm.

$$\frac{3}{4} \cdot 4 \cdot 4\pi = 12\pi \text{ cm}.$$

5.141 From the diagram, using angle
bisector theorem:

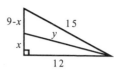

$$\frac{15}{9-x} = \frac{12}{x}$$ gives us $x = 4$, and

the Pythagorean theorem gives us $12^2 + 4^2 = y^2$.
Solve for y to get $y = 4\sqrt{10}$.

5.150 If the edge length is 2cm, then BC is the
diagonal of a square of side length
2cm. BC = $2\sqrt{2}$. AC is the hypotenuse of a triangle whose legs are 2
and $2\sqrt{2}$ cm. $2^2 + (2\sqrt{2})^2 = (AC)^2$.
AC = $\sqrt{12} = 2\sqrt{3}$ cm.

5.151 The side lengths are ten times the original, which will
make the area 10^2 times greater, or **12,600 units²**.

5.160 If CZ = BY = AX = 1, then BZ = CX = AY = 2, and
XZ = ZY = XY = $\sqrt{3}$, making the ratio of the sides
$\sqrt{3}/3$, and the ratio of the areas $(\sqrt{3}/3)^2 = $ **1/3.**

5.161 In the case where angle B = 90°, AB would be 15 (long
leg of an 8-15-17 Pythagorean triple) and length x
would be $\sqrt{226}$, slightly bigger than 15. As angle B
becomes more obtuse, x decreases until angle B
approaches 180°. Length x must be greater than
10cm because triangle ACD has sides 7 and 17.
Therefore, $\sqrt{226} > x > 10$, which means x may be 11,
12, 13, 14, or 15cm for a total of **5** integral lengths.

5.170 Label the length AX = x and the
circle radius r. AC = $16 + x$, and
AD = $16 - x$.
In ADE: $16^2 + (16 - x)^2 = r^2$.
In ACB: $8^2 + (16 + x)^2 = r^2$.
Substitution yields
$16^2 + (16 - x)^2 = 8^2 + (16 + x)^2$.
Solve for x to get $x = 3$. AD = 13, and DE = 16, so
AE = $\sqrt{13^2 + 16^2} = \sqrt{425}$. The area of the circle is
$\pi\sqrt{425}^2 = 425\pi$ cm².

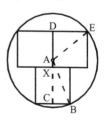

5.171 We find EC = $3\sqrt{5}$ using the Pythagorean theorem, and angle bisector theorem (angle ABD = CBD = 45°) gives us EX:CX = 1:2, so EX = $\sqrt{5}$ cm.

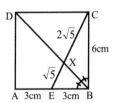

5.180 The distance between opposite vertices is $\sqrt{(4-1)^2+(5+2)^2} = \sqrt{58}$. We divide by $\sqrt{2}$ to get the side length: $\sqrt{29}$. Square this length to get the area: **29 units²**.

5.190 The horizontal line between $(-7,2)$ and $(14,2)$ can be used as the base of length 21. The height to the point $(-1,10)$ is 8 units. Half the base times the height equals **84cm²**. Alternatively, use the distance formula to get side lengths 21, 10, and 17. Use these values in Heron's formula to get 84cm². Many triangle area problems on the plane are best solved by drawing a rectangle around the triangle and subtracting the area outside the triangle from the rectangle (not necessary here).

5.200 Solve the equation $x + (2x) + (2x + 15) = 180$ for x to get $x =$ **33°**.

5.201 The surface area of a sphere is $4\pi r^2$. A hemisphere has half of the curved surface plus the area of the base: $2\pi r^2 + \pi r^2 = 3\pi r^2$. The volume of a hemisphere is $\frac{2}{3}\pi r^3$. Solve the equation $3\pi r^2 = \frac{2}{3}\pi r^3$ for r to get $r =$ **9/2**.

5.211 To use $f + v = e + 2$, we must find the number of edges. There are 20 kites, for a total of 80 sides, with each side shared by 2 kites. This gives us a total of 80/2 = 40 edges. $20 + v = 40 + 2$. $v =$ **22**.

5.220 If the interior angle measure is 171 degrees, the exterior angles measure 9 degrees and there are 360/9 = 40 sides, each of length 2cm for a perimeter of **80cm**.

5.230 Arc AB = 30. $(100-30)/2 = x$,
so $x = \textbf{35°}$.

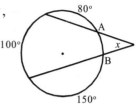

5.231 If we label length CX = x and the
radius of the circle is 3, then
EX = $3 + x$ and DX = $3 - x$.
(BX)(AX) = (DX)(EX), which
gives us: $2 \cdot 3 = (3+x)(3-x)$.
$6 = 9 - x^2$, $x^2 = 3$, so $x = \sqrt{3}$.

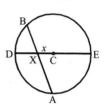

5.240 If we connect the centers of the
circles to the points of intersection, we create two equilateral
triangles (sides are radii of
congruent circles), which leaves
240° for each major arc, or 2/3 of each circle of
radius 3cm and circumference 6π:

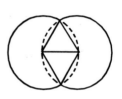

$$\frac{2}{3} \cdot 2 \cdot 6\pi = 8\pi \text{ cm.}$$

5.241 Using the Pythagorean theorem,
we get CD = $10\sqrt{10}$, and angle
bisector theorem gives us the
ratio of DX to CX is 15:35,
making DX = $3\sqrt{10}$ and CX =
$7\sqrt{10}$. Using the Pythagorean
theorem again we find BX = $3\sqrt{35}$. Triangles ACX
and DBX are similar, so AX/CX = DX/BX:

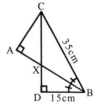

$$\frac{AX}{7\sqrt{10}} = \frac{3\sqrt{10}}{3\sqrt{35}} \text{ gives us AX} = \frac{210}{3\sqrt{35}} = \frac{70\sqrt{35}}{35} = 2\sqrt{35}.$$

AX + BX = AB = $5\sqrt{35}$.

5.250 Unfold the left side of the box to see that we are
solving for the diagonal length of a 9 by 40 rectangle.
The Pythagorean theorem gives us **41cm.**

5.251 The replica is 1/7 the height of the original, so its volume/mass is $(1/7)^3$ of the original, or 1/343. If the original weighs 27,440 pounds: 27,440/343 = **80lbs.**

5.260 The diagonals are $2\sqrt{2}$ cm. The altitude of an equilateral triangle creates two 30-60-90 right triangles with short leg $\sqrt{2}$ (half the side length) and long leg $\sqrt{2} \cdot \sqrt{3} = \sqrt{6}$. The area is:

$$\frac{1}{2} \cdot 2\sqrt{2} \cdot \sqrt{6} = \sqrt{12} = 2\sqrt{3} \text{ cm}^2.$$

5.261 Look first for a diagram that will help you solve the problem. To find each shaded area, use the diagram below.

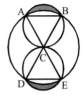

To find the area of shaded figure *P*, find the area of the smaller circle. The radius of the smaller circle is $\sqrt{3}$ **(p.199)**, so the area of the circle is 3π. Subtract the area of the triangle: $9\sqrt{3}/4$ and then divide by 3 (or multiply by 1/3) to get shaded area *P*:

$$\frac{1}{3}\left(3\pi - \frac{9\sqrt{3}}{4}\right) = \pi - \frac{9\sqrt{3}}{12}$$

To find the area of shaded figure *Q*, subtract the area of the triangle from the area of the sector, which is 1/6 the area of the larger circle:

$$\frac{1}{6} \cdot 9\pi - \frac{9\sqrt{3}}{4} = \frac{3\pi}{2} - \frac{9\sqrt{3}}{4}$$

Subtract to get the area of one lune.

$$\pi - \frac{9\sqrt{3}}{12} - \left(\frac{3\pi}{2} - \frac{9\sqrt{3}}{4}\right) = -\frac{\pi}{2} + \frac{18\sqrt{3}}{12} = \frac{3\sqrt{3}}{2} - \frac{\pi}{2}$$

Double this to get the combined area of the lunes:
$3\sqrt{3} - \pi \text{ cm}^2.$

5.270 CD is a leg of right triangles CDE and CDB. Label CE = x and EB = $2x$ (because AB is trisected at the points of intersection, CE is half the length of EB).

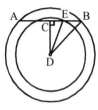

$7^2 - x^2 = (CD)^2$ and $9^2 - (3x)^2 = (CD)^2$, so $7^2 - x^2 = 9^2 - (3x)^2$. Solving for x we get $x = 2$, so AB = **12cm**.

5.271 Triangles BAD and ADC are similar, so: $\dfrac{8}{x} = \dfrac{x}{18}$. $x^2 = 144$ and $x = 12$, so the area of the figure is $\dfrac{12(8+18)}{2} = $ **156cm²**.

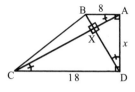

5.280 Label AX = x, then the side length of the square is $2x$, and CA = $2x - 15$ (the side of the square minus the radius CY=15). CX is 15. In right triangle CAX: $x^2 + (2x - 15)^2 = 15^2$. Solving for x we get $x = 12$. The area of each square is $(2x)^2 = $ **576cm²**.

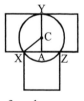

5.290 With the lines drawn as shown, it becomes clear that the two circle segments which make the "football" shape could be used to fill the white space outside the isosceles right triangle. We only need to subtract the area of triangle ABC from the quarter-circle: $100\pi - 200$

5.300 The exterior angle measure is easiest to find: $360/15 = 24$, so the interior angle is its supplement: **156°**.

5.301 Find the total volume of water, then find the depth when half is in each container. The combined volume is $24\pi(4)^2 + 24\pi(3)^2 = 600\pi$ cm³. The half in the 4ft cylinder fills it to a depth of $300\pi/16\pi = 18.75$ feet, or 18ft 9in. The half in the 3ft cylinder fills it to a depth of $300\pi/9\pi = 33.\overline{3}$ ft or 33ft 4in. The difference is **14ft 7in.**

5.311 Draw a diagonal from one point of contact where the inscribed cylinder touches the sphere through the center of the sphere to a point of contact on the opposite side (this is a diameter of the sphere). This diameter is the hypotenuse of a right triangle with legs 6in and 8in, making the diameter 10in and the radius 5in.
The volume is $\dfrac{4}{3}\pi \cdot 5^3 = \dfrac{500\pi}{3}$ in³.

5.320 Connecting the midpoints of any quadrilateral creates a parallelogram in which all four sides are midsegments of triangles whose bases are the diagonals of the original quadrilateral. The sides are therefore half the length of the diagonals: $4 + 4 + 5 + 5 = $ **18cm.**

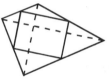

5.330 Angle BCA is inscribed in an arc measuring 30°, so its measure is 15°. The measure x is an exterior angle of triangle BEC equal to the sum of angles B and C. $x = $ **95°.**

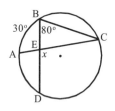

5.331 In similar triangles ABX and CDX, $30/x = 54/(56-x)$. Solve for x using cross-products to get $x = 20$. Find the height of triangle ABX using the Pythagorean theorem: $h = 5\sqrt{7}$ and the area is $15 \cdot 5\sqrt{7} = 75\sqrt{7}$.

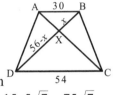

5.340 The side length of the hexagon is equal to the radius of the circle (3cm). This makes the diameter of the circle 6cm and the circumference 6π. Half the circumference is on the perimeter of the figure (3π). Add this to the six smaller segments (3cm each) to get $3\pi + 18$ cm.

5.341 The lengths of the sides are in the ratio $x : 2x : x\sqrt{5}$. We will label the parts of the short leg a and $a + 1$:

$$\frac{a}{2x} = \frac{a+1}{x\sqrt{5}}.$$

$$ax\sqrt{5} = 2ax + 2x$$

$$ax\sqrt{5} - 2ax = 2x$$

$$a(\sqrt{5} - 2) = 2$$

$$a = \frac{2}{\sqrt{5} - 2}$$

Rationalizing the denominator gives us: $a = 2\sqrt{5} + 4$. $x = a + (a+1) = 4\sqrt{5} + 9$, $2x = 8\sqrt{5} + 18$, and $x\sqrt{5} = 20 + 9\sqrt{5}$. The perimeter is the sum of these three sides: $21\sqrt{5} + 47$.

5.350 We look to "unfold" the box in a way that will give us the rectangle with the shortest diagonal. There are three ways in this case. Problem **5.250** gave us a 9 by 40 rectangle, using the top and the right sides give us a 10 by 39 rectangle, and using the top and the front gives us a 19 by 30 rectangle. To minimize the diagonal, we look for the rectangle whose sides are closest in length. The shortest distance is the diagonal of an 19cm by 30cm rectangle, $\approx$ **35.5 cm.**

5.351 The larger hemisphere has a surface area 4 times the original. If the areas are in the ratio 1:4, then the radii are in the ratio 1:2, and the volumes are in the ratio 1:8. The smaller hemisphere must have 1/8 the volume and mass of the larger one, or **1/4 pound.**

5.360 If we extend the sides as shown, we create 45-45-90 triangles on each corner, each with a hypotenuse of 1. This makes the length $a = \sqrt{2}/2$. The height of the octagon is $1 + 2a$: $(1+\sqrt{2})\,$ft.

5.361 The half-full cone is similar to and half the volume of the whole cone. If the ratio of the volumes is 1:2, then the ratio of the heights is $1:\sqrt[3]{2}$. If the height of the large cone is 20cm, we divide by $\sqrt[3]{2}$ to get the height of the small cone: $\approx$**15.9cm.**

5.371 If we add AX and BY, we get similar triangles CXA and CYB. This gives us the proportion:

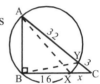

$$\frac{3}{16+x} = \frac{x}{35}, \text{ or } 105 = 16x + x^2.$$

Subtracting the 105 and factoring yields $0 = (x+21)(x-5)$, so $x = 5$ (the positive solution). Plugging this in, we see that triangle ABC has hypotenuse 35 and leg 21. This means that AB = 28 (not to scale), and the area of triangle ABC = **294** square units. Alternatively, we could add XY and solve using similar right triangles CYX and CBA.

5.380 Add segment BD parallel to AE. From the given information, we see that DE = 3, AB = 3, BC = 9 – 3 = 6, and CD = 12. This makes triangle CBD a 30-60-90 right triangle in which BD $=6\sqrt{3}=$ AE = FG. The

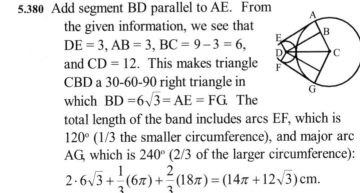

total length of the band includes arcs EF, which is 120° (1/3 the smaller circumference), and major arc AG, which is 240° (2/3 of the larger circumference):

$$2\cdot 6\sqrt{3} + \frac{1}{3}(6\pi) + \frac{2}{3}(18\pi) = (14\pi + 12\sqrt{3})\,\text{cm}.$$

5.390 From the diagram we have 30-60-90 triangle with short leg of length 2 (half the side of the hexagon). This makes $r = 2\sqrt{3}$ and $R = 4$, where r and R are the radii of the inscribed and circumscribed circles. The area of the annulus is $\pi(4)^2 - \pi(2\sqrt{3})^2 = 4\pi$ cm². Alternatively, we are looking for the difference between the radii squared and by the Pythagorean theorem, we see:

$R^2 - r^2 = 2^2$, so $\pi(R^2 - r^2) = 4\pi$. (See **5.071**).

5.400 Triangle ACB is isosceles with obtuse vertex angle B = 144°, making its base angles A and C **18°**.

5.401 The surface area of the cone is $\pi(3)^2 + \pi(3)s$ (*s* is the slant height of the cone). The surface area of the hemisphere is $3\pi(3)^2$. Set these equal to get $9\pi + 3\pi s = 27\pi$, so s = 6. The slant height (6) is the hypotenuse of the 30-60-90 right triangle whose short leg is the radius (3cm). The height is the long leg: $3\sqrt{3}$ cm.

5.411 If we label the side length of a cube *s*, the long diagonal of a cube is $s\sqrt{3}$, making the radius of the circumscribed sphere $s\sqrt{3}/2$. The radius of the inscribed sphere is *s*/2. The ratio of the surface area of the small sphere to the large sphere is:

$$\frac{4\pi\left(\dfrac{s}{2}\right)^2}{4\pi\left(\dfrac{s\sqrt{3}}{2}\right)^2} = \frac{s^2}{(s\sqrt{3})^2} = \frac{s^2}{3s^2} = \frac{1}{3}$$

5.420 Connecting two adjacent points to any other vertex will create a **5°** angle (see **5.620**).

5.430 Arc BCD is 360° minus arcs AB and AD, or 225°. Angle measure *x* is half the intercepted arc: **112.5°**.

5.431 In similar right triangles BDX and
ACX, BD = 44, and AC = 28. Label
segment AX = x and BX = $90 - x$.
This gives us the proportion:

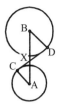

$\dfrac{28}{x} = \dfrac{44}{90 - x}$, and cross products

give us $2{,}520 - 28x = 44x$. Solving for x we get
$x = 35$, so AX = 35 and BX = 55. Substituting and
applying the Pythagorean theorem, we get CX = 21
and DX = 33. CX + DX = CD = **54 inches.**

5.440 Semicircle BC has an arc length of
9π. After the dog passes point B or
C, three feet of the leash are on the
side of the shed and the radius is
limited to 6 feet. The arc measure
of AB and CD is 60°. Their sum is
120°, which is 1/3 of a circle of
diameter 12. Therefore, arc lengths AB + CD =
$(1/3)12\pi = 4\pi$ and the combined length of the
dashed path is $4\pi + 9\pi = 13\pi$ feet.

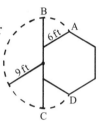

5.450 When we begin to climb, the triangle
formed between the floor, the ladder,
and the wall has lengths 14ft, 48ft,
and 50ft (recognizing Pythagorean
triples is key here) and when the
ladder slips, the 48 foot height
becomes 40 feet. The ladder (hypotenuse) remains
50, so the base of the ladder must now be 30 feet
from the wall (3:4:5 right triangle), so the base has
slipped $30 - 14 = $ **16 feet.**

5.451 The ratio of their altitudes is 3:4, so the ratio of their
volumes is $3^3 : 4^3 = 27 : 64$. Set up a proportion :

$\dfrac{27}{64} = \dfrac{30}{x}$ gives us $x = $ **(640/9)cm³**, about 71.1cm³.

5.460 If the perimeter is 24cm, the side
length is 4cm. Adding BX perpendicular to AC creates two 30-60-90
right triangles in which BX = 2 and
AX = CX = $2\sqrt{3}$, therefore
AC = $4\sqrt{3}$ cm.

5.461 20 triangles have a total of 60 sides, but each side
(edge) is shared by two triangles, so an icosahedron
has 30 edges. $f + v = e + 2$, gives us $20 + v = 32$,
and solving we get $v = 12$, so there are **12** vertices.

5.471 We only need to find the radius (r) of
the congruent semicircles. If we
add the lines shown, we notice that
triangle ABC is a right triangle with
BC = r and AC = $2r$ which means
that triangle ABC is a 30-60-90
triangle with AB = $r\sqrt{3}$. Segment AB is also equal
to the side length of the square (1) minus the radius:
AB = $1 - r$, so $r\sqrt{3} = 1 - r$. Add r to both sides:
$r\sqrt{3} + r = 1$. Factor out the r: $r(1 + \sqrt{3}) = 1$. Divide
and rationalize the denominator:

$$r = \frac{1}{1 + \sqrt{3}} \cdot \frac{1 - \sqrt{3}}{1 - \sqrt{3}} = \frac{1 - \sqrt{3}}{-2} = \frac{\sqrt{3} - 1}{2}$$

The combined area of the four semicircles is $2\pi r^2$:

$$2\pi \left(\frac{\sqrt{3} - 1}{2} \right)^2 = \pi(2 - \sqrt{3}) \, \text{units}^2.$$

5.480 Because DC = BE = 8.5 inches and
DE = 11 inches, DB = CE = 2.5
inches. This means that BC = 6
inches. BC is the hypotenuse of a
45-45-90 right triangle, so AB =
$3\sqrt{2}$ and the area of triangle ABC =
$(3\sqrt{2})^2 / 2 = $ **9in²**.

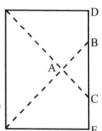

5.490 To find the area of the square, we will
begin by finding the length of AE
(the diagonal length of the square)
using the Pythagorean theorem with
right triangle AFE. We have learned
to find the height (AF) of an octagon (**5.360**).

AF = $2 + 2\sqrt{2}$. FE = 2. By the Pythagorean
theorem: $2^2 + (2 + 2\sqrt{2})^2 = (AE)^2$, so
$8\sqrt{2} + 16 = (AE)^2$. $(AE)^2 = (AC)^2 + (CE)^2$,
therefore $(AE)^2 = 2(AC)^2$. We are trying to find the
area of the square $(AC)^2$:

$$(AC)^2 = \frac{(AE)^2}{2} = \frac{8\sqrt{2} + 16}{2} = 4\sqrt{2} + 8 \text{ cm}^2.$$

5.500 We will label the angles $x - 28$, x, $x + 28$, and $x + 56$.
The sum of the angles is 360°, so $4x + 56 = 360°$.
Solving for x, we get $x = 76$. The largest angle
measure is $x + 56 = 76 + 56 = \mathbf{132°}$.

5.501 The radius of the hemisphere is equal
to the distance from the midpoint of
the base of the cube A to the vertex
of the cube C. AC is the hypotenuse of a right triangle whose short
leg AB is half the diagonal length of a square of side
length 2. Therefore AB = $\sqrt{2}$, BC = 2, and
$(\sqrt{2})^2 + 2^2 = (AC)^2$. AC = $\sqrt{6}$ and the surface area
of the hemisphere is $3\pi(\sqrt{6})^2 = 18\pi \text{ in}^2$.

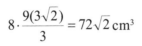

5.511 Eight triangular pyramids are removed.
The base of each is an isosceles
right triangle of area $(3\sqrt{2})^2 / 2 =$
9cm² and whose height is $3\sqrt{2}$ cm.
The combined volume of eight of
these pyramids is $8(Bh/3)$:

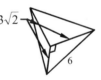

$$8 \cdot \frac{9(3\sqrt{2})}{3} = 72\sqrt{2} \text{ cm}^3$$

5.520 From number theory: $360/n$ equals the exterior angle measure, so for the exterior angle measure to be integral, n must be a factor of 360. 360 has 24 factors, but we cannot use 1 or 2 (a polygon cannot have 1 or 2 sides). $24 - 2 = $ **22** polygons.

5.530 Arcs AC and BD are twice the inscribed angles A and D, making AC = BD = 140°. If we add arcs AB + BC + CD we get 360° - 120° = 240°.
When we add arcs AC and BD we get 280°, which is equal to AB + BC + BC + CD.
If AB + BC + CD = 280° and AB + BC + BC + CD = 240° then arc measure BC = x = **40°**.

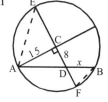

5.531 Segment AD = 17 by the Pythagorean theorem. EC = AC = 15 (both are radii). DF = 15 − 8 = 7. In similar triangles ADE and FDB, AD/DF = DE/BD: $\dfrac{17}{7} = \dfrac{23}{x}$, so $x = \dfrac{121}{17}$.

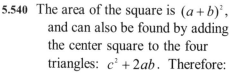

$$AB = AD + DB = 17 + \frac{161}{17} = \frac{289}{17} + \frac{161}{17} = \frac{450}{17}.$$

5.540 The area of the square is $(a+b)^2$, and can also be found by adding the center square to the four triangles: $c^2 + 2ab$. Therefore:

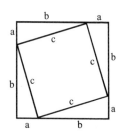

$$(a+b)^2 = c^2 + 2ab$$
$$a^2 + 2ab + b^2 = c^2 + 2ab$$
$$a^2 + b^2 = c^2$$

5.550 The length YZ$= \sqrt{b^2 + c^2}$, so XZ is the hypotenuse of right triangle XYZ. For diagonal XZ,
$(XZ)^2 = a^2 + (\sqrt{b^2 + c^2})^2$
so XZ $= = \sqrt{a^2 + b^2 + c^2}$.

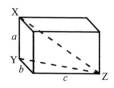

5.551 To increase the surface area 100 times, the edge length must be increased by a factor of 10, meaning the volume will be increased by a factor of 1,000. The new cube will have 1,000 times the volume of the original, or **3,000cm³**.

5.560 We are looking for the ratio AC:BD. Triangle ABC is isosceles with angle ABC = 120°. If we drop an altitude from B to AC, we bisect angle ABC creating two 30-60-90 triangles. Assign a length of 2 to BC, and we see that CE = $\sqrt{3}$ (you could also call length BC = 2x and CE = $x\sqrt{3}$, but we are only looking for the ratio, so it is fine to assign a number that is easy to work with). Double both values to get the lengths of the sides of the hexagons. AC = 2CE = $2\sqrt{3}$ and BD = 2BC = 4 so

$$\frac{AC}{BD} = \frac{2\sqrt{3}}{4} = \frac{\sqrt{3}}{2}.$$

5.561 Call the edge lengths *a*, *b*, and *c*. We are given that *ab* = 6, *bc* = 9, and *ac* = 12. We are looking for the diagonal length, given by $\sqrt{a^2 + b^2 + c^2}$ (**5.550**).

$$\frac{ab \cdot ac}{bc} = a^2 = 8, \; \frac{ab \cdot bc}{ac} = b^2 = 4.5, \; \frac{ac \cdot bc}{ab} = c^2 = 18.$$

The diagonal is therefore $\sqrt{8 + 4.5 + 18} \approx$ **5.5cm**.

5.571 If we add segments FD and FB we get similar triangles FDE and EFB (angles FED = BEF and EFD = EBF). Therefore, DE/EF = FE/EB:

$$\frac{8}{20} = \frac{20}{EB}, \text{ so EB} = 50. \text{ EC} = 20 \text{ so CB} = 30.$$

Triangles FDC and BAC are similar:

$$\frac{FC}{BC} = \frac{DC}{AC}. \; \frac{20}{30} = \frac{12}{AC}. \; \text{AC} = 18.$$

AF = AC + FC = **38cm**.

5.580 In the diagram, we see that triangles AXF and AXC are 30-60-90 right triangles. AF = 6, making AX = $3\sqrt{3}$ and XC = 9 which makes the area of triangle ACE = $9 \cdot 3\sqrt{3} = 27\sqrt{3}$.

5.590 We will do this the hard way to prove that the solution works for all cases. Labeling the semicircles by their diameters, the shaded area is equal to semicircle AC minus semicircle BC plus semicircle AB. The unshaded area is equal to semicircle AC minus semicircle AB plus semicircle BC. The areas of the semicircles are directly proportional to their radii squared, or even their diameters squared, so we will use x^2 to represent the area of semicircle AB, y^2 to represent the area of semicircle BC, and $(x + y)^2$ to represent the area of semicircle AC. The ratio AB to BC is $x{:}y$, and we are looking for the ratio of the shaded area to the unshaded area:

$$\frac{shaded}{unshaded} = \frac{(x+y)^2 - y^2 + x^2}{(x+y)^2 - x^2 + y^2} = \frac{x^2 + 2xy + y^2 - y^2 + x^2}{x^2 + 2xy + y^2 - x^2 + y^2} =$$

$$\frac{2x^2 + 2xy}{2y^2 + 2xy} = \frac{2x(x+y)}{2y(x+y)} = \frac{x}{y}.$$

Of course, we did not need to do all of this. It would have been easier to assign convenient values, but this allows us to see that for any ratio $x{:}y$ in the given diagram, the ratio of the areas will be $x{:}y$. If AB:BC = 1:3 then the ratio of the shaded to unshaded areas is also **1:3**.

5.600 If its interior angles measure 179°, its exterior angles are 1°, so it has 360/1 = 360 sides, each 2cm in length for a perimeter of **720cm**.

5.601 There are 38 total faces. We can solve for the number of edges with some common sense: 6 squares have 24 sides and 32 triangles have a total of 96 sides for a total of 120 sides, each shared by two faces. This gives us 60 edges. $f + v = e + 2$ can be used to give us $v = 24$. $v + e = 24 + 60 = $ **84**.

5.611 The triangle facing us is a 30-60-90 triangle (the water line will be parallel to the floor) with a long leg length 6in. This gives us a short leg of $2\sqrt{3}$ inches, making the area of the triangle $6\sqrt{3}$. Using the triangle as the base of a prism, we see that the prism's height would be 6in. The volume (Bh) is therefore $6(6\sqrt{3}) = 36\sqrt{3}$ in³.

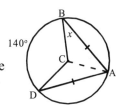

5.620 Triangle ACB is isosceles, so angle ABC = 170°. The exterior angles are 10°, and 360/10 = 36 sides of length 5cm makes the perimeter **180cm.**

5.630 Arcs AB and AD must be equal because they are intercepted by congruent chords, making each 110°. Angles CBA and CAB are base angles of isosceles triangle ABC and therefore equal, with angle BCA = 110°, both base angles must be 35°. $x =$ **35°.**

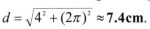

5.650 If we unroll the lateral surface of the cylinder, the path of the ant is the diagonal of a rectangle that is 4cm tall and half the circumference of the circle in width (2π cm). We use the Pythagorean theorem to find the diagonal length:

$$d = \sqrt{4^2 + (2\pi)^2} \approx \mathbf{7.4cm}.$$

5.651 The ratio of the diameters of the snowballs is 2:3:4, so the ratio of their masses is $2^3{:}3^3{:}4^3 = 8{:}27{:}64$. The mass of the smallest snowball is 80 pounds. Using our ratio, we get 270lbs for the medium and 640lbs for the large, for a total weight of **990lbs**.

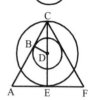

5.660 Segment AE = 4cm. Both AEC and BDC are 30-60-90 right triangles, so EC = $4\sqrt{3}$, CD = $2\sqrt{3}$, and BD = $\sqrt{3}$. The small circle therefore has an area of $\pi(\sqrt{3})^2 = 3\pi$ cm².

5.661 Call the edge lengths a, b, and c. We are given that $ab = 6$, $bc = 9$, and $ac = 12$ and we are looking for abc. $\sqrt{(ab)(bc)(ac)} = \sqrt{a^2b^2c^2} = abc$:

$$abc = \sqrt{(6)(9)(12)} = 18\sqrt{2}$$

5.671 The largest semicircle is inscribed as shown, with its diameter perpendicular to diagonal BD. Triangles BEF and DFG are congruent (both are 30-60-90 triangles with medium leg length r). This means that the ratio of BF to DF is 2:1, and because BD = 3, BF = 2 and FD =1. This makes $r = \sqrt{3}$, and the area of semicircle is $\dfrac{\pi(\sqrt{3})^2}{2} = \dfrac{3\pi}{2}$.

5.690 The diagonals of a rhombus are perpendicular and bisect each other, and the area is half the product of the diagonals. AC is the hypotenuse of a right triangle of short leg 8. We use the Pythagorean theorem to find long leg 15cm, making the long diagonal 30cm and the area

$$\frac{30 \cdot 16}{2} = \textbf{240cm}^2.$$

5.700 Ten 150° interior angles means there are ten 30° exterior angles for a total of 300°. For the exterior angle sum to equal 360°, the remaining exterior angle must measure **60°**, which is the largest.

5.720 If the perimeter of rhombus PQRS = 18cm, the side length is 18/4 = 4.5cm. The side of the rhombus forms the midsegment of triangle WXY, where WY is the base. WY is twice the midsegment = **9cm**.

5.730 Triangle CAB is isosceles (CA and CB are radii) with base angles A = B = 63°. Angle ACB is 54°, making arc AB 54° as well. Because parallel lines intercept congruent arcs, arc EG = 54°, angle ECG = 54°, and angle EFC = 36°. In triangle ADF, angle A = 63°, F = 36°, and the measure of angle D = x = **81°**.

5.760 There are many ways to solve this. The diagram to the right should be convincing. The area of an isosceles right triangle with hypotenuse length x is 1/4 the area of a square of edge length x, or **$x^2/4$**.

5.761 There are a lot of similar triangles in this figure. Mark congruent angles and convince yourself that triangles ABF, ADE, CBE, CDF, and EDF are all similar. We can use the

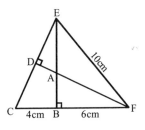

Pythagorean theorem in triangle EBF to find EB = 8cm, so the ratio of the short leg to the long leg in each of the similar triangles is 1:2. Using the Pythagorean theorem with triangle CBE we get CE = $4\sqrt{5}$, DE = $2\sqrt{5}$, and AD is DE/2 = $\sqrt{5}$ cm.

5.790 In the diagram, AB = BC = 1cm and AC = $\sqrt{2}$ by the Pythagorean theorem. We will find the area by:

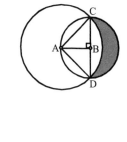

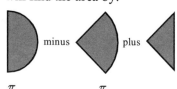

$$\frac{\pi}{2} \qquad -\frac{\pi}{2} \qquad +1 \qquad = \mathbf{1cm^2}.$$

5.800 The sum of the interior angles in a decagon is 180(8) = 1,440. To maximize the number of acute angles, we maximize the measure of the obtuse interior angles. The largest interior angle possible is just a hair smaller than 360°. With two (almost) 360 degree angles, the remaining 8 angles would have an average measure of slightly more than 90°, so we must have at least three obtuse interior angles and a maximum of **7** acute interior angles. One example is shown.

5.820 The diagonals of the rhombus intersect at right angles, so the sides of the rhombus form the hypotenuse of a right triangle of sides that can be labeled x and $3x$. This gives us:

$$x^2 + (3x)^2 = 10^2 \text{ or } 10x^2 = 100, \text{ which means}$$

$x = \sqrt{10}$. The area of a rhombus (it is just four right triangles) is half the product of the diagonals:

$$\frac{2\sqrt{10} \cdot 6\sqrt{10}}{2} = 60. \text{ The area is } \mathbf{60cm^2}.$$

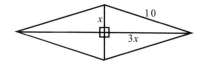

5.830 Quadrilateral ACDE is a kite with right angles ACD and DEA, which makes angles A and CDE supplementary, so angle CDE = 140°. Notice kites CBGD and DGFE as well, with diagonals DB and DF bisecting the vertex angles. This makes the measure *x* of angle BDF half the measure of CDE. *x* = 70°.

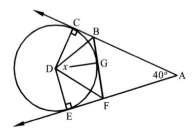

5.890 There are only a few triangles with integral side lengths *a*, *b*, and *c* that have perimeter = 15:
$(a, b, c) = (1, 7, 7)$ $(2, 6, 7)$, $(3, 6, 6)$, $(3, 5, 7)$, $(4, 5, 6)$ and $(4, 4, 7)$. It is easy to use Heron's formula here, because each has the same semiperimeter. We are looking to minimize the product
$(s-a)(s-b)(s-c)$, where $s = 7.5$. For each set above we get:
$(1, 7, 7)$: $(7.5-1)(7.5-7)(7.5-7) = 1.625$
$(2, 6, 7)$: $(7.5-2)(7.5-6)(7.5-7) = 4.125$
$(3, 6, 6)$: $(7.5-3)(7.5-6)(7.5-6) = 10.125$
$(3, 5, 7)$: $(7.5-3)(7.5-5)(7.5-7) = 5.625$
$(4, 5, 6)$: $(7.5-4)(7.5-5)(7.5-6) = 13.125$
$(4, 4, 7)$: $(7.5-4)(7.5-4)(7.5-7) = 6.125$
The (1, 7, 7) triangle is the smallest, now complete Heron's formula to find the area:
$\sqrt{7.5(1.625)} \approx \mathbf{3.49 cm^2}$.

5.900 The diagonal length must be greater than the difference between side lengths, making the shortest possible integer length **5cm.**

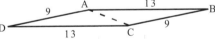

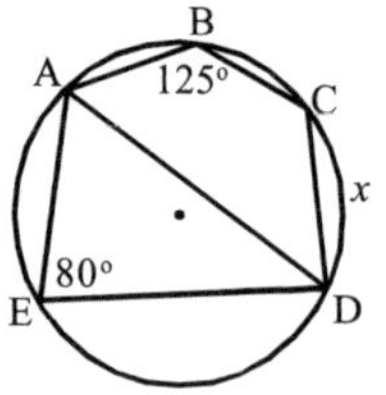

5.930 Angle B is inscribed in major arc ADC, which measures 250°. This makes minor arc AC = 110°. Angle E is inscribed in minor arc AD which measures 160°. The measure of arc CD = 160° – 110° = **50°**.

5.990 The area of the rhombus is half the product of its diagonals, or 24cm^2. The diagonals bisect each other at right angles, creating 3-4-5 right triangles where 5cm is the side length of the rhombus. The area of a rhombus can also be found by multiplying its edge length by its altitude (a) which gives us $5a = 24$, so the altitude is **24/5 cm**.

Appendix

Appendix
Chapter VII

In general, there are very few things that I recommend you just sit down and memorize. After solving a lot of difficult problems, you tend to build a mathematical vocabulary of items that are frequently useful. For example, most students who do well in mathematical competitions would not need to do any math to find the missing hypotenuse of a right triangle with legs of length 12 and 35 or the square root of 1,024.

Included in this chapter are formulas and values that are good to know. Much of this should be memorized, but don't spend too much time reciting numbers and formulas in your head. Refer to this section when you are not sure about a perfect cube or a formula and eventually you will start to remember them without ever having done much drill work.

It doesn't hurt to purposefully commit some of this material to memory. My memory is dreadful, and I have had to learn some patterns and tricks that help me recall most of the material in this section. Look for patterns that help you find ways to do the same.

Some of the material here is not covered in the text, but will be useful as you continue with practice from other sources.

Squares:	**Cubes:**	**Powers of 2:**
$11^2 = 121$	$1^3 = 1$	$2^0 = 1$
$12^2 = 144$	$2^3 = 8$	$2^1 = 2$
$13^2 = 169$	$3^3 = 27$	$2^2 = 4$
$14^2 = 196$	$4^3 = 64$	$2^3 = 8$
$15^2 = 225$	$5^3 = 125$	$2^4 = 16$
$16^2 = 256$	$6^3 = 216$	$2^5 = 32$
$17^2 = 289$	$7^3 = 343$	$2^6 = 64$
$18^2 = 324$	$8^3 = 512$	$2^7 = 128$
$19^2 = 361$	$9^3 = 729$	$2^8 = 256$
$20^2 = 400$	$10^3 = 1,000$	$2^9 = 512$
$21^2 = 441$	$11^3 = 1,331$	$2^{10} = 1,024$

Squaring a Number Ending in 5 (or .5):

The number will always end in 25. Find the leading digits by
    multiplying the first digit(s) by the next integer:

$25^2 = (2 \cdot 3) \, 25 = 625$

$35^2 = (3 \cdot 4) \, 25 = 1,225$

$45^2 = (4 \cdot 5) \, 25 = 2,025$

$55^2 = (5 \cdot 6) \, 25 = 3,025$

$65^2 = (6 \cdot 7) \, 25 = 4,225$

$75^2 = (7 \cdot 8) \, 25 = 5,625$

$85^2 = (8 \cdot 9) \, 25 = 7,225$

$95^2 = (9 \cdot 10) \, 25 = 9,025$

$105^2 = (10 \cdot 11) \, 25 = 11,025$

...

These come
up frequently:

$0.5^2 = 0.25$

$1.5^2 = 2.25$

$2.5^2 = 6.25$

$3.5^2 = 12.25$

...

First 50 Primes: (There are 25 primes less than 100).

2	3	5	7	11	13	17	19	23	29	31
37	41	43	47	53	59	61	67	71	73	79
83	89	97	101	103	107	109	113	127	131	137
139	149	151	157	163	167	173	179	181	191	
193	197	199	211	223	227	229 ...				

Don't be fooled by these prime-looking numbers:

91 $(7 \cdot 13)$ **119:** $(7 \cdot 17)$ **133:** $(7 \cdot 19)$ **143** $(11 \cdot 13)$

161: $(7 \cdot 23)$ **187:** $(11 \cdot 17)$ **203:** $(7 \cdot 29)$ **217:** $(7 \cdot 31)$

Pythagorean Theorem: For a right triangle with legs a and b with hypotenuse c: $a^2 + b^2 = c^2$

Pythagorean Triples:

Primitive triples and other common triples where $a \leq 20$.

a **is odd:**	a **is even:**
note: $a^2 = b + c$	$(6, 8, 10)$
$(3, 4, 5)$	$(8, 15, 17) : 8^2 = 2(15 + 17)$
$(5, 12, 13)$	$(10, 24, 26)$
$(7, 24, 25)$	$(12, 35, 37) : 12^2 = 2(35 + 37)$
$(9, 40, 41)$	$(14, 48, 50)$
$(11, 60, 61)$	$(16, 63, 65)* : 16^2 = 2(63 + 65)$
$(13, 84, 85)$	$(18, 80, 82)$
$(15, 112, 113)$	$(20, 21, 29)**$

* Also $(16, 30, 34)$ which is just twice the $(8, 15, 17)$ triple.

** Largest common primitive triple and does not fit easily into the patterns shown.

Less common primitive triples for $a < 40$:

$(28, 45, 53)$ $(33, 56, 65)$ $(36, 77, 85)$ $(39, 80, 89)$

Pascal's Triangle:

```
                    1   row 0
                  1   1   row 1
                1   2   1   row 2
              1   3   3   1   row 3
            1   4   6   4   1   row 4
          1   5  10  10   5   1   row 5
        1   6  15  20  15   6   1   row 6
      1   7  21  35  35  21   7   1   row 7
    1   8  28  56  70  56  28   8   1   row 8
  1   9  36  84 126 126  84  36   9   1   row 9
1  10  45 120 210 252 210 120  45  10   1   row 10
1 11 55 165 330 462 462 330 165 55 11 1   row 11
```

The 7th row is relatively easy to memorize. If you memorize the 7th row, the rows beneath are easy to construct.

Triangular numbers follow the third diagonal $(1, 3, 6, 10...)$.

The sum of the numbers in the nth row is 2^n.

Commonly Used Fractions:
Know all of these without having to think about them.
Obviously, this is not a comprehensive list. You should know
your tenths, hundredths, twentieths, etc. as well.

$$\frac{1}{8} = 0.125 \qquad \frac{1}{4} = 0.25 \qquad \frac{1}{3} = 0.\overline{3}$$

$$\frac{3}{8} = 0.375 \qquad \frac{1}{2} = 0.5 \qquad \frac{5}{8} = 0.625$$

$$\frac{2}{3} = 0.\overline{6} \qquad \frac{7}{8} = 0.875 \qquad \frac{3}{4} = 0.75$$

Sixths and Twelfths:

$$\frac{1}{12} = 0.08\overline{3} \qquad \frac{1}{6} = 0.1\overline{6} \qquad \frac{5}{12} = 0.41\overline{6}$$

$$\frac{7}{12} = 0.583 \qquad \frac{5}{6} = 0.8\overline{3} \qquad \frac{11}{12} = 0.91\overline{6}$$

Sevenths: Remember 1/7 and the rest come easy. The
order of the digits remains the same.

$$\frac{1}{7} = 0.\overline{142857} \qquad \frac{2}{7} = 0.\overline{285714} \qquad \frac{3}{7} = 0.\overline{428571}$$

$$\frac{4}{7} = 0.\overline{571428} \qquad \frac{5}{7} = 0.\overline{714285} \qquad \frac{6}{7} = 0.\overline{857142}$$

Ninths, 99ths, etc.:

$$\frac{1}{9} = 0.\overline{1} \qquad\qquad \frac{2}{9} = 0.\overline{2}$$

$$\frac{13}{99} = 0.\overline{13} \qquad\qquad \frac{7}{99} = 0.\overline{07}$$

$$\frac{101}{999} = 0.\overline{101} \qquad\qquad \frac{20}{999} = 0.\overline{020} \quad \text{etc.}$$

Area Formulas:

Square: $A = s^2$

Parallelogram: $A = bh$

Rhombus or Kite: $A = \dfrac{ab}{2}$ (where a and b are the diagonals, this works for any quadrilateral with perpendicular diagonals).

Trapezoid: $A = \dfrac{h(b_1 + b_2)}{2}$ (where b_1 and b_2 are the parallel sides).

Circle: $A = \pi r^2$ Circumference: $C = 2\pi r$

Triangle: $A = \dfrac{bh}{2}$

$A = rs$ (where r is the inradius and s is the semiperimeter).

$A = \dfrac{abc}{4R}$ (a, b, and c are the sides and R is the circumradius).

$A = \dfrac{1}{2}ab\sin c$ (useful trig. formula not used in this text).

Heron's Formula: Used to find the area of a triangle with side lengths a, b, and c where s is the semiperimeter (half the perimeter):

$$A = \sqrt{s(s-a)(s-b)(s-c)}$$

Volume:

Prism or Cylinder: $V = Bh$ Sphere: $V = \dfrac{4}{3}\pi r^3$

Pyramid or Cone: $V = \dfrac{Bh}{3}$

Surface Area:

Cylinder: $A = \pi r^2 + \pi r h$ Sphere: $V = 4\pi r^2$

Cone: $A = \pi r^2 + \pi r s$

Faces, Edges, and Vertices: $f + v = e + 2$

Ones!

$1^2 = 1$

$11^2 = 121$

$111^2 = 12,321 = (3 \cdot 37)^2$

$1,111^2 = 1,234,321 = (11 \cdot 101)^2$

$11,111^2 = 123,454,321 = (41 \cdot 271)^2$

$111,111^2 = 12,345,654,321 = (3 \cdot \boxed{7 \cdot 11 \cdot 13} \cdot 37)^2$

$\underset{1,001}{}$

...until the pattern breaks down after 12,345,678,987,654,321.

1,001 is boxed above because any six-digit number which repeats the same three digit is divisible by 1,001. Example: $317,317 = 1,001 \cdot 317 = 7 \cdot 11 \cdot 13 \cdot 317$

Clocks

Every minute, the minute hand on a standard clock travels 6 degrees and the hour hand travels 0.5 degrees. Perhaps more importantly, the angle between them changes by 5.5 degrees. This comes up often enough that it helps to have this memorized.

Permutations: $nPr = P(n,r) = \dfrac{n!}{(n-r)!}$

Combinations: $nCr = C(n,r) = \dbinom{n}{r} = \dfrac{n!}{r!(n-r)!}$

Linear Equations:

Slope: $m = \dfrac{y_2 - y_1}{x_2 - x_1}$

Point-Slope Form: $y - y_1 = m(x - x_1)$

Standard Form: $Ax + By = C$

Slope in Standard Form: $-\dfrac{A}{B}$

Slope-Intercept Form: $y = mx + b$

Quadratics: $y = ax^2 + bx + c$

Quadratic Formula: Used to find the roots (zeros) of a quadratic equation in the form $0 = ax^2 + bx + c$:

$$x = \frac{-b \pm \sqrt{b^2 - 4ac}}{2a}.$$

Vertex: The vertex is a maximum when $a < 0$ and a minimum when $a > 0$. The x-coordinate of the vertex is called the axis of symmetry and is found at:

$$x = \frac{-b}{2a}.$$

Sum of the Roots/Product of the Roots:

The sum of the roots of a quadratic in the form:

$$0 = ax^2 + bx + c \text{ is equal to } \frac{-b}{a} \text{ or } -\frac{b}{a}.$$

The product of the roots of a quadratic in the form:

$$0 = ax^2 + bx + c \text{ is equal to } \frac{c}{a}.$$

Special Factorizations:

Sum of Squares: $a^2 + b^2 = (a + b)^2 - 2ab$

Difference of Squares: $a^2 - b^2 = (a + b)(a - b)$

Difference of Cubes: $a^3 - b^3 = (a - b)(a^2 + ab + b^2)$

Sum of Cubes: $a^3 + b^3 = (a + b)(a^2 - ab + b^2)$

Sum of the First n Cubes:

$$1^3 + 2^3 + 3^3 + ... + n^3 = (1 + 2 + 3 + ... + n)^2$$

Harmonic Mean: Used to find an average rate of a and b:

$$H = \frac{2ab}{a+b}.$$

For $\{a_1, a_2, a_3, ...a_n\}$: $H = \dfrac{n}{\dfrac{1}{a_1} + \dfrac{1}{a_2} + \dfrac{1}{a_3} + ... + \dfrac{1}{a_n}}.$

Arithmetic Mean:

For $\{a_1, a_2, a_3, ...a_n\}$: $A = \dfrac{a_1 + a_2 + a_3 + ... + a_n}{n}.$

Sum of an Arithmetic Series: The sum of an arithmetic series with terms a_1 through a_n:

$$a_1 + a_2 + a_3 + ... + a_n = n \cdot \frac{a_1 + a_n}{2}.$$

Geometric Mean: Of two numbers, a and b: $\sqrt{ab}$.

For $\{a_1, a_2, a_3, ...a_n\}$: $G = \sqrt[n]{a_1 \cdot a_2 \cdot a_3 \cdot ... \cdot a_n}$

Sum of a Geometric Series: The sum of a geometric series with first term a and common ratio r:

$a + ar + ar^2 + ar^3...$ where $|r| < 1$ is found by:

$$S = \frac{a}{1-r}.$$

Triangular Numbers: The nth triangular number T_n is:

$$T_n = \frac{n(n+1)}{2} = \binom{n+1}{2}.$$

Sum of the first n Perfect Squares:

$$1^2 + 2^2 + 3^2 + ...n^2 = \frac{n(n+1)(2n+1)}{6}.$$